SAFETY THROUGH DESIGN

SAFETY THROUGH DESIGN

Editors:
Wayne C. Christensen, CSP, P.E.
Fred A. Manuele, CSP, P.E.

NATIONAL SAFETY COUNCIL MISSION STATEMENT

The mission of the National Safety Council is to educate and influence society to adopt safety, health, and environmental policies, practices, and procedures that prevent and mitigate human suffering and economic losses arising from preventable causes.

COPYRIGHT, WAIVER OF FIRST SALE DOCTRINE

The National Safety Council's materials are fully protected by the United States copyright laws and are solely for the noncommercial, internal use of the purchaser. Without the prior written consent of the National Safety Council, purchaser agrees that such materials shall not be rented, leased, loaned, sold, transferred, assigned, broadcast in any media form, publicly exhibited or used outside the organization of the purchaser, or reproduced, stored in a retrieval system or transmitted in any form or by any means, electronic, mechanical, photocopying, recording or otherwise. Use of these materials for training for which compensation is received is prohibited, unless authorized by the National Safety Council in writing.

DISCLAIMER

Although the information and recommendations contained in this publication have been compiled from sources believed to be reliable, the National Safety Council makes no guarantee as to, and assumes no responsibility for, the correctness, sufficiency, or completeness of such information or recommendations. Other or additional safety measures may be required under particular circumstances.

Library of Congress Cataloging-in-Publication Data
Safety Through Design: Best Practices/edited by Wayne C. Christensen, Fred A. Manuele.
p.cm.
ISBN 0-87912-204-8 (hc. : alk. paper)
1. Industrial safety. 2. Human engineering. 3. System safety.
I. Christensen, Wayne C. II. Manuele, Fred A.
T55.S217 1999
620.8'6—dc2l   99-30661
                                              CIP

3.5C0502   NSC Press Product No. 17644-0000

CONTENTS

Foreword ix

Preface..xi

Introduction..xiii

Part I. Introducing Safety Through Design

  1. Why Safety Through Design: What's in It for You? 3

  2. Concepts, Principles, and Methods for Safety Through Design 9

  3. Benchmarking for World-Class Safety Through Design............................23

  4. Achieving the Necessary Culture Change 37

  5. What Do Engineers Really Know About Safety?..49

Part II. Integration Into Business Processes

  6. Relating Principles to Quality Management....................................67

  7. Integrating Concepts Into the Design Process.....................................73

  8. Influence In Contracting and Purchasing 89

  9. Designing for Maintainability, Reliability, and Safety 109

  10. Proactive Ergonomics and Designing for Error-Free Work.....................119

  11. Using Concepts in Retrofitting Existing Operations 131

  12. Applying Concepts to Product Liability Prevention............................139

Part III. Safety Through Design in Industry

  13. Application in General Industry 155

  14. Application in Automotive Industry 171

  15. Application in Aircraft Manufacturing 185

  16. Application in the Chemical Industry..195

  17. Application in the Construction Industry 217

  18. Application in the Electronics Industry 241

  19. Beyond the Millennium—Safety Through Design in 2005.....................259

Appendix—Author Biographies...269

Index 273

FOREWORD

The National Safety Council has been in a leadership role in safety, health and environmental affairs since its inception in 1913, nearly 90 years. The content of this book causes us to realize that as much as things change rapidly in our world, some factors remain constant.

In reviewing past works, the First Edition of the Council's *Accident Prevention Manual (APM)* (1946) stated:

> *"...pre-planning requires the knowledge and skill of experienced engineers. To secure the highest efficiency in plant operations, provisions for workers' safety must be included in the design and layout."*

The Third Edition (1955) of the *APM* called attention to the need to design safety (including health and environmental considerations) into the job, rather than retrofit:

> *"Company policies should be such that safety can be designed and built into the job, rather than added after the job has been put into operation. The design engineer should be conscious of the fact that the safety department is most anxious to help in discovering job hazards and removing them.*
>
> *Each level of engineering should be given the responsibility for building safety into the job, right through the production phase. Such responsibility should extend to product design, machine design, plant layout and condition of premises, selection and specification of materials, production planning, time study, methods, duties of production foreman, and work of employees assigned to the job.*
>
> *When safety is properly inculcated in the planning of new operations or processes, there will be little need to secure management's backing for incorporating safety features before operations are started."*

The *APM* 11th Edition (1997) contains a chapter on "Designing for Safety." Today's business environment evidences an increasing compression of time between project/product concept and production. The luxury of delaying production because of safety concerns, when processes or equipment have reached the production floor, are no longer being tolerated by management. Safety, health and environmental concerns must be incorporated very early in the concept and design stages.

It is professionally gratifying to see this publication coming to fruition through the leadership of the Institute for Safety Through Design (ISTD). My thanks to the many individuals involved in this undertaking, including the co-editors and the Council staff. And, it is my pleasure to recognize two individuals, Fred A. Manuele, President, Hazards,

Limited, and Mike Taubitz, Global Safety Regulatory Liaison, General Motors, who were intimately involved with the establishment of the Institute and participants in its many accomplishments.

Jerry Scannell
President
National Safety Council

PREFACE

The Institute for Safety Through Design, when established in 1995, adopted the following Vision and Mission statements:

VISION - *Safety, health and environmental considerations are integrated into design and development of systems meant for human use.*

MISSION - *To reduce the risk of injury, illness and environmental damage by integrating decisions affecting safety, health and the environment in all stages of the design process.*

This book is another opportunity in the short life of the Institute to foster the concepts expressed in these statements. The 20 authors and co-authors sharing their knowledge and experience are to be commended for their leadership, contributions and willingness to provide their expertise. Yes, you will find different styles of writing and perhaps different points of view, but the experience of hearing more than one viewpoint will leave you richer in the knowledge of concepts and the importance of their application in your business environment.

Safety through design is not a precise science. Since it is not a "one size fits all" type of effort, it will require customization to your company. But the basic concepts of early involvement in the design stage, careful evaluation of hazards, and risk assessment are universally applicable.

Chapter authors bring you an introduction to the safety through design process and present approaches to integrating these concepts into business practices. They then enhance these details with points of view from various industries, providing an excellent cross-section of the efforts of leaders in the safety through design activity. The tools and information are there for you to start Benchmarking your efforts. It is satisfying to me that this book was completed during my tenure as Chair of the Advisory Committee of the Institute.

The work of ISTD is not only to have the safety through design concepts adopted by industry, but also to impact the university engineering education programs. ISTD, and others, are working to change the engineering curricula and produce graduates with increased knowledge of safety health and the environment. The Institute is developing curricula materials that can be embedded in existing curricula, and is supplying universities with materials to foster case studies on hazard analysis and risk assessment.

Your efforts to foster safety through design will be important. I personally encourage you to study this material and to challenge yourself and your company to move from the "retrofit" era to the "Safety Through Design" era.

James C. Rucker
Chair – ISTD Advisory Committee
Executive Director – Industrial Engineering
General Motors, North America Operations

INTRODUCTION

OBJECTIVE

This book—conceived, developed, and brought to fruition through the efforts of the Institute for Safety Through Design, an entity of the National Safety Council—is to fill a knowledge vacuum. Safety through design is defined as "the integration of hazard analysis and risk assessment methods early in the design and engineering stages and the taking of the actions necessary so that the risks of injury or damage are at an acceptable level." The concept encompasses facilities, hardware, equipment, products, tooling, materials, energy controls, layout, and configuration.

Observations were that engineers; managers; and safety, health, and environmental practitioners nurtured a hunger for information on safety through design concepts and the techniques used in other companies and industries to implement them. It was a labor of the Institute Advisory Committee and individual authors who contributed their time and effort.

The editors envisioned and secured a series of excellent authors having a diversity of background, business and industry experience, and success in their areas of expertise, that provided material based on industry experience and minimally on academic postulations. The authors and editors believe the concepts set forth in this book can be practically applied and most of all are necessary, if efforts to thwart the continuing large number of deaths, injuries, illnesses, and environmental incidents, both occupationally and off-the-job are to be successful.

Readers will find divergent viewpoints, which are acceptable, since there has been success with many different approaches to their application. The text is focused on providing significant insights into the concepts, and their potential integration and application in your operations. The material must be sorted, evaluated, and massaged to produce an appropriate blend for your operations, since safety through design is not a "cookie cutter" practice. Safety as a term is used in its broadest concept to include health and environmental aspects.

PART I. INTRODUCING SAFETY THROUGH DESIGN

CHAPTER 1. WHY SAFETY THROUGH DESIGN: WHAT'S IN IT FOR YOU?

Earnings per share, cost per pound of product, pre-tax earnings, return on net assets, incidence or severity rate reductions, reduced numbers of injured or ill employees, whatever your measure, if the principles are applied, the metrics will reflect substantive benefits. Significant reductions will be achieved in injuries, illnesses, damage to the environment, and attendant costs; productivity will be improved; operating costs will be reduced, and expensive retrofitting to correct design shortcomings will be avoided. This theme is reflected throughout the book either in direct savings, or in the benefit of accidents, injuries, illnesses, and environmental incidents, which are prevented.

The Model reflects the movement of safety from an afterthought to a forethought. It indicates efforts must be focused on moving these concepts upstream into the business planning or conceptual stage, and integrating them seamlessly into the design/build process. Safety through design must go far beyond minimums to accomplish acceptable risk goals.

Chapter 2. Concepts, Principles, and Methods for Safety Through Design

Risk is defined as "a measure of the probability of a hazards-related incident occurring and the severity of harm or damage that could result." Minimum risk, not zero risk (unattainable), is accomplished when all risks derived from hazards, throughout the life cycle of facilities, processes, equipment, and product, are acceptable. Then the design process should go forward to the "build" phase. Risk assessment is a key in the design process.

It is extremely important for the order of design precedence to be followed. A thought process for hazard avoidance, elimination, or control in the general design process is presented. Engineers and safety practitioners should have a hazard analysis and risk assessment matrix suitable to their needs. The goal to be met is that all residual risks will have been deemed to be acceptable.

Chapter 3. Benchmarking for World-Class Safety Through Design

Benchmarking is "a standard of excellence against which other similar things are measured or judged." It must be coupled with the current industry ongoing search for best practices that produce superior performance to facilitate Continuous Improvement. Both concepts are simple, fundamental, and critical. Business decisions and commitment is a direct outcome of management culture change, which must affect all organization level. Organizations will receive benefits from studying their own process and getting their act together before talking to world experts.

The activity is not a one-time event; it is an ongoing process. The time interval between design and downstream consequences may be substantial since one of the longest phases in the life of a design is the Operate/Maintain period. Benchmarking allows learning from experience without awaiting downstream experience to influence change in the Design and Build stages.

Chapter 4. Achieving the Necessary Culture Change

In many organizations a culture change will be necessary to establish effective safety through design concepts. It must involve management, hourly engineers, and safety in a collaborative venture. Culture is a set of perceptions, values, beliefs, and assumptions that determine how individuals see reality and affects how we behave. Change is difficult, and conformity is the norm. The best safety cultures are where people openly question assumptions and share ideas.

Delving into the need for organization culture change there is wonderment that people who are supposed to be most rational frequently give only lip service and no resources or personal leadership to safety through design efforts. Opposition comes from years of prejudice, or an interest in preserving the status quo. They may understand the concepts make sense, but are unwilling to pay the price in time, effort and dollars. To accomplish culture change, three strategic elements and six phases of planned cultural change are identified.

Chapter 5. What Do Engineers Really Know About Safety

Engineers (mechanical, electrical, civil) who design systems and products generally have received little formal education regarding the topics of safety, health, and the environment.

Efforts continue by organizations accrediting engineering programs to require these subjects be covered in the curriculum. ISTD and others are examining what engineers do know about safety and what they should know, and are working to develop materials to incorporate/integrate in the curricula.

Respondents to an ASME Design Division member survey indicated that while some felt safety was included in existing courses, most considered the coverage insufficient. In addition, lack of design safety education may limit an engineer's ability to identify safety concerns and potentials for the future. There is increased pressure to improve the level of safety of designs, and an additional massive task of growing current engineering staff knowledge of these topics.

PART II. INTEGRATION INTO BUSINESS PROCESSES

CHAPTER 6. RELATING PRINCIPLES TO QUALITY MANAGEMENT

There is a remarkable correlation between quality management and safety through design principles. The same processes that must be incorporated to ensure a product meets quality expectations will also ensure that safety expectations are achieved. Parallels exist between TQM, ISO 9000, and safety through design. By adopting these methods, establishing objectives, and starting at the design stage, the safety of workers and products can be impacted.

During the 1980s philosophies changed regarding the quality of products and approaches to producing better products. Old philosophies are now unacceptable and improved strategies for "speed to market" are being introduced, with the recognition that every day a new product is delayed from market introduction sales are lost that will never be recovered. These delays allow competitors to gain market advantage.

CHAPTER 7. INTEGRATING CONCEPTS INTO THE DESIGN PROCESS

The basic purpose and concepts of business are reviewed, emphasizing and offering insights into a wide variety of costs and their importance in relationship to the acceptance and implementation of safety through design concepts. Thoughts on business objectives of survival, return on investment, cost control and reduction, and their effect on operating managers and the bottom line serve as reminders that good data must be accumulated to support the social and moral considerations in promoting changes to reduce risks to an acceptable level.

Introduction of the concepts of life cycle costing and recycling costs as important tools in this whole process emphasizes the cradle to grave aspect of safety through design. The Product Design Process is also covered.

CHAPTER 8. INFLUENCING CONTRACTING AND PURCHASING

Contract specifications for building construction and buying machinery and the roles of the architect, contractor, code enforcement officials, machinery fabricators, owners and users are explored. Requirements in the United States and Europe, design responsibilities and the CE mark are discussed. Corporate culture, goals, guidelines, and checklists are shared. Thoughts are offered regarding prequalifying suppliers, which may minimize problems.

The purchaser really determines what is designed into a building. Satisfying codes and regulations deals with only minimum requirements, which may vary widely from country to country and city to city. Buying and constructing machinery offers different challenges than constructing buildings. For instance in the United States most purchasers specify that machinery must meet OSHA regulations; however, it is the *user* that is regulated and who therefore must be familiar not only with the OSHA requirements, but other industry codes, national standards, and applicable company requirements.

CHAPTER 9. DESIGNING FOR MAINTAINABILITY, RELIABILITY, AND SAFETY

In many businesses, maintenance workers in relation to their proportion of plant population have higher lost workday case rates than other groups. Engineers are encouraged to include consideration of safety in their design decisions for planned and unplanned maintenance that would affect maintainability and serviceability, and minimize the probability of failures (reliability) of equipment. Doing so achieves reductions in downtime and increases productivity.

Literature on maintenance, maintainability, and reliability is plentiful, but seldom addresses designing for minimum risk of injury for maintenance and related workers. Many organizations design for planned maintenance, but most do not know that unplanned maintenance will account for the vast majority of downtime. Safety through design requires that these tasks be defined.

CHAPTER 10. PROACTIVE ERGONOMICS, AND DESIGNING FOR ERROR-FREE WORK

The need for design engineers to consider ergonomics and human factors early in the design process is explained. The Engineering Life Cycle is detailed, together with Design Team compositions, poka-yoke (design for error-free work), and the Design For Assembly principles.

Manufacturing ergonomics is the study of natural laws of work, or the relationship between the worker and the environment. At the most fundamental level the engineer must deal with the relationship "fit" between the worker and the environment.

Ergonomic risk factors such as high force, awkward postures, repetition, inadequate rest, vibration and environmental factors and their interaction are discussed. Design for Ergonomics in Products is also reviewed considering the human as a component in a simple closed loop system model to create user-friendly products.

CHAPTER 11. USING CONCEPTS IN RETROFITTING EXISTING OPERATIONS

Error-provocative situations and the need for their elimination instead of toleration are discussed. Once the concept of avoiding error-provocative work situations is accepted, engineers and safety practitioners are in a good position to review existing situations with a different perspective. The importance of recognizing circumstances where retrofitting can come into play is stressed. There will be numerous instances where retrofitting of existing products, equipment, and processes will be necessary and safety through design principles can be applied.

In identifying situations requiring retrofitting, the role of safe job procedures, and accident/incident investigation in the process are reviewed. Modification of existing products, equipment, and processes provides an excellent opportunity to conduct a risk assessment of the original design and to evaluate it against the current state of technology.

CHAPTER 12. APPLYING CONCEPTS TO PRODUCT LIABILITY PREVENTION

An overview of product liability from an engineer's perspective and its relationship to safety through design is presented. Legal theories, elements of proof and the product liability process are discussed. Several cases relating to product liability cost to manufacturers are shared, together with thoughts on how these costs, injuries, and incidents, can be minimized, and the time spent on defense decreased.

Here, as in other areas, the evidence is that the earlier in a design process a hazard is identified, the easier, cheaper, and better it can be remedied. Costs are analyzed in relation to the cost by lawsuit and from the sales perspective. A review is made of data for product design decisions, since good design requires current, state of the art information.

PART III. SAFETY THROUGH DESIGN IN INDUSTRY

CHAPTER 13. APPLICATION IN GENERAL INDUSTRY

The process for integrating safety through design currently being implemented and used in a major manufacturing company is described. The basic process is versatile and can be used in most manufacturing and engineering organizations. In integrating the principles into the design process safety, Fitness-For-Use criteria are established. They must be measurable, mandatory, and realistic and are ultimately used to measure the project's success. Also described are the Engineering Design Safety Review, and the Walk-down of installed equipment and processes before start-up.

Measures to assess the safety through design process use and effectiveness, along with the challenges to its implementation and continuance, are discussed. An excellent hypothetical case study of the installation of an expansion of production operations in a manufacturing facility is provided.

CHAPTER 14. APPLICATION IN AUTOMOTIVE INDUSTRY

The history of safety through design as implemented for manufacturing equipment at Chrysler and General Motors is covered in the first portion. The focus in the balance of the chapter is on the design process within the General Motors North American Car Group.

There are two key requirements for the successful implementation of any process: stakeholders have clearly defined standards; and, there must be a system of checks and balances to assure the process is implemented and ongoing. A description is provided of the integration into the GM vehicle development process, of "design-in" safety principles and practices, with real world examples. Lessons learned are incorporated into the design standards to facilitate a living, breathing, "Design-in Safety" document. In view of the fact that people change within an organization, the need for a formalized process is discussed.

CHAPTER 15. APPLICATION IN AIRCRAFT MANUFACTURING

The safety-related challenges faced in manufacturing aircraft and their components are explored in this chapter. Integration of safety through design concepts into the process have produced improved injury and illness rates, productivity gains and heightened quality, which has been well received by manufacturing managers. Most aircraft manufacturers agree that 40% to 60% of their OSHA-required recordable incidents and costs are related to ergonomics.

The chapter therefore has a focus on the risk identification, and the process to implement safety through design concepts. A sample Policy is provided, together with ideas on building the infrastructure, training, and the very important area of capturing the cost. Several examples of the interdisciplinary approach to designing for safety are provided.

CHAPTER 16. APPLICATION IN THE CHEMICAL INDUSTRY

The tools and techniques for safety through design in the chemical process industry (CPI) are described in this chapter. The emphasis is on early consideration of safety and use of "inherently safer" concepts. The unique characteristics of the CPI, the life cycle of a chemical process and basic concepts are reviewed. Design strategies for safety and layers of protection are presented, followed by thoughts on design conflicts and trade-offs.

Tools for safety through design, such as Process Hazards Analysis (PHA), and Process Chemistry Guideword Hazard Analysis (PCGHA) are described and their application is discussed. Safety in design in connection with other important initiatives throughout the world, and safety and reliability in design are also reviewed.

CHAPTER 17. APPLICATION IN THE CONSTRUCTION INDUSTRY

Two aspects of construction design safety are covered. One is the safe design of a facility, bridge, highway, equipment, or other tangible end item to ensure that facility users and maintenance personnel are not injured. The second is to assure construction workers are not injured in completing the project. In the design to reduce user injuries a number of examples are provided. Use of system safety working groups is described, including provisions for customer input.

Policies are discussed, together with occupancy and contemporary facility design safety and health issues. An extensive "Building Design Safety Checklist" is included. It covers Planning and Administration as well as Specific Design Considerations. The author also provides web site references for additional information on tools mentioned.

CHAPTER 18. APPLICATION IN THE ELECTRONICS INDUSTRY

This chapter prepared by Intel Corporation and Novellus Systems, Inc, one of its suppliers, provides an insight into the culture and relationship of the two companies with respect to environmental, health, and safety (EHS) issues. The process can be complicated when conflicting expectations exist and can put a strain on both in performing to a level acceptable to customers.

Intel and Novellus equipment EHS design programs from tool design through installation and operations are reviewed. Basic activities of both organizations to achieve consistent high level programs are shared with the reader for potential use within their operations. First, the Intel EHS New Equipment Procurement Process is described, followed by the Novellus System Safety Program. Tangible Benefits in the form of several metrics are provided to share the beneficial results from designing to semiconductor industry consensus Guidelines.

CHAPTER 19. BEYOND THE MILLENNIUM—SAFETY THROUGH DESIGN IN 2005

A snapshot of major changes in the world that might affect safety through design is offered, along with the observation that by 2005 efforts to incorporate these concepts have been successful in a large number of organizations. Comments on changes in corporations, the workforce, and the unleashing of creativity by computers set the scene for discussion of safety through design concepts and practice in the new millennium.

Observations are offered on the impact of key changes in business practices and computers on engineers and safety practitioners. The results are surprising, with evidence of a clear need for an extremely cooperative effort between engineers as designers, management, and safety practitioners.

Part I

INTRODUCING SAFETY THROUGH DESIGN

Chapter 1

WHY SAFETY THROUGH DESIGN: WHAT'S IN IT FOR YOU?

by Fred A. Manuele

INTRODUCTION

This book is about improving earnings per share, or return on investment, or return on net assets, or internal rate of return—whatever the significant performance measures in your business. Its theme is that the following benefits will derive if decisions affecting safety, health, and the environment are integrated into the early stages of the design processes:

- → Significant reductions will be achieved in injuries, illnesses, damage to the environment, and their attendant costs.
- → Productivity will be improved.
- → Operating costs will be reduced.
- → Expensive retrofitting to correct design shortcomings will be avoided.

In your business, if competition has become so keen that you need to run smarter, better, and faster, this book is for you. Of course, we must make the case that integrating decisions affecting safety, health, and the environment in the early stages of the design processes will not only reduce risk but also improve productivity and lower operating costs. But, before we do so, we need to define what safety through design is all about, as well as the terms *safety, hazards,* and *risk.*

DEFINING SAFETY THROUGH DESIGN

Safety through design is defined as the integration of hazard analysis and risk assessment methods early in the design and engineering stages and the taking of the actions necessary so that the risks of injury or damage are at an acceptable level. This concept encompasses facilities, hardware, equipment, tooling, materials, layout and configuration, energy controls, and environmental concerns.

What is proposed for safety through design is not a program, with its attendant whistles, bells, slogans, and banners running to a sputtering end, to be forgotten as many programs are. What is needed is an agreed-upon and well-understood concept, a way of thinking, that is translated into a process that effectively addresses hazards and risks in the design processes.

SAFETY THROUGH DESIGN MODEL

The Figure emphasizes moving safety from an afterthought to a forethought in the design of facilities, processes, and products. Thus, considerations of hazards and risks would be moved as far "upstream" as possible in the design process. "Upstream" includes all aspects of the origination of business concepts, the relative decision making, and the design process, during which the greatest effectiveness can be achieved in hazard avoidance, elimination, or control.

As the Figure indicates, integrating consideration of hazards and risks early in the concept and design stages results in easier and less costly safety implementation, and avoids costly retrofitting in the build, operation, maintenance, and decommissioning periods.

THEORETICAL IDEAL

A goal in the adoption of the safety through design concept is to have the idea "seamlessly" integrated into the design process. A borrowing from *Why TQM Fails and What To Do About It*[1] will shed some light on that premise. Brown et al reviewed the quality programs in several companies. The authors say that some of the organizations they studied "don't have a total quality

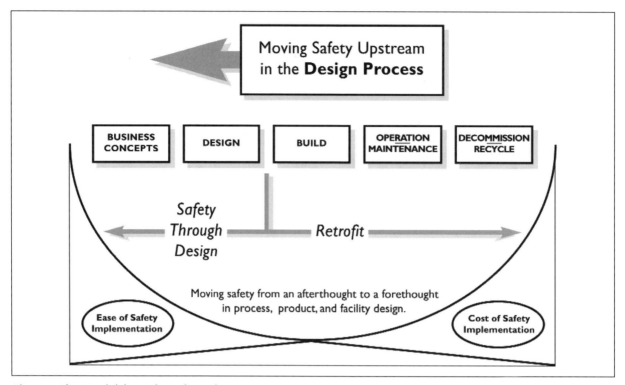

Figure. The Model for Safety Through Design.

management program; rather, they have a culture change initiative."

The authors also say, "Others insist that TQM is a macrochange strategy. The intent of these companies is to integrate TQM so completely into the organization that it is virtually indistinguishable."

In reading the following quotation from Brown et al, replace "TQM" and "quality" with "safety" and the substance of the statement remains sound.

> *When TQM is seamlessly integrated into the way an organization operates on a daily basis, quality becomes not a separate activity for committees and teams but the way every employee performs his or her job responsibilities.*

The theoretical ideal is reached when quality or safety is seamlessly integrated into an organization's culture and the way it operates on a daily basis. That ideal is what the authors of this book have in mind for safety through design. Some companies are close to that theoretical ideal in designing for the safety of products for general consumer use. Very few companies are at that

level when designing for the work place, processes, work methods, or environmental issues.

RELATING SAFETY THROUGH DESIGN TO DESIGNING FOR QUALITY

There is a remarkable kinship between sound quality management principles and sound hazards management principles. We borrow from W. Edwards Deming, who was world renown in quality management, to support that premise. Deming stressed, again and again, that "Processes must be designed to achieve superior quality if that is the quality level desired, and that superior quality can not be attained otherwise."

And the same principle applies to safety. For an example of what Deming intended, we quote the fifth premise in what Deming called a "Condensation of the 14 Points of Management," as listed in his book *Out of the Crisis*[2]. "Improve constantly and forever the system of production and service, to improve quality and productivity, and thus constantly decrease costs."

If you want superior quality, or superior safety, you must design it into new systems. You must also maintain a continuous improvement program for the redesign of existing workplaces and work methods. How interesting it is that Deming very successfully advocated a management system that encompassed the entirety of productivity, cost efficiency, quality, and safety.

DEFINING SAFETY, HAZARDS, AND RISK

In applying the safety through design concept, these definitions will govern:

- *Safety* is defined as that state for which the risks are judged to be acceptable.
- *Hazards* are defined as the potential for harm: hazards include the characteristics of things and the actions or inactions of people. Hazards encompass any aspect of technology or activity that produces risk.
- *Risk* is defined as a measure of the probability of a hazards-related incident occurring and of the severity of harm or damage that could result.

Designing to minimum risk—to acceptable risk—is a goal of this safety through design concept. That does not mean designing to zero risk, which is impossible.

RESEARCH—CASE STUDIES

To make the case that integrating decisions affecting safety, health, and the environment into the early stages of the design process is good business, we cite an experience in the development of a proposal to the National Safety Council that it create an Institute for Safety Through Design.

In the exploratory work, the chair of the study group needed to collect actual cases in which initiatives undertaken by safety professionals to resolve injury and illness problems also resulted in improved productivity and cost efficiency.

Eleven safety directors were asked for help. Much to the chair's surprise, every one agreed to provide success stories. That was an important indicator of how their jobs had changed. They were into productivity, cost efficiency, and performance measurement much more than expected.

Nine of the eleven safety directors actually responded with case studies. (Anyone who has done volunteer work will appreciate that such a response was remarkable.) More surprising was the number of success stories submitted. It was known that only five or six cases could be used

in the proposal being developed. Safety directors sent 22, and offered more if needed.

As a few of those cases are cited, keep this in mind. Each case defines shortcomings in operating methods that could have been eliminated in the design process; safety professionals initiated the studies because of injury experience; and risks were minimized, productivity improved, and costs were reduced.

COMPUTER MANUFACTURER

An electronic panel drilling machine was difficult to operate. A study indicated that workers had to bend and reach to perform tasks, and operator comfort, product quality and performance suffered. As a result of the study, new machines designed for better body mechanics were acquired. In the first year, labor costs were reduced by $270,000 and yield increased $420,000. Productivity was improved. Injuries were reduced.

AIRCRAFT MANUFACTURER

An assembly operation required standing on a platform to get visual and physical access to parts being assembled. Shoulder strain injuries resulted from installing operations, done above shoulder level. Work methods were redesigned. An assembly stand mounted on a hydraulic height-adjustable cart permitted drilling, riveting and installing parts in a hands-free operation performed below shoulder height, with good visual and physical access. No more strain injuries occurred. Production increased from 2 to 4 units a week. Estimated annual cost savings was $52,800.

COPIER MANUFACTURER

A copier product with highly repetitive assembly tasks was estimated to have workers' compensation costs 2.5 times higher than the corporate average. A redesign study revealed how hazards could be reduced <u>and</u> how simplifications could be made in product design (reduction in the number of parts, and standardization of parts for multiple use), with a substantial reduction in production costs.

CONSTRUCTION AND FARMING EQUIPMENT MANUFACTURER

On a backhoe assembly line, the design of the work, done within the operator's cab, required taking stressful and awkward positions and repetitive hand tool use. Back injuries were frequent and none but the youngest employees would accept assignment to the work. Wage rate ergonomic team members and the ergonomics coordinator proposed a new design that permitted the work to be done prior to installation of components in the cab, allowing the assembler to work in a good upright position. A major reduction in production time resulted and hazards were notably reduced.

AVOIDING COSTLY RETROFITTING

One of the purposes of designing to minimum risk early in the design process is to avoid costly retrofitting. As an indication of the benefits to be achieved by designing things right the first time, a study made by a computer chip maker is cited.

Because of the very high cost of constructing chip fabrication facilities, achieving cost effective design solutions through proactive design activity is essential. Great benefits were achieved when the application of sound engineering criteria resulted in human-compatible designs for manual material handling, workstations, controls, and displays, and for maintainability.

It was found that the costs of implementing solutions in the early design stages have an additional equipment cost impact of 0% to 5%, versus the 10% to 20% of costs for retrofitting to achieve the same ends.

RELATING TO INJURY EXPERIENCE

Consider these three cases which relate reducing risk in the design process to also achieving improved productivity and lower operating costs. Their subjects are generic and can be related to similar operations.

➝ Case 1

Parts weighing in excess of 25 lbs were handled several hundred times a day by employees in an automotive components plant in a very inefficient operation. Loading and unloading parts into metal hoppers involved twisting, turning, and bending. Numerous workers' compensation claims had been filed for back cases. Over time, a variety of remedial measures (back belts, focused training) had been tried.

It was not until automatic tilt tables for the part hoppers were provided, along with other steps to redesign the work, were the

ergonomic stressors reduced, as were the workers compensation cases. And productivity and efficiency were also improved.

Not only were training and personal protective equipment inappropriate to this situation, but the "fixes" cost far more than would have been the case if the issues were addressed in the original design of the equipment.

➝ Case 2

Because of a glitch in production scheduling, delivery of parts by a conveyor to a workstation ceased. The design of the conveyor was such that parts would regularly fall off and accumulate beneath it. This was not a well-designed and efficient system. An employee, wanting to keep up with production needs, went beneath the conveyor to retrieve the parts that had collected there. Her hair was caught in a drive belt, and part of her scalp was torn away.

At first, the causal factor for this incident was recorded as the unsafe act of the employee. Subsequently, it was realized that if parts had not fallen off the conveyor, there would have been no enticement for the worker to retrieve them. Questions were then posed about the design of the conveyor and the operating cost. Thus, the design of the conveyor was modified.

➝ Case 3

A worker failed to follow the established procedure to lock out and tag out the electrical power during a maintenance operation, and was electrocuted. The incident investigation report recorded the causal factor as "employee failed to follow the lockout/tagout procedure...."

But, it was also determined that the distance to the power shut off was 216 feet. That "encouraged" the employee's risky behavior. Obviously, the design of the lockout/tagout system did not consider efficient time use.

In the latter two cases, identification of planned and unplanned maintenance tasks in the design process would have resulted in a workplace design that improved employee *safety and productivity*.

DESIGNING TO AVOID ERROR-PROVOCATIVE SITUATIONS

Alphonse Chapanis is exceptionally well known in human factors engineering circles. He is an often quoted authority concerning the productivity gains to be made by addressing the capabilities and limitations of workers in the design processes, so that the design of the work is minimally error-provocative.

One of Chapanis' most interesting papers is his chapter titled "The Error-Provocative Situation: A Central Measurement Problem in Human Factors Engineering," in the William E. Tarrants book *The Measurement of Safety Performance*.[3] Chapanis stresses that if work is designed so that the probability of error is high, you can be assured that errors will occur. A central point in Dr. Chapanis' work is that "....The improvement in system performance that can be realized from the redesign of equipment is usually greater than the gains that can be realized from the selection and training of personnel."

DESIGNING IN CONSIDERATION OF THE POTENTIAL FOR HUMAN ERROR

Trevor Kletz wrote *An Engineer's View of Human Error*[4], which is a significant book. His views on the understanding of, and designing in consideration of, the potential for human error relate directly to the premise that integrating decisions effecting safety early in the design stages not only results in reduced risk but also impacts favorably on productivity and cost efficiency, and sometimes quality. The focus in the Introduction to his book has a significant bearing on safety through design. Kletz wrote that:

The theme of this book is that it is difficult for engineers to change human nature and, therefore, instead of trying to persuade people not to make mistakes, we should accept people as we find them and try to remove opportunities for error by changing the work situation, that is, the plant or equipment design or the method of working. Alternatively, we can mitigate the consequences of error or provide opportunities for recovery.

A second objective of the book is to remind engineers of some of the quirks of human nature so that they can better allow for them in design.

Whatever the consideration—productivity, cost efficiency, safety, or quality—Kletz's observation applies. If the potential for human error and the quirks of human nature are considered in the design process, the possible success of the operation is enhanced.

INTERNATIONAL INFLUENCES

American manufacturers who export machinery to Europe have already felt the influence of design standards issued by the European Union. Part 1 of En 292,[5] which is titled "Safety of machinery - Basic concepts, general principles for design" covers "basic terminology, methodology." Part 2[6] covers "Technical principles and specifications." This is the Scope in Part 1: "This European standard defines basic terminology and specifies general design methods, to help designers and manufacturers in achieving safety in the design of machinery for professional and nonprofessional purposes. It may also be used for other technical products having similar Hazards."

It is specified in Part 1 that

The designer shall, in all circumstances, in the following order: specify the limits of the machine; identify the hazards and assess the risks; remove the hazards or limit the risks as much as possible; design guards and/or safety devices (safeguards) against any remaining risks; inform and warn the user about any residual risks; and consider any necessary additional precautions.

As of 1997, most products sold in European Union countries are required to bear a "CE" mark. To obtain the mark, a "responsible person" (most often the manufacturer) must ensure that certain documentation concerning the safety of a product is available for inspection by enforcement authorities. That documentation is to satisfy, among other things, the procedures in the preceding paragraph concerning hazards and risks, which are central to safety through design. By affixing the "CE" mark, a manufacturer indicates that the product complies with all applicable directives in force. The "CE" mark is the passport for goods entering European Union countries.

Presently, there are no standards in the United States that require designers of machinery and equipment to document that hazards have been identified and analyzed, that risk assessments have been made, and that appropriate prevention and control methods have been taken. One group—which is developing an ANSI Technical Report For Machine Tools—was formed to develop a guideline for risk assessment for the machine tool industry in response to the European Union standard EN 1050, Safety of Machinery; Risk Assessment.[7] This subcommittee expects to issue its report in 1999.

EXPLORING THE OPPORTUNITIES

It is proposed that management personnel and engineers explore the historical information available to assess how integrating safety into the design process may have improved productivity, cost efficiency, and safety. That information is contained in the incident investigation reports completed after injuries and illnesses occur.

In such an exploration, responses to the following questions would serve as a starting point effecting new designs. To emphasize, the exploration would pertain to productivity and cost management, as well as safety, and perhaps quality.

- ➤ Could employee errors be attributed to design decisions?
- ➤ Is the design of the work place or work methods overly stressful?
- ➤ Is the design of the work place or work methods error-provocative?
- ➤ Did the immediate work situation encourage riskier actions than the prescribed work methods?
- ➤ Does the design of the work induce fatigue?
- ➤ Is the work very difficult or irritating?
- ➤ Is the work dangerous?
- ➤ Can maintenance work be accessed quickly and safely?

Undertaking such a process will provide an awareness of the impact that workplace and work methods design decisions have on operations, overall.

SUMMARY

This opening chapter establishes that integrating methods for hazard analysis and risk assessment early in the design and engineering stages will not only achieve significant reductions in injuries, illnesses, and damage to the environment—and their attendant costs—but also will result in improved productivity, cost efficiency, and the avoidance of expensive retrofitting to correct design shortcomings.

REFERENCES

1. Brown GM, Hitchcock DE, Willard ML: *Why TQM Fails and What to Do About It.* Burr Ridge IL: Irwin Professional Publishing, 1994.

2. Deming WE: *Out of the Crisis.* Cambridge MA: Center for Advanced Engineering Study, Massachusetts Institute of Technology, 1986.

3. Chapanis A: The error-provocative situation. In: Tarrants WE (ed). *The Measurement of Safety Performance.* New York: Garland Publishing, 1980.

4. Kletz T: *An Engineer's View of Human Error.* Rugby, Warwickshire UK: Institution of Chemical Engineers, 1991.

5. Safety of machinery - Basic concepts, general principles for design; Part 1. Basic terminology, methodology; European Standard EN 292-1, European Committee for Standardization; Central Secretariat: rue de Stassart 36, Brussels, 1991.

6. Safety of machinery - Basic concepts, general principles for design; Part 2. Technical principles and specifications; European Standard 292-2, European Committee for Standardization; Central Secretariat: rue de Stassart 36, Brussels, 1991.

7. Safety of Machinery - Risk Assessment; European Standard EN 1050; European Committee for Standardization; Central Secretariat: rue de Stassart 36, Brussels, 1997.

Chapter 2

CONCEPTS, PRINCIPLES, AND METHODS FOR SAFETY THROUGH DESIGN

by Fred A. Manuele

OBJECTIVES

This chapter provides design engineers and safety practitioners with a resource covering the concepts, principles, and methods applied in a safety through design initiative. Standards, regulations, specifications, design handbooks, and checklists that establish design minimums are plentiful, and they are very important. However, the concept of safety through design must go far beyond the application of standards and guidelines.

Trevor Kletz, in *Plant Design For Safety: A User-Friendly Approach*,[1] gives one example of a design concept that extends design goals far beyond standards and guidelines. He proposes that a highly significant purpose in designing for safety is to achieve a "user friendly" occupational setting. Consider the theme of his book.

In all industries, errors by operators and maintenance workers and equipment failures are recognized as major causes of accidents, and much thought has been given to ways of reducing them or minimizing their consequences. Nevertheless, it is difficult for operators and maintenance workers to keep up an error-free performance all day, every day. We may keep up a tip-top performance for an hour or so while playing a game or a piece of music, but we cannot keep it up continuously.

Designers have a second chance, opportunities to go over their designs again,

but not operators and maintenance workers. Plants should therefore be designed, whenever possible, so that they are "user friendly," to borrow a computer term, so that they can tolerate departures from ideal performance by operators and maintenance workers without serious effects on safety, output, or efficiency.

It is the theme of this book that, instead of designing plants, identifying hazards, and adding on equipment to control the hazards or expecting operators to control them, we should make every effort to choose basic designs and design details that are user friendly.

What needs to be established in an organization is a well-understood concept, a way of thinking, that is translated into a system that effectively addresses hazards and risks in the design processes—a way of thinking that is universally applied by all who are involved with designing.

PRINCIPLE RESOURCES FOR THIS CHAPTER

In writing this chapter, considerable extension was required of the bits and pieces taken from several sources, two of which are significant and deserve attribution. One is Military Standard System Safety Program Requirements, often referred to as MIL-STD-882C.[2] And the second is

William J. Haddon's energy-release theory as set forth in his papers, such as "The Prevention of Accidents"[3] and "On the Escape of Tigers: An Ecological Note."[4]

Military Standard 882C is the document containing the system safety program requirements for contractors to the Department of Defense. It is not written in a language easily transferable to the needs of design engineers. Nevertheless, it is a valuable resource.

Haddon's energy-release theory proposes that quantities of energy, means of energy transfer, and rates of transfer are related to the types of hazard-related incidents that occur, the probability of their occurrences, and the severity of their outcomes. Haddon also addressed the significance of avoiding unwanted exposures to harmful environments. Designing to avoid unwanted energy flows and unwanted exposures to harmful environments should reduce both the probability of harmful or damaging incidents occurring, and the severity of their outcomes.

ULTIMATE PURPOSE OF SAFETY THROUGH DESIGN

The ultimate purpose of applying concepts of safety through design to systems, the workplace, work methods, and products is to achieve safety—which is that state for which the risks are judged to be acceptable.

Some companies in the chemical industry have adopted a comparable philosophical approach in attempting to design "inherently safer" chemical processes. In the book *Inherently Safer Chemical Processes: A Life Cycle Approach,*[5] edited by Daniel A. Crowl and published by the Center For Chemical Process Safety (AICHE), the term "inherently safer" is defined as follows. "A chemical manufacturing process is *inherently safer* if it reduces or eliminates the hazards associated with the materials and operations in the process, and this reduction or elimination is permanent and inseparable."

In one company, "inherently safer" is defined as the pursuit of designing hazards out of chemical processes and equipment rather than the use of engineering or procedural controls to reduce the frequency or mitigate the consequence of potentially hazardous events.

The concept of "inherently safer" facilitates safety through design. It implies that the facility, system, process, or equipment has been rendered safer because of the efforts to design hazards out, or to mitigate the consequences of untoward events.

GENERAL PRINCIPLES AND DEFINITIONS

For the purposes of this chapter, the term *design processes* applies to the following:
→ Facilities, hardware, equipment, tooling, material selection, operations layout and configuration, energy control, and environmental concerns;
→ Work methods and procedures, personnel selection standards, training content, work scheduling, management of change procedures, maintenance requirements, and personal protective equipment needs; and
→ Industrial, commercial and consumer products for human use.

Those involved in the design process must attain an understanding of the elements of risk. *Risk* is defined as a measure of the probability of a hazard-related incident occurring and the severity of harm or damage that could result.

In the design and redesign processes, these two distinct aspects of risk must be considered:
→ Avoiding, eliminating, or reducing the *probability* of a hazard-related incident occurring; and
→ Minimizing the *severity* of harm or damage, if an incident occurs.

Minimum risk is sought with respect to new technology, facilities, materials and designs; in designing new production methods; in the design of products for human use; and in all redesign endeavors. Minimum risk is achieved when all risks deriving from hazards are acceptable. Minimum risk does not mean zero risk, which is unattainable. Establish and apply requirements for minimum risk in the acquisition or acceptance of new materials, technology, or designs, and prior to the adoption of new production, test or operating techniques.

In determining minimum risk, the decision factors will be the design objectives, the practicality of risk-reduction measures and their costs, and their probable acceptance by users. If a system—the facilities, equipment, and work methods—is not designed to minimum risk, superior results with respect to safety cannot be attained, even if management and personnel factors approach the ideal.

As a matter of principle, for an operation to proceed, its risks must be acceptable. All risks to which the concept of safety through design applies derive from hazards. There are no exceptions.

Thus, hazards must be the focus of design efforts to achieve safety—a state for which the risks are judged to be acceptable. Hazards are most effectively and economically avoided, eliminated, or controlled if they are considered early in the design process, and where necessary as the design progresses. Both the aspects of technology and human activity hazards must be considered in the design decision making.

A *hazard* is defined as the potential for harm; hazards include the characteristics of things and the actions or inactions of persons. In the identification and analysis of hazards, and their avoidance, elimination, or control the resulting risks are to be acceptable, throughout the *life-cycle of processes, equipment, and products.*

Early in the design process consider the risks attendant in the eventual disposal of facilities, processes, and products. If a hazard is not avoided, eliminated, or controlled, its potential may be realized, and a hazard-related incident may occur that has the potential to, but may or may not, result in harm or damage, depending on exposures.

Hazard probability is defined as the likelihood that the potentials of hazards will be realized and that a hazard-related incident will occur. Hazard probability is described in probable occurrences per unit of time, events, population, items, or activity. *Hazard severity* is defined as the aggregate of the worst credible outcomes of a hazard-related incident, considering the exposure.

Exposure includes the people, property, and environment that could be harmed or damaged if a hazard-related incident occurs. A *risk assessment* is an analysis that addresses both the probability of a hazard-related incident occurring and the expected severity of its adverse effects.

Hazard analyses and risk assessments must be integral parts of the design process.

For workstations, tools, equipment, and operating methods, and products for human use, design and engineering applications are the preferred measures for preventing hazard-related incidents since they are more effective. A fundamental purpose of design is to have processes and products that are error-proof, or error-tolerant.

Actions taken to identify and eliminate hazards and to reduce their attendant risks to an acceptable level are to be documented. The need for retrofitting of facilities and equipment to improve safety is minimized through the timely inclusion of safety features during research, technology development, and in purchasing and acquisition. Systems, equipment, and products are to be capable of operation, maintenance, and repair by personnel with minimum training.

When changes are made to design or work methods, have in place a management-of-change system that includes identification and analysis of hazards so that an acceptable level of risk is maintained. Significant safety data representing lessons learned are to be documented and disseminated to interested personnel.

ORDER OF DESIGN PRECEDENCE

To achieve the greatest effectiveness in hazard avoidance, elimination, or control, the following in order of precedence apply to all design and redesign processes.

1. *Design for minimum risk.* From the very beginning, the top priority is that hazards are to be eliminated in the design process. If an identified hazard cannot be eliminated, the associated risk is to be reduced to an acceptable level through design selection.

2. *Incorporate safety devices.* As a next course of action, if hazards cannot be eliminated or their attendant risks adequately reduced through design selection, reduce the risks to an acceptable level through the use of fixed, automatic, or other protective safety design features or devices. Make provisions for periodic maintenance and functional checks of safety design features or devices.

3. *Provide warning devices.* When identified hazards cannot be eliminated or their attendant risks reduced to an acceptable level through initial design decisions or through the incorporated safety devices, provide systems that detect the hazardous conditions and include warning signals to alert personnel of the hazards. Design warning signals and their application to minimize the probability of incorrect personnel reactions and standardize within like types of systems.

11

4. *Develop and institute operating procedures and training.* When it is impractical to eliminate hazards or reduce their associated risks to an acceptable level through design selection, incorporating safety devices, or warning devices, relevant operating procedures, training, and written warning advisories, signs and labels shall be used. However, do not use operating procedures and training, or other warning or caution signs and labels, or written advisory forms as the only risk reduction method for critical hazards. Acceptable procedures may include the use of personal protective equipment. Certain tasks and activities judged to be essential to safe operation may require special training and certification of personnel proficiency.

For many design situations a combination of these principles will apply. However, do not choose a lower level of priority until practical applications of the preceding level or levels are exhausted. First and second priorities are more effective because they reduce the risk by design measures that eliminate or adequately control hazards. Third and fourth priorities rely on human intervention.

GENERAL DESIGN REQUIREMENTS: A THOUGHT PROCESS FOR HAZARD AVOIDANCE, ELIMINATION, OR CONTROL

Some aspects of the following design requirements pertain to either or both unwanted energy flows and unwanted exposures to harmful environments. In presenting this outline, it is strongly emphasized that

→ the Order of Design Precedence previously given is to prevail;

→ ergonomics design principles apply, so that the work methods prescribed, and the procedures for the use of products for human use, are not error-provocative or overly stressful; and

→ the two distinct aspects of risk are to be considered in the design and redesign processes,
- avoiding, eliminating, or reducing the *probability* of a hazard-related incident occurring and
- minimizing the *severity* of harm or damage, if an incident occurs.

These design requirements could not possibly cover all situations; they are offered for consideration by those who would develop design requirements suitable to their operations.

1. Avoid introducing the hazard: prevent buildup of the form of energy or hazardous materials.
   - Avoid producing or manufacturing the energy or the hazardous material;
   - Use material handling equipment rather than manual means; and
   - Don't elevate persons or objects.

2. Limit the amount of energy or hazardous material.
   - Seek ways to reduce actual or potential energy input;
   - Use the minimum energy or material for the task (voltage, pressure, chemicals, fuel storage, heights);
   - Consider smaller weights in material handling;
   - Store hazardous materials in smaller containers; and
   - Remove unneeded objects from overhead surfaces.

3. Substitute, using the less hazardous.
   - Substitute a safer substance for a more hazardous one: when hazardous materials must be used, select those with the least risk throughout the system's life-cycle;
   - Replace hazardous operations with less hazardous operations;
   - Use designs needing less maintenance; and
   - Use designs that are easier to maintain, considering human factors.

4. Prevent unwanted energy or hazardous material buildup.
   - Provide appropriate signals and controls;
   - Use regulators, governors, and limit controls;
   - Provide the required redundancy;
   - Control accumulation of dusts, vapors, mists, and so forth;
   - Minimize storage to prevent excessive energy or hazardous material buildup; and
   - Reduce operating speed (processes, equipment, vehicles).

5. Prevent unwanted energy or hazardous material release: consider all forms of energy—mechanical, electrical, chemical, thermal, and radiation.

- Design containment vessels, structures, elevators, material handling equipment to appropriate safety factors;
- Consider the unexpected in the design process, to include avoiding the wrong input
- protect stored energy and hazardous material from possible shock;
- Provide fail-safe interlocks on equipment, doors, valves;
- Install railings on elevations;
- Provide non-slip working surfaces; and
- Control traffic to avoid collisions.

6. Slow down the release of energy or hazardous material.
   - Provide safety and bleed off valves;
   - Reduce the burning rate (using an inhibitor);
   - Reduce road grade; and
   - Provide error-forgiving road margins.

7. Separate in space or time, or both, the release of energy or hazardous materials from that which is exposed to harm.
   - Isolate hazardous substances, components, and operations from other activities, areas, and incompatible materials, and from personnel;
   - Locate equipment so that access during operations, maintenance, repair, or adjustment minimizes personnel exposure (e.g., hazardous chemicals, high voltage, electromagnetic radiation, cutting edges);
   - Arrange remote controls for hazardous operations;
   - Eliminate two-way traffic;
   - Separate vehicle from pedestrian traffic; and
   - Provide warning systems and time delays.

8. Interpose barriers to protect the people, property, or the environment exposed to an unwanted energy or hazardous material release.
   - Insulation on electrical wiring;
   - Guards on machines, enclosures, fences;
   - Shock absorbers;
   - Personal protective equipment;
   - Directed venting;
   - Walls and shields;
   - Noise controls; and
   - Safety nets.

9. Modify the shock concentrating surfaces.
   - Padding low overheads;
   - Rounded corners;
   - Ergonomically designed tools; and
   - "Soft" areas under playground equipment.

HAZARD ANALYSIS AND RISK ASSESSMENT

Hazard analysis and risk assessment methods must be used in the appropriate stages in the design process to evaluate risks and determine the risk management actions to be taken. A good hazard analysis/risk assessment model will enable decision makers to understand and categorize the risks and to determine the methods and costs to reduce risks to an acceptable level.

NEED FOR A HAZARD ANALYSIS AND RISK ASSESSMENT MATRIX

Design engineers must have available and use a hazard analysis/risk assessment matrix suitable to their needs. A good one follows in this chapter, which can be modified to suit individual requirements. There are others. Several texts include hazard analysis/risk assessment decision matrices, most all of which are adaptations from Military Standard - System Safety Program Requirements, known as MIL-Std-882-C.[2] Influence of that standard will be obvious in the remainder of this chapter.

Some guidelines follow that can be used in developing a hazard analysis/risk assessment decision matrix, and a thought process for its application.

↣ Keep it simple—you don't have to complicate things.

↣ Be aware that some situations defy statistical analysis.

↣ Hazard analysis/risk assessment is an art. It is not a science. It is suggested that designers and safety professionals be wary of numerologists, and also of risk scoring systems. A variation of a thought attributed to Descartes applies—if you can't know the truth, you ought to seek the most probable.

↣ To communicate with decision makers, terms must have been mutually defined. While identical terms may be used in the several hazard analysis methods described in the literature, those terms may have different meanings.

↣ Also, those who are to communicate with decision makers should have an understanding of their perceptions and tolerance of risk, and appreciate that perceived risks, elements of employee and public fear, and client interests may impact on risk decisions.

Table 2-A. Categories of Hazard Severity.

Description	Category	Definition
Catastrophic	I	Death, permanent disability, system loss, devastating property damage or environmental damage
Serious	II	Severe injury or occupational illness, or major system, property or environmental damage
Marginal	III	Minor injury or occupational illness, or minor system, property, or environmental damage
Negligible	IV	No medical attention required for a personal injury or illness; system, property, or environmental damage so small it can be tolerated

→ Implementing a logical hazard analysis/risk assessment model is more important than which model is chosen.

SEVERITY OF HAZARD

Categories of hazard severity displayed in Table 2-A provide guidance in developing a hazard analysis/risk assessment matrix. Adaptation of a variation of Table 2-A will require developing definitions of the terms selected for an individual operation. Particularly, definitions are necessary of the terms system loss or property damage, major or minor system or environmental damage, and severe and minor injury and occupational illness, if those terms are to be used.

HAZARD PROBABILITY

The probability that a hazard-related incident will occur is to be described in probable occurrences per unit of time, events, population, items, or activity. A qualitative probability may be derived from research, analysis, evaluations of the historical safety data on similar systems, and from a composite of opinions of knowledgeable people. Supporting rationale for assigning a hazard probability should be documented. Table 2-B is an example of a qualitative hazard probability ranking; category parameters would relate to the interval base chosen—unit of time, events, etc.

ACHIEVING ACCEPTABLE LEVELS OF RISK

Use of hazard severity and hazard probability tables produces a qualitative risk assessment from which determinations can be made that risks are acceptable, or not acceptable, and from which priorities can be set for actions to be taken.

It must be understood that the charts on hazard severity and probability are to serve only as guides and that definitions of terms within them must be refined to suit the needs of a particular operation.

For further guidance, Table 2-C shows an example indicating how a combination of the hazard severity and probability charts can be used to develop qualitative risk assessments.

CASE STUDY—RISKS ARE UNACCEPTABLE FOR PERSONNEL EXPOSURE BUT PROVISIONALLY ACCEPTABLE FOR PROPERTY DAMAGE EXPOSURE

While this chapter addresses concepts, principles, and methods for safety through design, much of what is written here also applies to decision making for existing operations. To promote an understanding of risk concepts and risk management, the following real world scenario is presented to illustrate that conclu-

Table 2-B. Rankings of Hazard Probability.

Probability Level	Category	Parameters
Frequent	A	Likely to occur often
Probable	B	Will occur several times
Occasional	C	Likely to occur some time
Remote	D	Unlikely but possible to occur
Improbable	E	So unlikely, it can be assumed occurrence may not be experienced

Table 2-C. Hazard/Risk Assessment Matrix.*

OCCURRENCE	SEVERITY OF CONSEQUENCE			
Probability	Catastrophic-1	Serious-2	Marginal-3	Negligible-4
A - Frequent	1A	2A	3A	4A
B - Probable	1B	2B	3B	4B
C - Occasional	1C	2C	3C	4C
D - Remote	1D	2D	3D	4D
E - Improbable	1E	2E	3E	4E

Hazard Risk Index	Suggested Category
1A, 1B, 1C, 2A, 2B, 3A	Unacceptable: risk reduction action is necessary
1D, 2C, 2D, 3B, 3C	Unacceptable if personnel are exposed to the hazards or if environmental damage may occur, wherein risk reduction is necessary: may be provisionally acceptable in operations, subject to a management decision if facility or equipment damage only may occur
1E, 2E, 3D, 3E, 4A, 4B	Acceptable, with management review
4C, 4D, 4E	Acceptable, without management review

* Note that for the "acceptable" categories, do not assume that action is not to be taken to eliminate or control the hazards.

sions as to risk categories may differ for personnel, environmental, or property damage exposures.

A metal coating facility has received an urgent order from a valued client for a short production run of coated parts. To meet the time requirement, use of older production equipment that has not been in service recently will be necessary. Maintenance and testing to assure proper operation of the older equipment have been deferred. Startup must begin during the next operating shift and continue on an overtime basis for several more shifts. There will be no opportunity for the overdue maintenance and testing.

The equipment uses high pressure etching with a toxic reagent as a part of the coating process. Blowout of pump and valve seals leading to a release of the reagent is an identified hazard.

Reagent vapors can be fatal if inhaled in high concentrations. On contact with moisture in the air, they are energetically caustic, threatening damage to nearby equipment.

Using the organization's hazard/risk assessment matrix, past risk assessments for this hazard produced these results.

	SEVERITY	PROBABILITY
Equipment	*Marginal*	*Occasional*
Personnel	*Catastrophic*	*Improbable*

Probability determinations differ because the equipment is constantly exposed to the hazard, while personnel are exposed infrequently, on a walk-through basis.

The Plant Maintenance Supervisor and the Operations Manager question the integrity of the pump and valve seals, and call on the safety professional to produce a current risk assessment, assuming that operations are nevertheless to proceed. This is the result.

	SEVERITY	PROBABILITY
Equipment	*Marginal*	*Probable*
Personnel	*Catastrophic*	*Remote*

The three conclude that the risk to equipment might be provisionally acceptable while the risk to personnel is unacceptable. To meet the schedule, they propose to the plant manager that the equipment be operated as it is, and that a strictly enforced "no-approach" rule be imposed, effectively restricting personnel to a protected control room. For personnel, this administrative procedure, in their judgment, reduces the probability of a harmful incident from "remote" to "improbable." Thus, the risk is judged to be acceptable, and the operation can proceed. It is understood that, as soon as the run is completed, the delayed maintenance and inspection will be performed.

In this situation, the management actions taken resulted in an arrangement whereby the risks deriving from hazards to which facilities or equipment only are exposed are judged to be provisionally acceptable, while those same risks are deemed to be acceptable for personnel.

CONDUCTING A HAZARD ANALYSIS AND RISK ASSESSMENT

In every one of the following steps, it is vital to seek the counsel of experienced personnel who are close to the work or process. Reaching group consensus on the judgments made, generally, would be the goal. For all but exceptionally simple equipment, multiple hazards analyses and risk assessments will be necessary.

1. *Establish the analysis parameters.* Select and scope a manageable task, system, or process to be analyzed, and define its interface with other tasks or systems, if appropriate.

2. *Identify the hazards.* A frame of thinking should be adopted that gets to the base of causal factors, which is hazards. A determination would be made of the potential— repeat, potential—for harm or damage that arises out of the characteristics of things and the actions or inactions of people. Hazard potential should be kept separate at this point in the thought process, which prompts recognition of severity potential for itself.

3. *Consider the failure modes.* Define the possible failure modes that would result in realization of the potentials of hazards.

4. *Describe the exposure.* This is still an identification activity. Its purpose is to establish and get agreement on the number of people, the particulars of the property, and the aspects of the environment that could be harmed or damaged, and the frequency of their endangerment. It is not easy to do, and help should be solicited from knowledgeable sources. Several subjective judgments will be made in this process.

5. *Assess the severity of consequences.* Informed speculations are to be made on the number of fatalities or injuries or illnesses, on the value of property damaged, and on the extent of environmental damage. Historical data can be of great value as a baseline. On a subjective judgment basis, agreement would be reached on the severity of consequences. After a severity category is selected (catastrophic, critical, marginal, or negligible), a hazard analysis will have been completed.

6. *Determine the probability of the hazard being realized.* Unless empirical data is available, and that would be a rarity, the process of selecting the probability of an incident occurring (frequent, probable, occasional, remote, or improbable) will again be subjective. Probability has to be related to intervals of some sort, such as a unit of time or activity, events, units produced, or life-cycle.

7. *Define the risk.* Conclude with a statement that addresses both the probability of an incident occurring, and the expected severity of adverse results.

8. *Develop remediation proposals.* If the risk is unacceptable, alternate proposals for the design changes necessary to achieve an acceptable risk level should be recommended. For each proposal, remediation cost should be determined and an estimate would be given of its effectiveness in achieving risk reduction.

RISK RANKING AND PRIORITY SETTING

The preceding material pertains to individual hazard and exposure scenarios. To properly communicate with decision makers, a risk-ranking system should be adopted so that priorities can be established. Since the hazard analysis and risk assessment exercise is subjective, the risk-ranking system will also be subjective.

RISK IMPACT

To discriminate between hazards having the same hazard/risk index, a risk impact determination is necessary. An impact determination consists of a review of the effect of an event economically, socially and politically. (Example: A release of a small amount of chemical into a stream may not cause measurable physical damage, but extreme political and social damage could result.)

RESIDUAL RISKS

No matter what actions are taken to avoid, eliminate or control hazards, some residual risks will still exist. If the safety process meets its goal, none of the residual risks will be unacceptable.

CONSIDERING REMEDIATION COSTS

Costs to reduce risk surely are a part of the management decision making. But, those costs should not be included in the hazard analysis/risk assessment exercise.

Some risk assessment systems include in their formulae a factor for the cost of reducing risk. In those systems, hazard-related incidents with low probability of occurrence and high severity of consequence, classed as catastrophic or critical, may be given a subordinate ranking if the cost to reduce risk is substantial. If those risks are given a subordinate ranking, management is denied the information it ought to have concerning catastrophe potential.

BEING ATTENTIVE TO OSHA'S HAZARD ANALYSIS REQUIREMENTS

Estimates indicate that the requirements for hazard analyses established through OSHA's *Rule for Process Safety Management of Highly Hazardous Chemicals*[6] could apply to as many as 50,000 places of employment. *Many of those locations are not within chemical companies.* Being attentive in the design and redesign processes to the risk elimination or control outcomes expected through the application of those requirements is good business. The rule requires that the following steps are taken:

➤ The employer shall perform an initial hazard analysis (hazard evaluation) on processes covered by this standard. The process hazard analysis shall be appropriate to the complexity of the process and shall identify, evaluate, and control the hazards involved in the process.

➤ The employer shall use one or more of the following methodologies that are appropriate to determine and evaluate the hazards of the process being analyzed....What-If; Checklist; What-If/Checklist; Hazard and Operability Study (HAZOP); Failure Modes and Effect Analysis (FMEA); Fault Tree Analysis; or an appropriate equivalent method.

➤ Also, the hazard analysis shall address:
- The hazards of the process
- The identification of any previous incident which had a likely potential for catastrophic consequences in the workplace
- Engineering and administrative controls applicable to the hazards and their interrelationships
- Consequences of failure of engineering and administrative controls
- Facility citing
- Human factors
- A qualitative evaluation of a range of the possible safety and health effects of failure of controls on employees in the workplace.

Under the requirements for *Pre-startup safety review*, the employer is required to provide a process hazard analysis, among other things, for new facilities and for significant modifications. The OSHA *Rule for Process Safety Management of Highly Hazardous Chemicals* does not mention occurrence probability. This appears in the preamble to the standard.

OSHA has modified the paragraph (editorial note - paragraph on consequence analysis) to indicate that it did not intend employers to conduct probabilistic risk assessments to satisfy the requirement to perform a consequence analysis. Yet, design engineers and safety practitioners will have to consider incident probability in ranking risks and in giving advice to decision makers.

APPROPRIATION REQUESTS, PROJECT REVIEWS, CONTRACT SPECIFICATIONS

An organization's system for the preparation of appropriation requests for new projects or major alterations should include a design review procedure that requires hazards analyses and risk assessments, both internally and by suppliers of equipment. One purpose of addressing hazards in the design process is to avoid retrofitting, which may be excessively costly or impossible when construction projects are in progress or new equipment does not meet the requirements of good hazard management.

When contract specifications clearly set forth safety requirements, the probability of that sort of problem occurring is reduced. Having a well-crafted checklist for project reviews and for the development of contract specifications would be beneficial to design engineers and safety professionals. A sample checklist to serve as a guide only is provided in Chapter 8, "Contracting and Purchasing." It should be customized to meet the needs of each organization.

CULTURE CHANGE—INITIATING A HAZARD ANALYSIS AND RISK ASSESSMENT SYSTEM

In some organizations, implementing more formal procedures for hazard analysis and risk assessment may require significant changes in management practices and significant changes in the organization's culture. Thus, the concepts applicable in successfully achieving a culture change would apply.

A planned effort will be necessary to convince decision makers that adopting more formal hazard analysis and risk assessment concepts will be valuable. Small steps forward, proving value, are recommended. It is suggested that those who are to undertake such an initiative do the following:

➤ Develop an awareness of risk tolerance beliefs held by decision makers.
➤ Study the approach to be taken with decision makers; consider history, risk tolerance, their needs, and how decision makers could be influenced to conclude that what is being proposed helps in achieving their goals.
➤ Work with a team of knowledgeable people and obtain agreement on the benefits to be obtained from the use of an additional hazard analysis/risk assessment system, the methods to be used, and meanings of terms to be used in a Hazard Analysis and Risk Assessment Decision Matrix.
➤ Determine which risks deserve priority consideration.
  • Select one or two higher category hazard/risk situations.
  • Follow the steps in conducting a Hazard Analysis/Risk Assessment.
  • Continue to try, assess, modify, and try again.

For more information on changing the corporate culture, see Chapter 4, "Achieving the Necessary Culture Change."

MODEL POLICY AND PROCEDURE STATEMENT ON SAFETY THROUGH DESIGN

Recognizing the extensiveness of the culture change needed to successfully implement a newly adopted safety through design concept and the hazard analysis and risk assessment procedures integral in the design process, some companies issue policy and procedure statements as a beginning. An example follows. It announces that hazards must be identified and addressed early in the design process, and as an integral part of a concurrent engineering program.

EXAMPLE. POLICY AND PROCEDURE STATEMENT: SAFETY IN THE DESIGN PROCESS

Our continuing policy is to provide employees with a safe work environment, and to assure a proper treatment of environmental hazards deriving from our operations.

To meet this objective, it is necessary for personnel having design responsibilities to consider hazards during the early concept stages when developing new products, manufacturing processes, technology, and facilities that may impact on occupational safety and health and on the environment.

Designing for safety, health, and environmental considerations is most cost effective when done upstream where the ability to influence is greatest. In addition to reducing risk, the concept of "Safety in the Design Process" has also been demonstrated to accomplish the following:
➤ *Increase worker productivity;*
➤ *Improve people and processing flexibility;*
➤ *Facilitate uptime;*
➤ *Reduce costs;*
➤ *Reduce hazards in service and maintenance activities; and*
➤ *Achieve effective environmental controls, upstream.*

Conversely, the cost of secondary engineering to retrofit for hazards impacting on safety, health, and environmental needs after the initial design and deployment of the manufacturing process is excessive, and often includes burdensome constraints on our manufacturing and production systems.

During the early conceptual stages for product and process development, anticipating service and maintenance tasks and identifying employee and environmental exposures are critical first steps in developing the safeguarding and engineering controls necessary. That same concept includes designing to avoid or control hazards and designing in the necessary safeguarding protection for operators and supporting maintenance personnel, considering both planned and unplanned service of the equipment and facility.

Engineering design should strive for elimination of hazards. Only when elimination, substitution or engineering controls are not feasible should reliance on physical barriers, warning systems, training, and personal protective equipment be considered.

The concept of "Safety in the Design Process" requires a coordinated effort between the Engineering and the Safety, Health, and Environmental communities. Our bulletin titled (xyz) establishes when safety, health, and environmental studies are necessary in the consideration of new facilities, products, technology and manufacturing processes. Please review current and future programs to assure that safety, health, and environmental issues are considered in the early stages of concept and design.

Safety, health, and environmental personnel are to assist as technical resources in achieving our "Safety in the Design Process" goals.

MODEL OPERATING PROCEDURE GUIDE FOR SAFETY THROUGH DESIGN

How can an organization put into practice a policy requiring that hazards be addressed in the design process, recognizing the significance of the culture change implicit in the adoption of a safety through design concept? Very few procedure statements exist that could serve as references. An example of a modified procedure guide issued by a multi-location company with diverse operations follows. This example can be modified for use by other organizations.

EXAMPLE. OPERATING PROCEDURE GUIDE—PROCESS DESIGN AND EQUIPMENT REVIEW

PURPOSE
To provide operations, engineering and design personnel with guidelines and methods to foresee, evaluate and control hazards related to occupational safety and health, and the environment, when considering new or re-designed facilities, equipment, and processes.

SCOPE AND DEFINITIONS
This guideline is applicable to all facilities, processes, systems, manufacturing equipment, and test fixtures regardless of size or materials used. These conditions will be necessary for an exemption from design review:

➤ No hazardous materials are used (as defined by 29 *CFR* 1910.1200);
➤ Operating voltage of equipment is <15 volts and the equipment will be used in non-hazardous atmospheres and dry locations;
➤ No hazards are present that could cause injury to personnel (overexertion, repetitive motion, error-prone situations, falls, crushing, lacerations, dismemberment, projectiles, visual injury, etc.);
➤ Pressures in vessels or equipment are <2 psi;
➤ Operating temperatures do not exceed 100F/38C;
➤ No hazardous wastes as defined by 40 *CFR* 26 & 262 and/or 331 *CMR* 30 are generated; and
➤ No radioactive materials or sealed source devices are used.

If other exemptions are desired, they are to be cleared by the safety, health, and environmental professional.

PHASE I. PRE-CAPITAL REVIEW
This review is to be completed prior to submission of a project request or a request for equipment purchase, in accord with the capital levels out-

lined in Bulletin xxx. Pre-capital reviews are crucial for planning facilities needs such as appropriateness of location, power supply, plumbing, ventilation, et cetera. Process and project feasibility are determined through this review. A complete hazard analysis using a "What If" process or *designsafe...the hazard analysis and risk assessment guide (designsafe),*[7] in accord with Bulletin yyy, is to accompany the request. Noncapital projects should also be reviewed utilizing these procedures, but a formal "What If" or *designsafe* hazard analysis is not required.

PHASE II. INSTALLATION REVIEW

This review requires a considerably more detailed hazards and failure analysis relative to equipment design, production systems, and operating procedures. Detailed information is to be documented, including equipment operating procedures, a work methods review giving emphasis to ergonomics, control systems, warning and alarm systems, et cetera. A hazard analysis utilizing *designsafe* is to be used, and documented. The Project Manager shall be responsible for establishing and managing a Hazard Review Committee.

HAZARD REVIEW COMMITTEE

This committee will conduct all phases of design review for equipment and processes. In addition to the Project Manager, members will include the safety, health, and environmental practitioner, the facilities engineer, the design engineer, the manufacturing engineer, and others (for example, financial, purchasing) as needed. For particular needs, outside consultants for equipment design or hazard analysis may be recommended by the safety, health and environmental practitioner.

RESPONSIBILITIES

Project Manager

For all phases of the design review, the Project Manager will be responsible, from initiation to completion. That includes initiation of the design review, having the hazards analyses/risk assessments completed, forming the design review committee, compiling and maintaining the required information, document distribution, setting meeting schedules and agendas, and preparing the final design review report. The Project Manager will coordinate and communicate with all outside design, engineering, and hazard analysis consultants.

Department Manager

Department Managers will see that design reviews are completed for capital expenditure or equipment purchase approvals, and previous to placing equipment or processes in operation, as required under "Installation Review". Signatures of Department Managers shall not be placed on asset documents until they are certain that all design reviews have been properly completed, and that their findings are addressed.

Design Engineer

Whether an employee or a contractor, the design engineer shall provide documentation to the Project Manager and the Review Committee includin:

➤ detailed equipment design drawings;

➤ equipment installation, operation, preventive maintenance and test instructions;

➤ details of and documentation for codes and design specifications; and

➤ requirements and information needed to establish regulatory permitting and/or registrations.

For all of the foregoing, information shall clearly establish that the required consideration has been given to safety, health, and environmental matters.

Safety, Health, and Environmental Practitioner

Serving as a member of the Hazard Review Committee, the safety, health, and environmental practitioner will assist in identifying and evaluating hazards in the design process and provide counsel as to their avoidance, elimination, or control. Special training programs for the review committee may be recommended by the safety, health, and environmental practitioner.

Also, consultants may be recommended who would complete hazards analyses, other than for the "What If" system.

Administrative Procedures

In this section, the administrative procedures would be set forth, such as the amount of time prior to submission of a capital expenditure or equipment purchase request is to be allowed the Hazard Review Committee for its work, information distribution requirements, advance notice time requirements for Installation Review meetings, procedures to assure that findings of hazards analyses are addressed, and how differences of opinion of Hazard Review Committee members are to be resolved.

RESOURCES ON HAZARD ANALYSIS AND RISK ASSESSMENT TECHNIQUES

Many hazard analysis and risk assessment techniques have been developed. In addition to those cited from OSHA's *Rule for Process Safety Management of Highly Hazardous Chemicals,* these are some mentioned in the literature: Preliminary Hazard Analysis; Gross Hazard Analysis; Hazard Criticality Ranking; Catastrophe Analysis; Energy Transfer Analysis; Human Factors Review; The Hazard Totem Pole; and Double Failure Analysis. P. L. Clemens discussed 25 such systems.[8]

In addition to traditional tools, new computer based hazard analysis and risk assessment software has become available to aid engineers and safety professionals in working through the process.

SUMMARY

The guidelines given in this chapter serve as a reference only, for design engineers and safety practitioners who undertake the culture change necessary to have safety through design concepts integrated into the design process. They will help in the development and writing of the principles, definitions, order of design precedence, design requirements, and the policies and procedures applicable in their organizations. In every case, for the safety through design concept to work effectively, policies and procedures must require that hazard analyses and risk assessments be made early in the design process.

REFERENCES

1. Trevor K: *Plant Design For Safety: A User-Friendly Approach.* New York: Hemisphere Publishing Corporation (Taylor Francis), 1991.

2. Military Standard System Safety Program Requirements (MIL-STD-882-C). Department of Defense, Washington DC, 1993.

3. Haddon WJ Jr: *Preventive Medicine. The Prevention of Accidents.* Boston, 1966.

4. Haddon WJ Jr: On the escape of tigers: An ecological note. *Technology Review,* May, 1970.

5. Crowl DA: *Inherently Safer Chemical Processes: A Life Cycle Approach.* New York: Center For Chemical Process Safety, American Institute of Chemical Engineers, 1996.

6. *Process Safety Management of Highly Hazardous Chemicals.* OSHA Standard at 1910.119, Feb 1992.

7. *designsafe...the hazard analysis and risk assessment guide.* Itasca, IL: National Safety Council.

8. Clemens PL: A compendium of hazard identification & evaluation techniques for system safety applications. *Hazard Prevention,* Mar/Apr, 1982.

Chapter 3

BENCHMARKING FOR WORLD-CLASS SAFETY THROUGH DESIGN

by Robert T. George
D. Thomas Peterson

OBJECTIVES

This chapter covers the role of benchmarking in the overall process of improving safety performance through design. Readers will be introduced to some basic principles of benchmarking methods through examples from the DuPont experience. It is our intent to share the value we have for the benchmarking process and how it can be properly applied to promote safer processes and designs.

INTRODUCTION

There is tremendous value to a business in just understanding the power of designing safety into a process, system, or product. Safety through design can be done well or not at all, and the only way to ensure that it is done well is to measure it, understand how you do it, look beyond yourself to observe how the best do it, and adapt those "best practices" to your process. These steps of quality improvement are called benchmarking.

What is *benchmarking*?

Webster's Definition: Benchmark—A surveyor's mark....of previously determined position... used as a reference point.

Business Definition: A standard of excellence against which other similar things are measured or judged.

Continuous Improvement Definition: The ongoing search for best practices that produce superior performance.

As you can see by the definitions above, benchmarking is simple and fundamental. It is using an external perspective to help improve performance. It has been learned repeatedly that internally focused, closed economic systems tend to decay, and that companies must bring to bear the perspectives of others who are performing the same processes with different perspectives and often better results. DuPont has put a great deal of thought into designing safety into our products and processes. It is hoped that by sharing some of these insights, you will be able to adapt them to your own designs.

BACKGROUND OF BENCHMARKING FOR BUSINESS IMPROVEMENT

Industry has been using benchmarking in business processes since the late 1970s, when Japanese firms began undercutting Xerox's copier business. By learning from the Japanese through benchmarking, Xerox was able to design its copiers for better cost, quality, and ease of repair. Xerox extended benchmarking to business processes, and Bob Camp wrote, "Benchmarking: The Search for Industry Best Practices That Lead to Superior Performance"[1] that chronicled their work with the L.L. Bean Company. L.L. Bean helped Xerox understand how to improve the process of servicing their installed base of machines with repair parts. Companies began to study Bean's excellence at shipping small quantities of different sized products and at providing excellent customer service, and the process improvement business has not been the same since.

DuPont started using benchmarking in the mid-1980s as a way to make changes in a number of key business processes such as maintenance, employee health care, and new product development. Still, benchmarking was not really a new concept in DuPont. Early in DuPont's history, it was recognized that the safety performance in making black powder was unsatisfactory and a commitment to reduce injuries was developed. For the past 200 years, best practices have been applied from everywhere they could be found to achieve improvement. Today the goal is zero failures, a goal that extends beyond injuries to health and environmental failures. DuPont cannot reach that goal without designing safety into processes and designing out the opportunities for failures.

A number of global safety, health, and environmental benchmarking projects have looked at cost and efficiency, but few have dealt with the process of designing safety into manufacturing and business processes. In the early 1990s, numerous studies looked at the design of new products, with the specific goal of finding a "design for X." The concept was to design for the desired outcomes of a product: capital utilization, manufacturability, assembly, repair, improved cycle time, ergonomics, and of course safety. Because safety is such an integral part of product design and the effects of poor design can take so long to show up, modifying the safety performance of a product or process can take a long time. In fact, especially in today's litigious society, a "proven technology" used without incident for years (such as silicon breast implants or externally mounted tractor-trailer gas tanks) may ultimately reveal design-based flaws that manifest themselves in personal injury.

DuPont receives two or three requests a week to "benchmark" our safety processes. Sitting down for a few hours listening to us talk passionately about this subject rarely if ever results in changes in the benchmarker's organization. But what has been done is put together courses and engagements that help determine root causes of problems and explain the practices that lead to safe performance.

REQUIREMENTS OF BENCHMARKING

Common quality tools (such as six sigma, process mapping, and pareto analysis, for exam-ple) can improve organizational performance and contribute to improved designs. However, virtually all process improvement requires the external perspective brought by benchmarking. A former CEO of DuPont has said that all of the major changes at DuPont over the past decade have been driven by benchmarks of performance. It has been a robust process for leading change in a staid older company.

The value of benchmarking comes from four areas: rigor, suspension of disbelief, accountability, and culture change.

RIGOR (MAKING SURE THE TARGETS ARE SET HIGH ENOUGH)

From DuPont's early benchmarking study of plant maintenance, it was found that the best companies measured how much of their maintenance was planned and how much of it was reactive to equipment failure. DuPont found that only about a third of its maintenance was planned. One plant set a goal to plan 70% of its maintenance. They thought this was an optimistic objective, that it could never be achieved, but that it was worth going after. As the goal was getting closer, planned maintenance was benchmarked and it was found that the best practitioners were planning well over 90% of their maintenance. The consequences of this best practice was less maintenance overtime, lower maintenance cost, and longer equipment uptime.

How do you set your safety goals? How do you know if they are high enough? Are they realistic? You can't know if your goals and objectives are adequate without looking by benchmarking.

SUSPENSION OF DISBELIEF (CONVINCING OURSELVES THAT WE CAN ACCOMPLISH THE RESULTS)

If you don't think you can do something, you usually can't. Conversely, if you see others doing something, you usually think you can do it too. In a recent benchmarking study of maintenance, plant turnarounds were viewed. This is where you bring a refinery or machine center down for a period of time to do maintenance on the equipment when it is off-line. The American automotive industry was found to have been chasing Honda over the years. In the old days it took months in the summer to re-tool for new models, and the lost productivity and waste were substantial. Honda showed the industry that retooling could be done in weeks and then days and now hours. The secret was designing in the process for faster turnarounds. Now all the companies know it can be done and a number are right behind Honda.

DuPont's safety performance is widely recognized, but very few companies seriously benchmark our processes. One company did and took almost a year to benchmark their safety processes. They put some of their best people on the team, led by a senior vice-president. They worked with the DuPont safety business unit that transfers safety technology internally and externally to customers. The resulting commitment to excellence produced a ten-fold improvement in safety performance by the benchmarking company. One of their retired plant managers, returning to the plant for an annual picnic, apologized to the employees for the hundreds of incidents that didn't need to have happened while he led the plant. He said, "I didn't know we could be this good."

ACCOUNTABILITY (ASSIGNING RESPONSIBILITY)

Benchmarking is applied in today's organization to provide an ongoing process for measuring performance and prompting continuous improvement. Within DuPont and many global enterprises, the process of leadership includes the ongoing improvement of a business or function and the continuing examination of this performance versus the best. The best companies institutionalize the auditing of process design and do root-cause analysis of failures.

CULTURE CHANGE (REDIRECTING AN ORGANIZATION'S FOCUS)

Benchmarking leads to being an outward-looking company, rather than one internally focused. This is often what causes the major step change in the organization.

One of DuPont's best textile fibers customers developed metrics for each of its products (denim, corduroy, and so forth) that were based on their customer's perceived values. They then compared themselves with their competitors and found that they were the best in a number of categories and usually in the top three. The CEO didn't trust the results so he brought in a world-renowned textile professor. The consulting professor reported back that, yes, they were in fact the best, but only among U.S. producers. When they compared themselves with European and Asian producers, they weren't the best in any fabric category. The CEO was pleased to see the opportunities for improvement for his entire product line and it began to change the mindset of his employees to becoming global competitors.

As you can see, the business value of benchmarking is broad. It is a tool that can bring best practices to bear on products. (For example, a new car offers passengers a better survival rate at higher speeds because the engine is designed to drop down and give more room to absorb the crash). In addition, benchmarking can focus on business processes such as the new product development process; for example, the cycle time to bring out a new safety feature can be reduced with the use of the best practice of concurrent engineering.

Figure 3-1 is the map of the DuPont benchmarking process that was adapted from Xerox, AT&T, and Citibank to support the DuPont benchmarking procedures that have been developed over the years. It can be useful as we think through the application of the benchmarking tool on safety through design.

THE BENCHMARKING PROCESS

PHASE I: PLANNING (PLAN)

To deliver world-class performance, you must keep score (measure process performance) and understand your customer's desires, the best you can provide, and the best your competitors can provide. In addition, you must understand what the external world is doing and how they are achieving those results. By applying the benchmarking tool, a quantitative and qualitative assessment of our practices is provided for comparison to those of the outside world.

It is important to describe early what part of the process you are benchmarking. In other words, what is "safety through design" based on?
- Safe to design?
- Safe to build?
- Safe to operate?
- Safe to dismantle?
- Safe disposal?
- All of these?

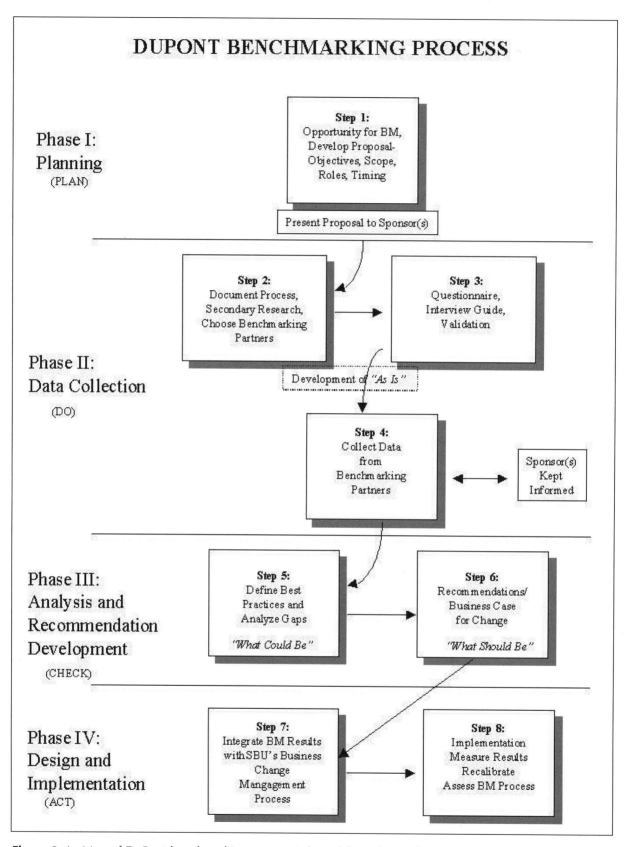

Figure 3–1. Map of DuPont benchmarking process (adapted from those of Xerox, At&T, and Citibank) to support the DuPont benchmarking procedures developed over the years.

Next, what are the potential systems categories to be reviewed during the study?

➤ How do you measure the safety through design process?

➤ What are the roles of the different members of the organization in safety through design?

➤ What are the consequences of poor safety through design performance in the organization?

➤ What are the rewards for good safety through design performance?

➤ What are the consequences to individuals who disregard appropriate safety through design on all their work?

➤ How is a concept like safety through design introduced into an organization?

➤ How are safety through design results communicated through the organization?

➤ What is the safety through design expectation for suppliers and contractors supporting an organization?

➤ What percentage of time is dedicated to safety through design and other safety items each month?

➤ What are the best practices that enable safety through design?

Finally, are you going to focus on benchmarks of cost and cost/benefit analysis, or on an external analysis of safety performance results (percentage hazards uncovered during development, percentage construction injury, percentage lifecycle process incidents recorded)?

PARTICIPANTS IN THE BENCHMARKING PROCESS

> Choosing the right participants to sponsor, lead, resource, and participate in the benchmarking engagement is critical to its success.

Who in the organization should be involved in the safety through design benchmarking process? A critical insight of any change process is "you can't learn for someone else and you can't benchmark for someone else." The organization must benchmark for itself, so it is critical that participants in the benchmarking process represent both leadership and content expert viewpoints. Choosing the right participants to sponsor, lead,

facilitate, and participate in the benchmarking engagement is critical to success. Each participant has a role to play and each contributes to the success of the benchmarking process.

Strategic management

➤ Safety through design is a paradigm that, when understood, leads to business decisions and commitment to the engineering of safety.

➤ When it is an integral part of ongoing business execution, the business should want to benchmark, asking the question "how do we compare to others that apply this process?"

➤ Resources and funding must be approved at strategic levels to ensure success.

➤ Management must be willing to hear the facts, behave in a nonjudgmental manner, and adopt the findings.

➤ Agreement must be reached on the kind of results expected from everyone, and which results are to be measured.

➤ Management must help define which partners will have credibility when bringing back the practices.

➤ Sponsors need to follow through with audits to monitor application of safety through design concepts.

➤ Participants must continuously go back and repeat the process, upgrading and improving it.

Line management

Line management must be able to

➤ plan for data collection and analysis as an integral part of the overall work plan;

➤ review, interpret, understand, and adjust to benchmarking data to drive improvement;

➤ integrate benchmarking into resource planning; and

➤ measure results and provide immediate feedback.

Operations

These participants need a defined (written) plan for data collection and must be kept informed of how results are used to drive improvement (safer facilities, for example).

Customer of services

➤ What are the safety consequences to the user of services downstream of the design (operators, contractors, general public)?

➤ Can the individual/team who prepared the design receive and evaluate downstream results?

Specialists/safety consultants/process resource
Content experts can often accelerate cycle times through their industry contacts and increase the level of inquiry because of a higher level of understanding of the process and its feedback. Benchmarking may be conducted best by third-party specialists when there are proprietary concerns or issues of data collection, analysis, and reporting. Third-party specialists collect and display data (without disclosing individual sources), provide a filter for confidential information, and ensure compliance with legal restriction on information exchange. Consultants can provide consistent guidance, accurate interpretation, trend analysis, and real-time feedback.

Generally, a study will go 20% faster and cover at least 20% more information with the participation of a benchmarking process resource. The role of the resource can include
➤ performing project management;
➤ engaging secondary research;
➤ providing access to external partners;
➤ developing a questionnaire and interview guide; and
➤ developing skills such as interviewing techniques and data analysis.

The resource does not lead the study, but accelerates the learning and deployment of best practices.

FRONT-END LOADING
It is critical to plan for the front-end loading of the study. Usually an organization gets more than half of the benefit from a benchmarking study through studying their own process. For an effective study, you must understand your own process before you ask others how they perform. One of the quality tools that help capture a process is mapping. It is useful to have the team draw a picture of the process and gain consensus regarding the current state, how it is measured, and what level of performance is being achieved. It is important but always difficult to define those measurable leading indicators that translate into downstream performance. Innovation is a primary driver of business profitability: 3M, for example, uses "percent of sale from new prod-

ucts" as a metric for the level of innovation; DuPont uses safety performance as a leading metric for the health of operations processes.

> Usually an organization gets more than half of the benefit from a benchmarking study through studying their own process.

Each organization, team, or task group needs to "map" its work process to understand leading and lagging indicators. In this chapter, the authors are trying to aid in understanding the benchmarking process and the leading indicators so that downstream results can be improved. It may be possible to isolate units of work so that they can more easily be measured, benchmarked, and modified.
➤ Determine (and chart) who is responsible for accomplishing each work unit.
➤ Determine if the work processes the same way each time to normalize benchmark comparisons.
➤ Determine who makes the decisions on how to design a new process, who controls the safety design decisions, and who controls the budget.
➤ Determine whether designing for safety is to be treated as "added work" or an "integral design activity."

Because you must have the most knowledgeable people on the project core team and they almost always have "day jobs," they have to make about 20% of their time available for the study. Since benchmarking is part of all of our jobs, that shouldn't be too difficult—but it always is. Make sure the team has the resources in time, administrative support, and funds for travel and research.

PHASE II: DATA COLLECTION (DO)
You might save a couple hours in the library by scheduling a benchmarking visit right away, but this is called "industrial tourism" and is frowned upon in benchmarking circles. The first rule of the benchmarking process is get your act together before you go out and talk to the world's experts. Do your homework first and see what the latest thinking is on your subject. You don't know, what you don't know, and you may find

that many of your questions can be answered by secondary research from public information. That doesn't mean that there won't still be a lot gained by questioning and interviewing practitioners. Even if all of the best practices are well defined, you may want an external counterpart to share what their implementation problems were. Know as much as you can before you go out.

> The first rule of the benchmarking process is get your act together before you go out and talk to the world's experts.

In many business processes such as call centers, Web page design, and safety, there are organizations that have not only the understanding of best practices, but the capability to transfer the technology. This is often the most productive way to transform an organization. However, before you spend your money on these consultants, "benchmark" their services. Find examples of successful clients and less successful clients you can interview to make sure there is a fit for your organization.

Structure your questions in a questionnaire for quantitative information and an interview guide for qualitative questions. Make sure you validate both instruments before you go outside. If your organization can't answer the questions, it is likely that others can't either.

Developing criteria for partners is an important part of the implementation of a study. The wrong partners can waste your time in talking to people who don't understand the concept of safety through design or whose design processes have very little overlap with yours. You usually learn a few things from everyone if you have done your homework, but it is often true that you will learn most from one or two of the partners.

➤ Focus on developing criteria for partners and then choosing partners that are closest to the criteria.

➤ Identify individuals, teams, and companies who do the things you are trying to accomplish in a "world class" fashion. Benchmark targets may be identified in businesses that are quite different from yours but that have similar work processes. Try to map typical industries to identify possible matches with individual blocks on your work map.

➤ Look for businesses with a strong public vision statement on safety commitment.

➤ Look for industries and businesses with good overall long-term performance. An organization is probably not going to have an extended growth record without demonstrating some consideration of safety through design.

➤ Some of the best practices can be derived from a company that had a significant failure in its process. These significant events can be a real wake-up call, and even though the organization may not have institutionalized the changes, they can be excellent sources of best practices. Companies like Exxon, Dow Corning, Union Carbide and DuPont have all had to respond to significant safety through design issues.

➤ Look for organizations that have a strong record in environmental excellence and employee satisfaction. Safety through design will be closely linked to these items.

➤ Consider adding safety through design items to existing data-sharing or benchmarking exchanges.

➤ Look for opportunities to benchmark internally among individuals or business sectors.
  • Review relative trends over time to understand the relationship between leading indicators and final results.
  • Analyze absolute performance to improve understanding of performance between similar and different sub-sets of the same organization.

➤ Pick a couple of partners that are outside of your obvious area or someone from the public sector. (For example, a manufacturing company might wish to benchmark against Disney or the postal service.)

➤ Think globally.

➤ Keep focused on the future; the best process over the last decade may not be competitive for the next one.

➤ Efficiency of handling may be as important as volume. If you were trying to improve the accounts payable process for a college engineering department that handles a few hundred invoices a month, you wouldn't necessarily want to benchmark your performance against AMEX, which may handle 3 million an hour.

→ Don't look for the Holy Grail. You usually can only learn a little more than you know. Be realistic—your objective may be to become world-class, but you must be able to walk before you run. Don't go after the Nobel Prize-winning expert when there are teachers closer to home from whom you can learn a great deal.

Keep the sponsors apprised of what you are finding as you go through the study. It takes time to learn, and significant change will often require some time to absorb the lessons.

PHASE III: ANALYSIS AND RECOMMENDATION DEVELOPMENT (CHECK)

Early examination of successful benchmarking studies showed that both resources and elapsed time are equally divided among the preparation, the actual interviewing for metrics and best practices, and the analysis. Pull together the best practices from the survey and share them with your partners. This provides the partners with an incentive to participate in the process, and it lets you validate your findings.

As you develop your plan to take out the findings of your study, you will see the value of front-end loading a project. If you have done your homework, the organization will be pushing you for results and chafing at the bit to start deploying the changes.

From the set of best practices and metrics, you will adapt recommendations for your organization. Many organizations have an institutionalized change process that lets them deploy resources and process improvements as part of their ongoing operating process.

This is a critical part of the process as you plan for the transfer of the best practices. But just as with safety through design, the way to ensure success is to design it into the process, which means

→ keep sponsors informed;
→ conduct good secondary research;
→ define the topics and information required to improve the process;
→ develop sound criteria for partners;
→ assign the right people to the core team; and
→ provide the resources.

PHASE IV: DESIGN AND IMPLEMENTATION (ACT)

How are you going to deploy the results? Improvement to a process or design based on input from benchmarking requires the ability to aggressively look for and incorporate change. Organizations need a robust change management process, which requires setting milestones and providing resources to deploy the changes.

→ Determine how the organization provides incentive for, and recognizes and rewards, a change agent. Why would an individual/team want to do a better job of safety through design? (The incentive could be as basic as survival of a business.)
→ Be able to view and present ideas in terms that the organization can understand and value. Present the case for life-cycle cost savings from safety through design versus exclusive focus on possible higher first cost.
→ Conduct (and document) formal safety item reviews during the design phase of a project to determine if the organization's stated best practices are being applied and if knowledge from previous benchmarking studies has been incorporated. (This must be a top-down process.)
→ Post both internal and external benchmarking results so that the individuals/teams doing the work can monitor how they are performing.
→ Show the relationship between safety through design performance and compensation.

BARRIERS TO DEPLOYING CHANGE

DESIRE FOR A QUICK FIX

Now that the elements of a benchmarking study have been reviewed, what are the mechanisms of change? It has been found that with the pressure of global competition, individuals are often looking for a magic solution, which is virtually never available. Improving the impact of benchmarking involves a change process—the ongoing search for practices that can be applied to the business for continuous improvement. Improving the safety through design process is not a one-time event; it is an ongoing process. Manage the expectations of the organization so that you can make incremental changes. It is important that everyone recognize that this is a continuous evolution. Expectations for a single quick fix can be a major barrier to deploying change.

> Improving the safety through design process is not a one-time event; it is an ongoing process.

FALSE PERCEPTION OF UNIQUENESS

A second roadblock to accepting external benchmarks and best practices is the attitude that "we're different." Individuals and organizations like to think of themselves as unique—and in some ways they are right. There are very few "best practices" that can be adopted directly into an organization. In fact, the term "best practices" is a misnomer because practices are inherently "best" only in the context of the overall process. Still, it is useful to use the term best practices (they are best for someone) as a way of describing enablers of business processes that may be adapted to achieve superior results. To take an extreme example: if my business goal is to design a garment to protect the wearer from being shot, what is the "best practice" for thickness? The answer is "it depends." Who is the garment being designed for? If for an infantryman who may encounter repeated fire into one place on the garment, you would have a thick bulky vest. But if it is for a businessman traveling in an area where kidnapping is a problem, it needs to be able to fit unobtrusively into the lining of a raincoat or it won't be worn.

FEAR OF "COPYING"

Not everyone endorses benchmarking. There are individuals who have an aversion to benchmarking because they think of it as plagiarizing. This attitude is frustrating because it can result in an internally focused organization that is not competitive. When children are sent to school to learn math, they aren't expected to invent algebra, geometry, and calculus themselves. Process leaders shouldn't be expected to make up their own business processes as they go, when instead they can learn from the best.

CULTURE AND MANAGEMENT PROCESSES

Designing-in safety includes designing it into managing processes and organizational behavior. An organization's culture and organizational behavior plays a big part in determining what practices can be successful in an organization. Some cultures have managing processes that can overcome higher levels of risk. When deploying best practices and process improvement steps, make sure you look at the whole "system." The cause of the explosion of the NASA Space Shuttle Challenger was O-rings failing at cold temperatures. If NASA had designed a more robust decision-making process on deciding when to launch, the O-ring information would have been included and acted upon, and the incident probably would have been avoided.

APPLICATION OF BENCHMARKING TO SAFETY THROUGH DESIGN

To ensure that safety through design concepts are incorporated into work processes and systems, it is necessary for the responsible individual/organization to have appropriate standards and expectations defining what this concept should look like in the final product. Ultimately, engineering work processes should be executed to deliver products and facilities that are safe to build, operate, dismantle, and dispose of.

Benchmarking provides a means for defining what is possible in safety performance, establishing specific safety goals, and driving continuous improvement in areas such as reduction in personal injuries, property damage, and environmental incidents. Awareness of these goals and expectations coupled with feedback on how existing facilities and processes actually function can provide valuable information to those researching and designing similar new processes.

ENGINEERING PROCESS MODEL

In a typical engineering work process, there may be a significant time lag between when a design is issued and when the downstream consequences are realized. In fact, there may be cases where there are no recognized incidents to trigger improvement on what is actually an inherently unsafe design. The same unsafe design(s) could thus be repeated time and again before any need for a change is evident. Making corrections

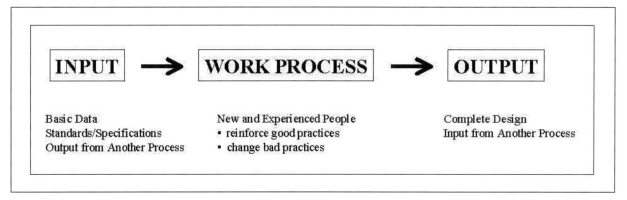

Figure 3–2. The flow of input to the work process to produce design-based deliverables is shown.

based on this blind approach is more extensive and costly than managing an effective system to establish goals and provide knowledge feedback to do things right the first time. A quality benchmarking process and an efficient, robust real-time feedback mechanism are absolute necessities for managing and improving safe and competitive engineered facilities.

Much engineering work can be broken down into a series of discrete activities. The generic model (Figure 3-2) describes the steps of the process model.

Input to the work process may take different forms and could possibly include basic data, management instructions, business objectives, standard policies, output from other work processes, and feedback from downstream processes. The work process step is where the input data/material is processed through one or more iterations to produce design-based deliverables. Engineers, designers, and other specialists use generic design tools, automated engineering systems, and individual experience-based techniques to do this work. The output from this work process could be a complete design or input to additional processing steps.

EXAMPLES OF THE NEED FOR EXTERNAL BENCHMARKING

Great amounts of time may elapse between initial design and final dismantle phases (Figure 3-3). Clearly, though, there may be lessons learned during the dismantle phase that could in retrospect have significantly improved the work of the original design phase; but the time between the two phases makes this impossible for a company that only learns from its own experience.

Benchmarking, however, makes it possible to "learn from experience" that you haven't even had yet, by looking at the experience of others who have. For example, after several disastrous oil leaks occurred in single-hull tankers at sea (in the operate/maintain phase), shipbuilders around the world began incorporating double-hull technology into their designs, regardless of whether or not their own single-hull ships had ever had an incident.

This kind of benchmarking uses the experiences of others to accelerate your own safety through design progress. For this reason, even though the greatest impact of safety through design will be realized in the build and operate/maintain phases, we can best review benchmarking to improve safety through design by starting from the dismantle phase and working *back* through the previous steps.

DISMANTLE

There is need to direct attention toward understanding how to safely dismantle and dispose of (or reuse) facilities that are no longer useful. Safety consideration needs to be directed to rigging and lifting, isolation, product and equipment decontamination, soil and drainage treatment, working in restricted areas, etc. These considerations are quite remote from someone working the project design phase, but any significant knowledge should be shared within organizations, associations, and consortiums if possible. Examples of knowledge that could be shared could include the fact that special consideration needs to be made for vessels and pipe that could contain "frozen" process material that could become unstable (explode or burn) if the vessel were heated while

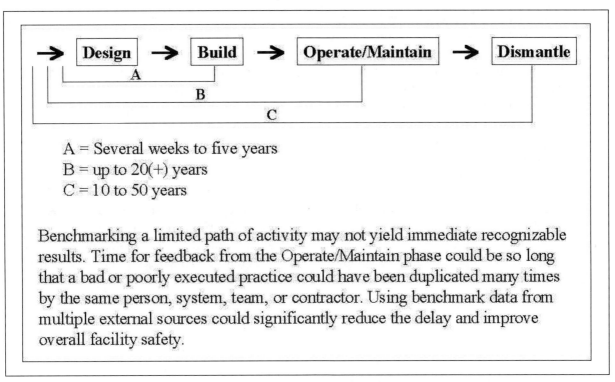

A = Several weeks to five years
B = up to 20(+) years
C = 10 to 50 years

Benchmarking a limited path of activity may not yield immediate recognizable results. Time for feedback from the Operate/Maintain phase could be so long that a bad or poorly executed practice could have been duplicated many times by the same person, system, team, or contractor. Using benchmark data from multiple external sources could significantly reduce the delay and improve overall facility safety.

Figure 3–3. Benchmarking to improve safety through design is best done by starting at the dismantle phase and working back through the previous steps.

being cut or torched. Are more drains needed (at the design phase) for this rare event? Can double-wall or clad-wall vessels be safely handled and separated? (There is design work required to plan/design a major or complex dismantling, and safety through design should be applied.)

OPERATE/MAINTAIN

This is the phase of the project with the greatest exposure time, highest product handling risk, and best opportunity to establish benchmarking practices. Significant operations items that may be directly related to safety through design include
- number and seriousness of injuries;
- number and type of environmental incidents;
- regulatory agency interventions;
- frequency of ergonomic incidents;
- labor issues based on safety matters; and
- overall facilities downtime due to safety related issues.

There are numerous approaches on how to select and audit or benchmark these performance items. Benchmarking data can be collected by and compared within trade associations, consortiums, educational institutions, regulatory agencies, and labor organizations.

The benchmarking data can be used to measure how others in similar processes and industries perform, and might be used to set new standards of safety performance within an organization. Consideration must be given to changes in organizational culture, expectations of line management, labor relations, perceived and real costs of implementation, and tools and training. Other chapters in this book will address these issues in more detail. These benchmarks are real-time for the operate/maintain but occur after design is complete.

We are focusing on safety through design, but it is necessary to appreciate that the industry-specific data collected while benchmarking operate/maintain will require careful analysis to isolate specific design-related material. Items that contribute to safety incidents during operate/maintain may be due to more than one cause. For example, a process release that also burns an employee may be a combination of operating error, inadequate design (for the application), and poorly maintained equipment.

To produce meaningful feedback to people who can effect change early in current design processes, it is necessary to conduct a thorough incident investigation, isolate details of specific design shortcomings, document improvement recommendations, and assure wide communication within the entire organization. It may be that during the original design review for a project, it was determined (and documented) that an administrative procedure negated the need for a more complex (costly) design solution. If internal or external benchmarking begins to identify repeat similar incidents, then the original design safety review logic and design need to be examined and reconsidered. A similar type of analysis can be conducted for ergonomic and environmental incidents.

An example would be the repeated spilling of a hazardous product at a filling station. Investigation revealed the original design was to include level control instrumentation and automatic shutoff capability. This was rejected due to cost and the fact that an operator would be present during the filling cycle. The installation, as built, relied on the operator to monitor the level of the product in the container and manually stop flow when the level reached a predetermined point. The operator became distracted while monitoring other activities during the filling cycle, which caused the container to overflow repeatedly and create a hazardous situation. The solution was to review the operator job assignment and training; install instrumentation per original design to automate the process and eliminate the source of the problem; and to give formal wide distribution of this knowledge through the safety network.

BUILD

Except during the final build activities, there is probably no process-related exposure to be managed. There are, however, different serious construction-related safety issues that need to be addressed in the design phase. During the build phase, a large work force is being exposed to a complex, dangerous environment that changes daily. Safety through design needs to consider how the facility will be assembled and if there are better ways to accomplish this task. Considerations like designing to minimize work at elevated heights and modularization of subassemblies at remote, less congested locations not only reduce safety exposure but probably make good economic sense also. Items and

activities to benchmark during the build phase could include

- injuries (minor and lost time);
- environmental incidents;
- ergonomic incidents;
- potential incidents; and
- labor safety issues.

Business and construction management needs to set goals and expectations of performance for each job. As with the operate/maintain phase, benchmarking can be used to identify what is feasible and what the advantages are for improved performance. There are several ways to plan benchmarking for the build phase:

- Compare competitors in the same industry;
- Compare the same construction contractor for different clients;
- Compare internally against other similar projects; and
- Compare against business management's or the contractor's established standards.

Throughout the design phase, an investigation similar to that described for operate/maintain needs to be conducted for each incident to isolate the design safety items. Feedback needs to be made promptly.

It should be evident that it is impossible to do an adequate safety through design process unless the design leaders include knowledgeable build and operate/maintain representatives as integrated members of the design team. Their contributions are not to be added after the design, but rather fully integrated to ensure the safest product/process/facility possible.

DESIGN

The design phase of the project is the home base for safety through design, even though many basic concepts and safety audits have already been proposed, evaluated, selected, and fully documented in predesign reviews. The consequences of safety decisions at this phase will not be realized until some time in the future. Feedback from benchmarking audit data in the later phases of other projects is very useful in the appropriate selection of design solutions and equipment. Knowledge from previous operate/maintain reviews on administration and design in safe concepts can be used as the basis for policy issues. Difficulties and problems with previous start-ups and dismantling operations also provide real experiences to help avoid similar conditions (or at least allow a realistic life-cycle cost analysis).

Benchmarking during design can track both leading indicators and quality of current work performance. Leading indicators would include the status of the following:

➤ Project design safety audits;
➤ Fire and safety reviews;
➤ Process hazards reviews;
➤ Risk analysis;
➤ Ergonomic reviews;
➤ Environmental reviews;
➤ Electrical classification reviews;
➤ Control safety reviews;
➤ Process relief safety reviews;
➤ Labor safety reviews;
➤ Operations safety review;
➤ Building code review; and
➤ Regulatory safety reviews.

All of these reviews provide valuable information on the adequacy of the design to meet all safety, environmental, and ergonomic requirements and standards as established by the owner, operators, and regulatory agencies. Most of these reviews can be conducted using established procedures and checklists (assuming users are knowledgeable) to ensure total safety coverage.

Unless the identical team conducts every safety review step, there will be variability in the products. There will be obvious differences for different process and types of production facilities being designed. There may also be differences due to culture of the workplace, geographic locations, complexity of the process, skill/training of those conducting the reviews, access to information, budget limitations, time constraints, and so forth.

A second type of design-phase benchmarking is auditing the quality of the various reviews listed above to determine how well the reviews themselves satisfy the safety through design concept. This type of periodic benchmarking audit can be done on a static sampling. Knowledgeable experts in each audit category perform this benchmark. They would check to ensure that selected safety reviews were correctly done and documented. This across-the-board review by a select team allows a check for consistency of application of the correct design tools and can

identify common (or individual) deficiencies, need for training/standards, and perhaps need for corrective action if significant shortcomings are noted. This benchmarking requires strong management support to achieve success and should not be viewed or used as an evaluation of individual performance.

Open lines of communication are needed to ensure a positive safety through design experience. The organization must have a managing process that institutionalizes the knowledge learned from this feedback. As knowledge acquired from the benchmarking, operate/maintain reviews, and difficulties with start-ups comes together, the organization must capture this information for future action.

SUMMARY

We have seen that a benchmarking program for safety through design is only as strong as its weakest link. Equal care and attention must be given to

➤ quality of measurements and analysis;
➤ effective feedback communications network; and
➤ management commitment to apply learnings to ongoing planning and processes.

Achieving the goal of ever-improving safety performance requires the external perspective provided by benchmarking. This search for best practices to adapt to your phases of design, build, operate/maintain, and dismantle ensures an ongoing improvement process. Seeing examples of excellence will suspend disbelief in major changes and can provide an organizational culture that is less internally focused, more accountable, and more comfortable with setting rigorous standards for continuous improvement.

How good is your design process? How do you measure your rate of improvement? Is safety designed into the process? Who does it better? What are their practices? These are the questions that can be answered with the tool of benchmarking. References 2-6 have been added to provide additional resources on the benchmarking process.

The material in this chapter is a distillation of ideas, insights, and anecdotes that we have found useful in understanding the benchmarking process and how it influences safety through design. We want to thank the safety professionals and design process leaders within DuPont and the National Safety Council who have shared their wisdom with us over the years and made this chapter possible. Any failure here to capture the robust value of the benchmarking tool and the profound impact of designing safety into a process is ours alone.

REFERENCES

1. Camp RC: *Benchmarking: The Search for Industry Best Practices that Lead to Superior Performance.* Milwaukee: ASQC Quality Press, 1989.

2. Bogan CE, English MJ: Benchmarking: A wakeup call for board members (and CEOs too). *Planning Review* 21:28, 1993.

3. Boxwell RJ: Benchmarking for Competitive Advantage. New York: McGraw-Hill, 1994.

4. Camp RC: *Business Process Benchmarking: Finding and Implementing Best Practices.* Milwaukee: ASQC Quality Press, 1994.

5. Hammer M, Champy J: *Re-engineering the Corporation: Manifesto for Business Revolution.* New York: Harper Business, 1993.

6. Zairi M, Leonard P: *Practical Benchmarking: A Complete Guide.* London: Chapman & Hall, 1994.

Chapter 4

ACHIEVING THE NECESSARY CULTURE CHANGE

by Steven I. Simon, PhD

INTRODUCTION

A full explanation of what culture change is and is not, who is involved, why it is necessary and can achieve world class safety through design, and how to make it happen is provided in this chapter.

It would appear self-evident that integrating safety concepts early into the design process would pay dividends for a company in terms of reducing injuries, as well as increasing production and improving the bottom line. It is, after all, the ultimate in common sense. Then why do some of the people who are supposed to be the most rational in the organization, such as senior management and technical leaders, frequently give only lip service, but neither the resources nor personal leadership to intensive safety through design efforts? Look at it from an historical perspective: Why have people resisted any prevention measure? What blocks them (and us) from embracing what is clearly a great benefit?

Engineers, in the writer's experience, are traditionally among the most resistant employees when it comes to safety culture change ideas and initiatives. Even for this book, there were a couple of skeptics who wondered why there was even going to be a chapter on the subject. "It's so obvious," they said, "why bother?" Another reading of this might be, "It does 'Not Apply' to us, so why bother?"

Well, it does apply. And, since many of the readers of this book will be engineers, it's important to acknowledge and confront the norm among many engineers that culture issues are 'Not Applicable' to good safety, even in circumstances where those issues obstruct the effective implementation of their own safety engineering solutions. There is probably not one single engineer who could not do a much better job if only they were allowed to do it—not held back by management opacity, given the requisite resources, and not foiled by unfriendly users.

IGNORANCE VS. CULTURE

If it is not ignorance, then it is clearly cultural. So it is important to identify what those cultural elements, those blocks, are. If we can identify the forces that stand in the way of change and progress, then, hopefully, we can overcome them. These blocks are the cultural norms and assumptions that are obsolete or unfounded, but nevertheless they are clearly accepted as given. Generally they require complete demolition, because they are so deeply held, based as they are on years of experience and extreme prejudice, e.g., it's the way we've always done things and it's always worked fine.

What is evident to the convert, or even the uninitiated, may be resisted by those whose perceptions and beliefs are conditioned by past practices and/or who have a vested interest in preserving the status quo. The machinist who has never worn eye protection and has never had an incident may resist the use of a foreign and somewhat uncomfortable piece of equipment. If, in addition, users have to pay for their eyewear, or the exam to prove a prescription is really needed, they will be even less inclined to make the change.

This is similar to the manager who is asked to embrace a new safety through design initiative. On one level, the manager may understand that safety through design makes perfect sense, but may not want to do things differently (it is uncomfortable) and may not want to pay for it. And engineers are not immune to this virus. In spite of the obvious benefits of safety through design, they may not want to change the way they have traditionally worked and they may not want to engage safety practitioners, line management, even operators, in early design decisions.

These are examples of safety culture in the workplace—negative safety culture. On the other hand, when employees in a plant urge each other, visitors or contractors, to wear their safety glasses or hard hats, it is an example of a positive culture, or a positive element of the safety culture. Managers, likewise, can exhibit positive or negative safety culture, but their attitudes, behaviors and decisions often affect the physical safety of many, not just a few.

Although there are some skeptics among contributors to this book, my co-authors generally recognize that a culture change is a necessary element in any safety through design initiative. They point out, and they are correct, that top management must be converted to the cause; that is absolutely essential. But, in referring to a true culture change, we must make sure to go beyond using historical data and case studies to convince decision-makers that safety through design will contribute positively to the bottom line. That may, in fact, be nothing more than sound, old-fashioned salesmanship. You go in, make the case, and get the okay. But have we really changed culture? Has management bought the program or bought into it? Will management act as change leaders or simply go along with the wishes of a few importuning safety and engineering professionals? Do they see safety through design as a complement to other health and safety programs or a substitute?

One danger is that you could end up creating a creature like Dr. Dolittle's Pushme-pullme. It has been seen before with behavioral safety programs versus technical improvements. One approach may unwittingly be supported at the expense of the other. As one manager related, "Since behavior is responsible for 90-plus percent of all accidents, we can modify behavior... and reduce capital outlays for safety-focused technical enhancements." Contrarily, if it is believed that safety through design can protect the worker, in spite of all his flaws, there may be a short-changing of training and other worker improvement programs. A culture like that will end up fostering competition, rather than cooperation, with various interest groups vying for scarce safety resources.

Ultimately, the only kind of culture change that is worth doing in order to achieve safety through design is one that involves all levels of the workforce—management, supervisors, hourly employees, and design professionals—and engages them in a durable, collaborative venture. Without leadership at all levels, as well as communication and cooperation among the people who design the machines and those who operate them, we are doomed to push and pull against ourselves.

N/A...N/A...N/A....

According to one safety practitioner, the engineers at his facility "march to the beat of a different drummer, particularly when it comes to safety." They worked at a manufacturing facility of one of the nation's largest and most prestigious companies, in a New England town that we will call Fallsbluff. Since it was an engineering center for their division, there were 100 engineers out of a total plant population of 800. But they might as well have been on Mars for all that they were integrated into the daily life of the facility.

The writer consulted there for three years in the not-too-distant past and, although the plant's safety record at the outset was more-or-less average, their safety culture was truly in a sorry state. The safety practitioner administered a safety culture survey at the start, to as many of the employees as he could round up (more than 400), and a number of focus groups were held to get specific feedback and anecdotal information. The results indicated that Fallsbluff had a generally poor safety culture, with some of the lowest ratings the writer had seen on scales across the board. As predicted by an enlightened health and safety staff, the survey and focus groups indicated a great deal of mistrust and suspicion between management and labor—a gulf the size of the proverbial Grand Canyon. Workers questioned whether management really cared about their safety, instead worrying only about numbers; and management suspected workers sabotaged safety innovations and falsified some of their injury claims.

The good news was that there was hardly any gap between the perceptions of management and labor in assessing the situation. Both groups looked at conditions honestly and critically, often scoring within a few percentage points of each other on almost all categories and questions in the survey. This was certainly something positive to build upon. No one, apparently, was hiding his head in the sand. Well, almost no one; the surveys returned by the engineering group looked like checkerboards, with a very high number of "N/A" (Not Applicable) responses to the 51 questions, many times higher than any other group in the plant. Apparently when it came to plant safety, many of the topics did "Not Apply" to them.

What kinds of things did "Not Apply"? There were 51 questions on the survey, measuring 12 sub-scales, including the safety of the work environment, safety leadership, social process, safety considerations of their jobs, the safety practices of their co-workers, etc. They defined their work environment as their own offices, counted only fellow engineers as their co-workers, and considered that their jobs were without inherent hazards.

Still, one might argue, it might be possible for an engineer who thinks and works apart from the general hubbub to design a safer machine, a better mousetrap as it were. Possibly, but that was definitely not the case in Fallsbluff. The great divide between engineering and the general population also interfered with the successful design, installation, and use of safeguards. Engineers, for example, followed a strict policy of designing attachments to any machine over 35 pounds. They sent out a memo about it, but were frustrated to see that the attachments were not being used. They did not say anything to operators on the floor, however, because of fear of operator reaction.

Engineers also complained that people in manufacturing did not attend unit reviews. They felt that while they were working on plans six months out, the operators were focused only on day-to-day concerns.

The view from the other side was no less grim. Operators in the main bay felt that the cranes they were using were unsafe, that the parts had gotten bigger, but the cranes were not designed to pick up the heavier units. Rather than saying much about this, operators simply rotated equipment as best they could, knowing that what they were doing was "unsafe." There was also a grinder that was long considered unsafe, but it was not "till a kid lost fingers" in it that it was finally corrected.

It was not surprising, therefore, that in response to the statement, "Our jobs are designed to be as safe as possible," only 43 percent of hourly and 55 percent of management agreed that this was true. Even fewer respondents, 28 percent of hourly employees and 30 percent of management, agreed that "Our work environment is as safe as technology can make it." Many engineers simply thought these statements did "Not Apply" to them.

While it might be theoretically possible to design a perfect machine and a perfect work environment, clearly this could not happen in a culture where accurate information does not flow smoothly back and forth, and where trust and personal involvement and identification are so weak.

Perhaps the most telling result of the initial research came from some remarks made during one focus group. Some engineers were complaining that their favorite vending machine was in the machine shop (where there were typically flying particles). Up until a year earlier, they could just go in there and buy snacks and sodas, but then there was a new policy that safety glasses had to be worn by anyone going into that area, whether they worked there or not. The engineers didn't think the eyeglass policy should apply to them, and they weren't happy about it.

Perhaps cultural safety people tend to focus too much on this type of small, symbolic act, but it sends a powerful message. If engineers in Fallsbluff refused to wear PPE in designated areas, how could they expect workers to comply? Workers will continue to leave their glasses on top of their hats, walk through yellow tape, and frustrate the best efforts of those same design engineers, until the overall plant culture turns against those unsafe behaviors. And members of the engineering group are a key component of that culture; they, above all others, must demonstrate that they understand that safety issues Do Apply to their own group.

WHAT IS SAFETY CULTURE?

So far, it has been established that safety culture is more than management's current thinking about safety; and safety culture change is more than changing management's mind about how to achieve safety goals. So what is safety culture and why in the world would there be a need to change it?

Culture, in its broadest sense, is that set of perceptions, values, beliefs, and assumptions that determine how we as individuals see the reality around us, and how it affects the way we behave. These constructs can be visible or invisible, accurate or inaccurate. Before Copernicus, it was believed (known) that the sun revolved around the earth. It rose on one side and went down on the other, then came around again the next day. Likewise, during most of the history of mankind, people observed that the earth was flat as a pancake. To keep members of the group from falling off, the edge of the known world was marked on maps with dragons and other signs of peril. This is harmless enough, unless one is interested in global exploration and progress. In that case, it can be a major impediment.

To posit an opposing theory (no matter how true) to the accepted belief was (and still is) a sure way to risk the opprobrium or persecution of society. For society—group, tribe, or civilization—is an intolerant dictator. We like people to think the way we do. It reinforces our faith in ourselves, our society, and in our leaders. Consequently, change is difficult and conformity is the norm.

Gaining acceptance of a new idea or change, even having the new theory accepted by the academy and the royal court, is not the end of it. Culture is a continuous process. Today, more than 500 years after Columbus, fifty percent of children under the age of ten believe that the world is flat. Only by passing on our hard-won knowledge—through teaching, training and example—can change be sustained.

Research indicates that culture plays a crucial role in the productivity, quality and safety performance of our present-day organizations. The culture model helps people realize that individual actions spring from group norms and traditions, as well as individual traits. Once people are aware of these influences, they can make better choices. Normally, for instance, people do not give any thought to the way they walk up stairs. Walk into a DuPont facility, however, and people will strongly suggest that, for your own good,

you hold on to the handrail. In the best safety cultures, people question the old assumptions and share better ideas with their colleagues.

We are living in an age when culture is more assailable and changes are more readily achieved. If culture were once a nearly impregnable fortress, it is now simply a fort. Instead of taking a few decades to effect change, we can now often accomplish it in a few years.

Culture is effected by a myriad of influences. There are policies and procedures; all employees and visitors must hold on to the handrail when ascending or descending a staircase, stay to the right, use your inside hand, palm down. There are signs and symbols; the billboard at the plant gate, the pictographs at the top and bottom of each staircase. Communication; the article in the employee newsletter about handrail safety, the speech at the all hands meeting. There are rewards and punishments; the mugs, caps, and dinners for consistent handrail safety, the bad evaluation for non-compliance. There is peer pressure; "Hey, kid, smarten up and use the handrail." Setting an example; the plant manager always holding on with one hand. And, there is better engineering; a stronger handrail designed to fit the hand better.

One influence alone rarely changes the culture quickly enough to prevent incidents. Plant management has considerable power to wield, mandating change. Engineering can, perhaps, design a fail-safe system, e.g., a stair gate that only opens when you take hold of the handrail. Ultimately, however, changing the safety culture has to be a combined effort of management, labor, and professional staff, eventually engaging every member of the tribe in changing the organization's core values.

WHY BOTHER WITH CULTURE CHANGE?

Why bother with culture change? After all, it's supposed to be extremely difficult to change assumptions that are so deeply grounded. What if you change everything else, the stuff you have control of: technologies, management systems, some behaviors, reallocated resources? Wouldn't that work? How about letting the culture take care of itself? Sooner or later, it's bound to come around.

Unfortunately, that is too often the approach. Change everything but... But where the culture remains sour, where there is mistrust and lack of communication, even the best plans can go astray.

An example at a major public utility comes immediately to mind. They were a good company with a good safety record and a strong commitment to safety. Management was squarely behind all safety initiatives, including brand-new grassroots safety teams.[1] To test the effectiveness of the teams, one of the members, an electrician, made a request to fix something that had been bothering her for years and had never gotten any action. A couple of times a year, she needed to go up on a parapet, hang over the edge and turn a certain valve. It was awkward at best, potentially injurious.

The field location engineer came and took a look at the problem. He designed a safe, effective solution, relocating the pipes and valve to ground level. The only problem was that it would cost $10,000 to do it and there was no way that the company was going to go along. The team meeting where this was presented turned into a full-blown disaster complete with accusations and name calling. The next day both parties complained to management; the engineer swore he would never go back, that he was not going to take that kind of abuse; the workers accused the engineer of not being responsive.

Clearly, the two sides were out of touch with each other's needs, expectations, and forms of expression. The engineer thought that the team's request was frivolous, the workers ignorant of design, and the process demeaning. For their part, the team members thought the engineer was high-handed, unrealistic, and patronizing. It could have ended right there, with a widening credibility gap. Fortunately, management had no intention of giving up at the first sign of an impasse. Both parties were sent back to research alternative proposals and to work together doing it. Eventually, they came up with additional proposals: to erect a permanent platform for $5,000; and to buy $500 worth of scaffolding and set it up each time it was needed. They went with the periodic scaffolding, but more importantly, the parties learned to work together. Afterward, the engineer regularly attended team meetings and from an engineering point-of-view input was added to the process.

Even in the arena of safety through design, engineers have in fact frequently been frustrated by culture—production pressures, cost choices and other organizational and cultural influences blunting the use of their many skills and tools.

These are examples of negative culture at work; but what corporation, bureaucracy, or department does not have its share of inept managers, ignorant coworkers, foolish procedures, and misguided projects? The idea is to minimize their effect, improve trust and communication, and overcome obstacles; ergo, improve the culture.

HOW TO ACCOMPLISH A CULTURE CHANGE: THREE STRATEGIC ELEMENTS

We have alluded to the importance of norms and assumptions, but barely touched on the subject of how to change the culture of which they are constituents. If the culture is to change, three essential elements must exist for a reasonable chance of success. Not all organizations are ready to launch a culture change initiative. Minimally, you need to have the following:

➤ Driver(s) for change;
➤ Management support; and
➤ Structure for managing the change process.

DRIVER(S) FOR CHANGE

There are four customary ways that cultural change is driven in organizations. The most common is top-down leadership actions. Frequently, the CEO or plant manager perceives a need to change the culture of the organization, then oversees the development and execution of a planned change. Occasionally, the change is initiated at the grassroots level, sometimes by an individual and sometimes by an employee team. A third driving force can be the persistent efforts of experienced safety and health practitioners. In the case of safety through design, the professional driver might be the engineering group. The fourth driver is often referred to as the Significant Emotional Event, such as a catastrophe like Bhopal, a giant EPA fine, a monster lawsuit, or a fatality.

Clearly, the last driver is the one to be avoided. On the other hand, contrary to popular belief, "top-down" is neither the best nor even the preferred means for driving sustainable culture change. Some combination of the first three is more desirable, since it involves more members of the tribe. We might refer to the ideal combo as a "club sandwich," with *leadership* from the top (company and union management), the middle (safety practitioners, engineers and supervisors), and the bottom (hourly workers).

MANAGEMENT SUPPORT

Where the driver for change is not top-down, management support must be enlisted for a culture change such as safety through design to get off the ground. Depending on the size and organization of the company, this could involve a few key leaders or many individuals on corporate and division levels. The prejudice among culturists, like the writer, is to be inclusive rather than exclusive, informing and involving as many people as feasible. There is more than one instance where an influential vice president who was left out of the loop early in the process felt slighted and whose resistance to the change resulted in its failure to take hold.

Initially, management needs to be sold according to the rational and business arguments detailed elsewhere in this book. While safety improvements are a plus at any point in the process, they are most economical, efficient, and elegant when conceived in the design phase and not carried out after-the-fact, as kludgy retrofits. Use whatever data you can muster, from pilot projects, from the experience of other companies, university studies, and so on. Make reasonable projections in terms of start-up costs, payback period, and eventual savings. In short, safety through design will contribute positively to the bottom line—through fewer incidents, lower workers' compensation costs, higher productivity, greater quality, and customer satisfaction. Try to win support rather than just approval. You want management to give you more than a nod of the head and a long length of rope. You also need the resources and the structure to get the job done.

STRUCTURE FOR MANAGING THE CHANGE PROCESS

Having a clear driver for change and a healthy budget is no guarantee of success. Without a dedicated, formal infrastructure for managing the transition from the present culture to the future culture, individuals who lead the charge may find that they have entered hostile territory, having left the army and the supply lines far behind. This state of isolation is no fun. Thus, the need for a proper support structure that lasts throughout the life cycle of the culture change. This structure is often neglected, sometimes at considerable cost.

A company absolutely committed to safety spent a year developing a super sophisticated tool for evaluating all 250 elements of their safety program. The chairman, president and CEO personally revealed the dismal results of the initial assessment to 150 of the top people in the company (average score of 15%) and challenged them to bring it up to 100 percent by the year 2002. There was no structure in place for accomplishing this and little prior thought given to it. Many of the managers—all of whom already had full plates—despaired over the assignment and a few pointedly expressed the feeling that they had been set up, albeit inadvertently, for failure.

There are three accepted structures for managing change: (1) using the existing hierarchy; (2) appointing a czar or czarina; and, (3) creating a transition team.

Using the existing hierarchy is most commonly used and the least likely to work—for a number of reasons. As with the company above, most managers are already sufficiently burdened and not able to take on important new responsibilities. In addition, maintaining the existing structure also sends a somewhat contradictory message. "We want change, but not too much of it."

Alternatively, the company can appoint a czar or czarina with plenipotentiary powers to oversee the change. Often, this is done with new initiatives, such as TQM, to good effect. The limitation is having the process tied to and identified with a personality. When the personality leaves, continuity is at risk.

The third method, use of a transition team, has the best chance of being effective. It combines the advantages of the other models: like the existing hierarchy, it involves many people rather than one; and, like the czar/czarina, it is single-minded. Additionally, members of the transition team should be motivated, part-time participants, who come together with no history and no ulterior motives, for the exclusive purpose of managing the transition from the present culture to the future culture. The life cycle of the team begins with the baseline safety culture and usually concludes once the transition to the new culture is complete.

SIX PHASES OF CULTURE CHANGE

Assuming that you have the three strategic elements—a clear driver for change, management support, and a dedicated transition infrastructure you are nearly ready to embark upon the six phases of planned cultural change. Change does not happen by itself; strong, visible leadership is needed to catalyze the elements. Keep in mind that leadership should not be confused with what is referred to above as management support.

To paraphrase Schein,[2] management is administration within the organization, and leadership is shaping the culture. Leadership can come from any quarter. In the case of safety through design, leadership can come from the engineering department, it can come from the environmental, health, and safety department, or it can come from the shop floor. Regardless of its source it will require individuals who are able to inspire, motivate, communicate and change others, and even themselves.

There are six phases in the culture change model. They apply to any organization-wide culture change, such as safety through design. Make no mistake, by the time it is completed, these concepts will involve and impact the entire safety culture of the organization.

The six phases are as follows:
- ➤ Define and communicate the need for change;
- ➤ Envision a desired future;
- ➤ Assess the culture;
- ➤ Strategic planning;
- ➤ Implement; and
- ➤ Evaluate;

The following sections are not meant to be an exhaustive explanation of how to implement culture change; rather, they provide a brief description and rationale of the various phases.

DEFINE AND COMMUNICATE THE NEED FOR CHANGE

Major changes require that people recognize the need for change. The first step is to analyze and describe the external pressures for change, such as customer demand, the competitive environment and regulatory requirements. The next step is to inform people about the changes and why they must take place. Use all the arguments and back-up material you can muster. You must gain management support and then seek the support of those who will directly be affected.

Communicate the need for change at a meeting where people have the opportunity to ask questions. If the change will have a negative impact on individuals, they should be allowed to vent their frustrations. If this is not done, negativity will simply go underground and subvert the change process.

ENVISION A DESIRED FUTURE

Providing a vision can help people let go of the past because they need to believe that something better will replace what they have now. The vision must inspire employees and managers alike to commit significant amounts of time and energy. Since safety through design holds the promise of saving lives and keeping people whole, it should not be difficult to prompt a strong emotional response.

The process of creating a vision is more powerful if it is participatory. This phase of the intervention presents an opportunity to set up the intensive communication systems, which will be needed later, along with the channels to facilitate involvement and participation. An ongoing team, with representatives from engineering, safety, management, and labor, would be ideal, meeting regularly to oversee the entire safety through design process.

ASSESS THE CULTURE

A culture assessment saves time and resources because it insures that the organization will be addressing problems, not symptoms. It should describe the present state (organizational and cultural), evaluate organizational readiness for change, identify affected parties and determine the areas of intervention.

The culture assessment should be conducted in a highly inclusive and participatory manner. If a survey is used it should be filled out by various levels of the organization. Interviews or focus groups should provide a cross section of all departments. This will insure an accurate picture of the organization and serve to initiate involvement and ownership in the process.

Once the assessment results have been tabulated, they should be fed back to the rest of the organization. Remember, for safety through design to work, you want as much feedback from as many areas of the company as you can get. You can never tell where the next great idea or suggestion will come from; and you will need the support of many people for implementation to go smoothly. Supervisors, operators, even engineers may respond to the assessment results with passive, if not overt, aggression, if left out of the process.

STRATEGIC PLANNING

The ultimate aim of strategic planning is to develop a set of objectives that will help the organization achieve its desired safety performance and to select a strategy to get there. Once the strategic objectives have been determined, an analysis of the assessment results will indicate how the culture needs to change in order to achieve those objectives.

Different organizations have greatly different needs that can change over time. One plant may only require minor adjustments to implement a safety through design program, since it might fit handily with a quality or productivity program already in place. Another organization, which may have sustained a significant emotional event, could require a major reexamination of its safety processes and culture, involving much more than the way it conducts engineering.

If the organization is looking for a major improvement in safety performance, this planning effort will need to be led by a leadership team that includes the top manager—at either the company, division or plant level. Members of the organization must believe that the head person is in charge and serious about accomplishing these objectives.

It is not expected that all planning, and implementation will be done by the leadership team. Once a strategy has been mapped out, many responsibilities can, and should, be pushed down in the organization, with the formation of sub-committees or grassroots teams, tapping the skills, insights and energy of those who are closer to the work.

IMPLEMENT

In reality, implementation has already begun with the envisioning, assessment and strategic planning interventions. There is no point in waiting until the total strategic plan is designed to begin to take action. In fact, it aids the change process to get a couple of easy but significant successes under your belt. At one Canadian plant, for example, the simple creation of the grassroots teams deflected, and amicably resolved, most of the grievances that would, otherwise, have gone to the Labor Ministry. The same plant also saw a significant drop in reported incidents—even as the grassroots process was beginning.

The same could be true with establishment of the safety through design team and the gathering of information. Simply having team members—including engineers and managers—actively and visibly assessing the design safety needs of the plant can help inspire the interest of employees. Cynical as they may be on the surface, wary of so-called flavor-of-the-month programs, workers quickly become enthusiastic when they actually witness movement on their behalf. Often, the most skeptical worker or supervisor becomes the most vocal supporter—once positive change is perceived. But it won't help if you keep it a secret. Follow the advice often given to authors: tell them what you're going to do, tell them what you're doing, and then tell them what you've done.

The inclusion of employees on the safety through design team is an even more direct means of gaining employee involvement. If a strategic goal is to have employees take personal responsibility for their safety and the safety of others (using the technologies and training that are provided), a long-range plan is needed to set up the empowered safety teams that will eventually involve a large number of employees.

EVALUATE

The purpose of measurement is to provide a mechanism to determine if we met our objectives. Keeping incident statistics is helpful, but they are lagging indicators that measure after-the-fact performance. Evaluation also needs to be based on such leading indicators of the safety process as employee perceptions of the safety culture and safety behavior observations in order to maintain an ongoing measurement of preventive factors that effect end results.

Ongoing evaluation is essential. A follow-up survey and mini-assessment every year or so provides a yardstick for measuring progress. Conducted consistently, these assessments can also provide a way to help interpret incident statistics, to place in context so that appropriate action can be taken.

USE A MODEL AND START CULTURAL REALIGNMENT OF ORGANIZATIONAL SYSTEMS

It is never too early to examine the organization from a whole systems perspective, and begin the task of realigning systems with the values, assumptions and norms of the new culture. This is the difficult task of cultural realignment. It entails changing the norms and assumptions of the organization so that they will support new objectives and serve as an aligned mechanism in influencing individual safety behaviors. In this activity, organizational members must ask themselves, "What are the current assumptions that determine the way we think and make decisions about safety at this time?" "Are these current assumptions helpful or do they cause us to make unsafe decisions?"

It does not necessarily matter if the assumptions are true or false in determining what is useful in building a positive safety culture. At one power generating facility, 70% of workers believed that safety was their personal responsibility while only 45% of managers agreed. Management needed to adjust their thinking and "get with the program." At another plant, workers mistakenly felt that management only cared about numbers and would not support new safety programs; as a consequence, they never requested resources. Once this misapprehension was clarified, many new initiatives were proposed and approved.

Just as no department or unit operates in a tower separate from the rest of the organization, the organization itself is subject to outside pressures, influences, and forces. Culture change leaders must utilize a comprehensive framework to analyze the systems, culture and structures that affect performance. They cannot rely on single-factor methods or theories. Thus, it is helpful to use a model for examining the key factors involved in systems realignment for new safety culture objectives. Only from a comprehensive systems perspective is it possible to assure long-term safety improvements. This perspective will help managers realize why simplistic approaches such as changing a job description or changing a policy are ineffective.

Use of a model enables systematic and ongoing review of the multiple factors that need to be aligned with the new cultural objectives. The Simon Open System Model is one such model.[3] It takes into account the factors that influence safety performance at the environmental, organizational, and cultural level, and provides a road map to design strategy and cultural realignment.

In this model, the external environment that influences safety performance includes government regulations, customers, stockholders, workers' compensation costs, and the market place. Pressures from any of these groups influence the company's safety strategy and objectives. For example, a rise in workers' compensation costs could result in a company objective to reduce incidents. A strategy is then formed to achieve these objectives. For this reason, strategy is viewed as "input" to the organization.

The organizational influences and culture of a company form the transformational process, which determines the quality of "outputs" or safety performance of the company. Ideally, the structure and processes of the organization are in line (aligned) with the strategic objectives. The two-direction arrows between the culture and organizational influences symbolize a reciprocal influence. Structure influences culture, and culture influences structure, and so forth. Norms and assumptions are depicted as a shadow behind the culture because they are invisible, although they are an integral part of the safety process.

Finally, the environment gives positive or negative feedback to the organization on its outputs. For example, increased incidents could result in higher insurance costs, shareholder discontent, government penalties or community resentments. This feedback will, in turn, affect organizational strategy and the cycle begins again.

This open systems model provides insight into the interactive and systemic natures of the cultural, technical, and environmental components affecting safety performance. If safety

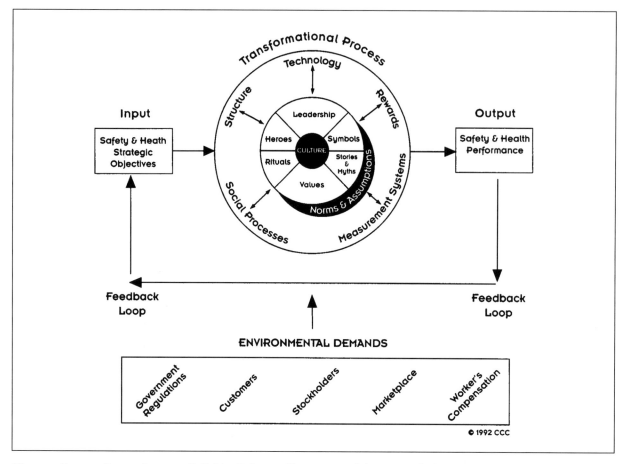

Figure. Simon Open System (S.O.S.) Culture Change Model™. A Whole Systems Model for Cultural Realignment.

through design is developed with these concerns in mind, it will be more successful in creating safer workplaces.

SAFETY CULTURE DOES APPLY— BEGIN WITH YOUR OWN DEPARTMENT

Three years ago the writer started consulting with a large aerospace defense contractor that employed more than 1,000 engineers. One senior manager, the Vice President of Engineering, was incredibly enthusiastic about setting up safety culture leadership teams.[1] His core group went through three days of team formation meetings and training. At the outset, he planned the composition and charter for the new teams. He said he had given the subject a lot of thought and he knew exactly what was needed and what the three teams should be doing. And then he named three areas that they should be studying and working on—ergonomics, emergency egress and safe lifting procedures.

It was impossible to fault his commitment, support and energy, and those three areas did need a lot of work, but that is not what we mean by changing the culture. That is thinking and working like a traditional engineer—highly rational. Design it, build it, and they will use it. The top engineer identifies a problem, sets up a team (of engineers) to study it, they work on coming up with a solution, and they report back to him. That is done every day and it solves many problems. The team might work for a month or a year, but eventually, the team disbands when the problem is solved. This is the perfect scenario for a project-based task force.

But that is not always the way things work. This should not be the case, above all, with a safety through design culture change team. The team should be ongoing, not transitory, and made up of representatives from different areas, not just the engineering department. Their mission, being culture-based, is to identify the strengths and deficiencies in the culture that promote or undermine excellent safety performance anything from mistrust to lack of responsiveness to the perception that production always takes precedence over safety. Soft issues, yes, but cultural issues that do correlate with hard results.

The VP of Engineering in our story understood the real-world impact of soft issues, and promised to hold back his task- and goal-oriented proclivities, or at least channel them in another direction. With culture change, one has to trade linear thinking for a holistic approach. It is great to set up an ergonomics task force, as he wanted to, but wrong to confuse it with culture change if all it does is replace one machine with another. If the child has trouble reading, you might get him a pair of better reading glasses and this may solve the problem. It may be all that is needed, or there may be other contributing factors, or symptoms of an underlying issue: the teacher may be punitive, the child may be dyslexic, assigned to the wrong class level, may have a different medical problem, psychological or emotional disturbances, or family difficulties. Without a whole systems review of the child and his or her environment, even if the reading problem is fixed, you can be sure that you have *not* addressed all the factors that influence the education and well-being of the child.

The engineering department of this company went ahead with the culture change project, set up permanent teams, and has had considerable success changing assumptions, behavior and safety processes over the course of three years. At any one time, thirty to forty people, from all levels of the engineering group, are actively involved in the teams and attending bi-weekly safety culture team meetings.

One small incident is worth recounting. After about six months, the VP of Engineering remarked how astounded he was to discover how much had been overlooked about safety within his own department. It was not just workers on the shop floor who needed to worry about ergonomics and posture; it was also his people working at drafting tables and computer terminals. Although he had long possessed the intellectual knowledge that his own people could get hurt, it wasn't until he really focused his care and attention on the issue of the safety culture in his own department, that he found out how much safety *Did Apply* to his own backyard.

It's a great place to start. In fact, the lesson can, and should, be applied to starting up any safety through design culture change. You might begin with a pilot project in your own engineering department. Explore how safety culture issues affect your group. Make a study of them, identify needs. Find out what happens when you make a request for capital improvements for ergonomic equipment for your own group. See how the existing hierarchy deals with your demands. Measure the gap between your expectations for how safety should be implemented in your company and the response to your department's improvement proposals.

Too often the health and safety of engineers and office workers are given short shrift. The cultural assumption is that no one gets hurt working at a desk, and, as a consequence, this reinforces the belief that safety issues, once again, do "Not Apply." In point of fact, as we know, there are sick buildings, there are carpal tunnel injuries, there are back ailments and vision problems that are the result of conditions in the workplace.

By achieving a culture change in your own backyard, you not only help protect your own employees' health and safety, you also change the mind-set of department personnel. Members of the engineering department in the case above, for example, reported that as a result of participating in their own multi-year culture change process, they began to incorporate a heightened safety value in all areas of their work.

SUMMARY—GOING BEYOND THE TECHNICAL

All current efforts to make safety through design a national movement are to be applauded. As a society, we have suffered too long building and using machines that injure people, machines that have to undergo costly retrofitting to function safely. We won't have to react to incidents if we can prevent them.

This book should help further that goal. It brings attention to the cause and gives professionals in the field the tools so that they can engage the challenge to bring about safety through design within their organizations. It makes the arguments that need to be made in order to persuade decision-makers of the justness of the cause. The book is a compendium of valuable and useful information, but are we introducing anything *really* new and revolutionary? Haven't we had sufficient expertise and technical know-how for a long time? So why, knowing all that we know, have we failed to meet the challenge of designing safe machines and equipment the first time out of the gate?

The major impediments to safety through design are not technical. They are the negative aspects of our safety culture, which interfere with our efforts to carry out logical and achievable safety-enhancing programs. If this chapter does nothing else, the writer hopes that it will make readers more attuned to the fact that safety culture is ignored at our peril.

Those who are responsible for leading the charge with safety through design must account for the underlying cultural aspects. Keep in mind that it is not always a rational process. Working on the safety culture often involves dealing with emotions, misconceptions, and mistrust. We are all subject to strong cultural forces—habit, peer pressure, hidden assumptions—forces that may interfere with the rational application of our skills and tools. In order to achieve the necessary safety culture change, we not only have to apply our technical expertise, we must also identify and remove negative safety norms, lead by personal example, and engage and inspire others to share a vision of a new culture. Although this may be a difficult process, it is the best and only guarantee of sustainable success.

REFERENCES

1. Simon SI, Carrillo R: *Grassroots Safety Leadership™ A Handbook for Designing and Implementing Culture-Based Safety Improvement Strategies,* 3rd ed. Seal Beach, CA: Culture Change Consultants, 1995.

2. Schein EH: *Organizational Culture and Leadership.* San Francisco: Jossey-Bass, 1991.

3. Simon SI: The culture change model of behavioral safety. *Light Up Safety in the New Millennium,* Feb 1998, pp 192–207.

Chapter 5

WHAT DO ENGINEERS REALLY KNOW ABOUT SAFETY?

by Bruce W. Main

OBJECTIVES

This chapter presents research data on what engineers, and engineering faculty, know about safety, health and the environment. It shares concepts evolved from the Symposium on what engineers should, or need, to know about safety, health and the environment. The implications to engineering educators and practicing engineers, and methods to affect change will be outlined.

INTRODUCTION

Design engineers face increasing pressure to improve the level of safety in their designs. Such pressure takes the form of product liability, workers' compensation costs, increased costs or unavailability of liability insurance, and incident and medical costs, among others. In some industries (for example, motorcycle helmets, light aircraft, and ladders), these costs have become dominant, exceeding the costs of either design or manufacture. In virtually every industry, the costs are believed to be high and rising. This chapter examines what engineers know about safety, and what they should know.

The Accreditation Board for Engineering and Technology (ABET) evaluates engineering schools to assure that graduate engineers have requisite knowledge and abilities upon completion of their education. ABET is governed by engineering societies. ABET has implemented new accreditation standards, and changes in its evaluation criteria which increase the likelihood that safety, health and environmental knowledge will be considered when degree programs are reviewed (ASEE Prisim, 1997).

The ABET criteria known as "Engineering Criteria 2000" was adopted November 2, 1996, and becomes effective for all engineering programs beginning in the fall of 2001. Criterion 4, Professional Component states that "...curriculum must prepare students for engineering practice... incorporating engineering standards and realistic constraints that include most of the following considerations: ...environmental...health and safety..." This is consistent with the concern for the safety and well-being of the public expressed in the Engineers' Code of Ethics written by the engineering societies.

The new ABET criteria continues to be the subject of much discussion concerning the application, implementation and evaluation of the specific requirements. Activity is noted in education institutions to modify curricula to include basic safety, health and environmental knowledge. The net result of these modifications is that institutions will not be effective in implementing this knowledge unless substantial assistance in developing curricula materials is provided to faculty.

ABET criteria does not provide specific safety, health and environmental criteria or evaluation methodology. Therefore, the knowledge and education engineers receive can vary greatly across universities. Such variance can produce limitations in knowledge, unless similar materials are provided to all institutions and the faculty has been oriented. The techniques and abilities to evaluate the effectiveness and knowledge transfer of the curricula will be based on the safety, health, and environmental concern, capability, and knowledge imparted to the evaluation teams selected by the engineering societies.

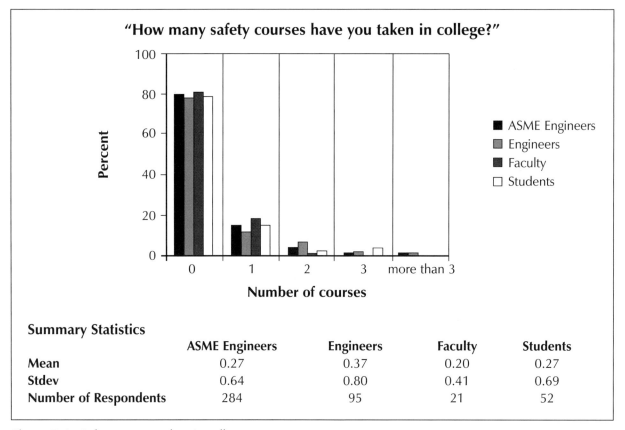

Figure 5-1. Safety courses taken in college.

To understand how engineers incorporate safety in design, a survey was conducted of both current and future design engineers. The survey results provide a basis for understanding what engineers actually do in their design efforts regarding safety, and suggest how this might be improved. Examining what engineers should know about safety was addressed at a symposium in 1997. The results are reviewed and discussed. The implications of the gap between what engineers know and what they should know are explored in the discussion.

WHAT IS KNOWN—A SURVEY
BACKGROUND
The survey was administered to four population samples: practicing engineers (randomly selected from the ASME Design Division membership), practicing engineers known to the authors (located throughout the country), University of Michigan faculty in the Mechanical Engineering/Applied Mechanics Department, and University of Michigan students in senior and graduate design classes. The survey was administered through the mail with the exception that the stu-

dent survey was personally administered. The total number of responses was 311 for the random sample with a response rate of 62%.[6]

RESULTS
As shown in Figure 5-1, nearly 80% of the respondents had not taken a safety course in college. This is true across all population samples.

Figure 5-2 indicates that well over 60% of the respondents had not taken any safety short courses. Note that 90% of the faculty had not taken a safety short course. Figure 5-3 indicates that 80% of the faculty and students had not attended any safety conferences. Both engineer populations responded similarly, slightly less (70%). Figure 5-4 is notable by the absence of faculty who had attended safety lectures (about 70% had not attended safety lectures). In contrast, approximately 60% of the other three populations had attended at least one safety lecture. Table 5-A shows that self-study is a significant source of safety education in that 30%–47% of the respondents had engaged in self-instruction or study pertaining to safety.

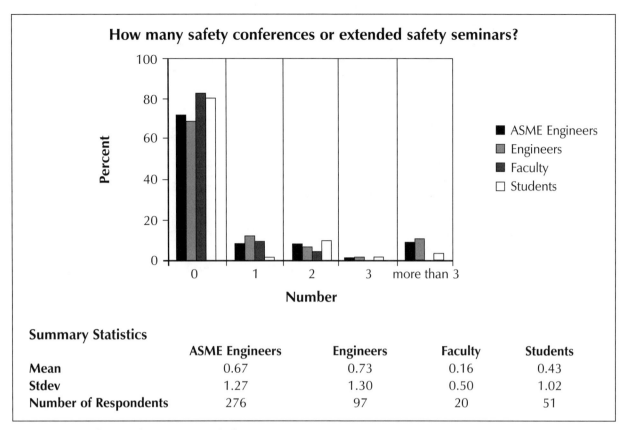

How many safety conferences or extended safety seminars?

Summary Statistics

	ASME Engineers	Engineers	Faculty	Students
Mean	0.67	0.73	0.16	0.43
Stdev	1.27	1.30	0.50	1.02
Number of Respondents	276	97	20	51

Figure 5-2. Safety conferences attended.

The respondents were asked to provide a self-rating of their knowledge with respect to safety. Figure 5-5 shows the responses to this question. Of particular note is the contrast between the two response groupings; the faculty and students view themselves much less knowledgeable than the practicing engineer populations. This contrast is also reflected in Figure 5-6, where respondents rated the effectiveness of the methods they use. The average means for these groupings are very similar for both questions.

In the open-ended questions about improving the design process, respondents advocated more safety education in several areas. The primary suggestions included: more engineering education (seminars/workshops), more classes in school, a required college course, greater emphasis in the engineering curriculum, incorporation of safety issues in design and project management courses, and more formal education covering the theory of safety. Although a few respondents suggested that all engineering courses include safety concerns, most respondents considered this insufficient.

Main and Ward[6] have shown that design engineers usually are not aware of the tools and techniques used in design safety (including health and environment). The obvious answer to the lack of awareness issue is to provide engineers training in design safety. However, it is too simple to suggest that a lack of awareness is the root problem. In a cascade effect, engineers' awareness of design safety is low because they have not received training in design safety methodology. This lack of training results from a lack of instructional materials and literature describing design safety. Therefore, even employers and faculty motivated to teach design safety methods cannot find instructional materials to do so. This lack of materials is a measure of the emerging state of the art of design safety.

WHAT ENGINEERS SHOULD KNOW
PROPOSAL

In 1996, Dembe observed that:

> *Despite calls for the integration of safety into engineering curricula and the establishment of ABET requirements for*

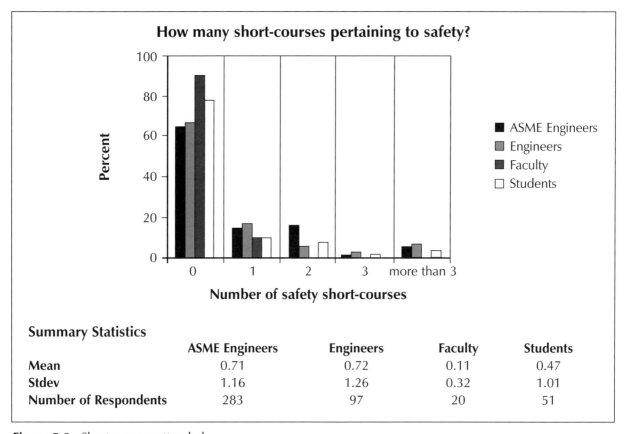

Figure 5-3. Short courses attended.

Summary Statistics

	ASME Engineers	Engineers	Faculty	Students
Mean	0.71	0.72	0.11	0.47
Stdev	1.16	1.26	0.32	1.01
Number of Respondents	283	97	20	51

safety-related instruction, few engineering colleges have instituted formal course offerings focusing on safety and health. Impediments include the lack of room for additional coursework in the standard curriculum, the perceived unavailability of qualified faculty and instructional materials, and a widespread conviction among faculty and administrators that safety is not critical to engineering education. Attempts to address this need by developing special instructional safety modules or enrolling students in full-semester safety courses have met with limited success. An alternative approach is to use safety-related examples and case studies to portray conventional engineering principles. Rather than separating safety instruction into a distinct course or modules, this approach would present safety prin-

ciples as a fully-integrated part of traditional engineering practice. To make this idea a reality, appropriate examples and cases will need to be developed and disseminated. In addition, industry involvement, government backing, and financial support is required.

Dembe also notes that:

According to the Professional Engineers' Code of Ethics, one of the "fundamental canons" of the engineering profession is to "hold paramount the safety, health and welfare of the public in the performance of their professional duties." It is hard to image how an engineer can be expected to fulfill this maxim unless he or she receives appropriate education in safety engineering principles.

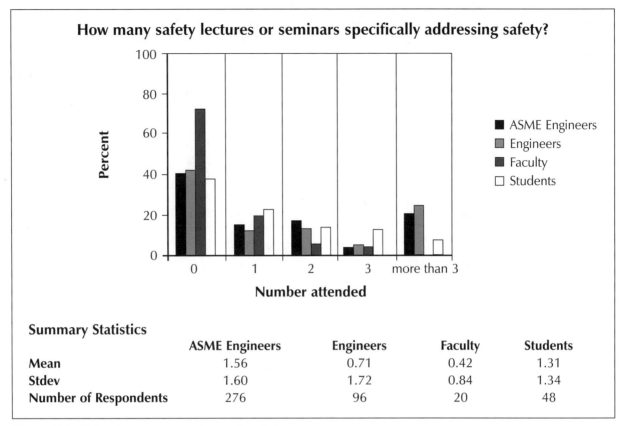

Figure 5-4. Safety lectures or seminars attended.

ISTD SYMPOSIUM

BACKGROUND

In September 1996, the ISTD convened a Symposium with a specific objective:

To identify the safety, health, and environmental knowledge an engineer should possess upon completion of a baccalaureate degree.

The Symposium focus was on all engineering disciplines with primary emphasis on the "classic" disciplines of chemical, civil, electrical and mechanical engineering. Although some chemical and industrial engineering departments are actively incorporating safety, health and environmental materials into existing courses, much work remains to achieve a truly sound basis of safety, health and environmental concepts for all engineering graduates.

Recent studies by the American Society of Engineering Educators (ASEE) and others call for reshaping curriculum to include an understanding of societal, economic, ethical and environmental impacts of engineering decisions. Corporations, large and small, are facing increasingly complex requirements to assure operations

and products do not create risks to employees, customers, and the community.

FORMAT

The Symposium employed a Delphi (panel of experts) methodology to identify the safety, health, and environmental knowledge an engineer should possess upon completion of a baccalaureate degree. Attendees were selected by application with an intentional effort made to obtain a representative mix of knowledgeable experts from many areas including the following:

➤ Academe (from a cross section of various engineering departments);

➤ Industry engineering departments;

➤ Industry engineering consultants;

➤ Labor representatives; and

➤ Safety practitioners.

Academe representatives were department heads and faculty who are involved with actions to incorporate safety, health and environmental materials into engineering courses and curricula. Industry representatives involved in successful safety through design activities were particularly qualified to offer insight on safety, health and

Table 5–A. Safety Training Through Self Study.

Specific self instruction or study pertaining to safety?

	ASME Engineers	Engineers	Faculty	Students
Number of Respondents	264	88	18	46
Percent No	53	58	61	70
Percent Yes	47	42	39	30

environmental knowledge that would be beneficial to engineers performing the work.

The Symposium was a working session rather than a learning conference. Assembled presenters and participants sat at round tables with each table having a mixture of presenters and participants from industry, business, labor, and academe.

The Symposium employed the following format:

➤ A challenge was placed before the assembled members;

➤ A speaker introduced the challenge;

➤ Subsequent speakers presented viewpoints, experiences, and beliefs pertinent to the challenge;

➤ Each round table was provided with a general discussion questions structured around the challenge; and

➤ Considerable time was allowed for discussions wherein the tables developed a consensus on ways and means to meet the challenge.

A complete description of the Symposium and results including summaries of round table discussions, papers and presentations was published.[3]

RESULTS

The engineers, educators, labor representatives, and safety practitioners present deliberated thoughtfully and long, often through breaks and lunch. They considered the transition from today's world to an ideal when engineers would emerge with a baccalaureate degree and an understanding and concern for the safety, health and environment of individuals affected by facilities, process or product designs. They identified the knowledge an engineer should possess, and made substantial contributions on the method to achieve the desired educational outcome. Discussions resulted in a conclusion that the engineering curriculum was full, and additional courses would not be accepted by engineering departments. Even if presented as an elective, there would be no assurance all graduates would take the elective and leave with the desired knowledge.

Three challenges were placed before the participants. The results are organized around these three challenges.

CHALLENGE 1

Identify techniques for overcoming resistance to incorporating safety, health and environment into curriculum including faculty and department heads, and with facilities and curriculum materials.

Department Heads and Professors

Although the department heads are the Leaders, the participants felt more attention should be devoted to the faculty. Attention should be given to department heads in connection with evaluations, such as for tenure, and to create motivation for professors to overcome resistance to change and to take time to prepare for new subjects/topics. There is a need to find champions of the safety through design cause, and for techniques to recognize those who expend effort to become knowledgeable and initiate instruction.

Concurrently, industry and the Institute must communicate the importance of safety to recruiters and to engineering personnel who sit on university Advisory Committees. Other areas such as grants, chairs, contracts, reverse co-ops, and research opportunities must be used to create a climate for incorporation of safety, health and the environment into the curriculum. Another idea was to develop a resource such as a register of qualified speakers who could make presentations to students to validate safety, health, and the environment.

Curriculum

Needs to be holistic, provide applied industry (real world) problems, and in the coming years start incorporating these into textbooks. Subsequently, there have to be related cased studies and problem sets for safety through design, and a toolbox of materials and resources.

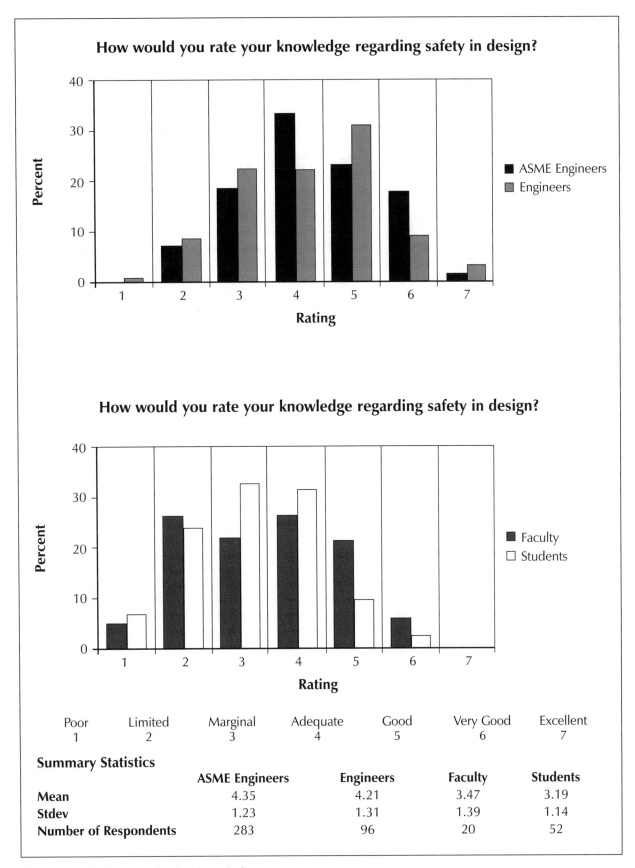

Figure 5-5. Self rating of safety knowledge.

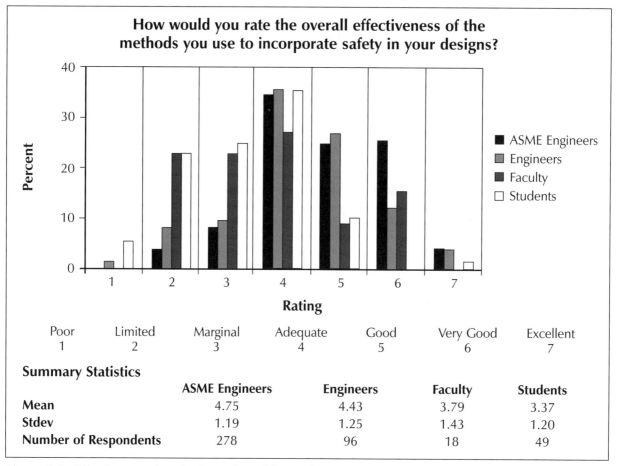

How would you rate the overall effectiveness of the methods you use to incorporate safety in your designs?

Rating	Poor	Limited	Marginal	Adequate	Good	Very Good	Excellent
	1	2	3	4	5	6	7

Summary Statistics

	ASME Engineers	Engineers	Faculty	Students
Mean	4.75	4.43	3.79	3.37
Stdev	1.19	1.25	1.43	1.20
Number of Respondents	278	96	18	49

Figure 5-6. Effectiveness of methods used to address safety.

Facilities
Do not seem to be an issue at this time.

CHALLENGE 2
Identify the knowledge an engineer should have upon completion of a baccalaureate degree.

Results
Industries with good safety through design programs should employ students and expose them to these practices and philosophies. Both students and faculty must be sensitized to the importance of safety, health and environmental issues. An ideal would be to have faculty specialists who would be the "go to" people and emphasize the qualitative aspects of safety through design. Stress teamwork concepts and practice.

CHALLENGE 3
Identify techniques and subjects where safety, health and environmental principles might be incorporated and to list in order of relative pri-

ority the knowledge of safety, health and the environment that should be acquired.

Each round table prepared a one page response to this challenge and shared a brief presentation with the group. The responses are contained in the Compendium.[3]

Results
Safety, health, and environmental principles and philosophies to be incorporated charted by academic year. There should be homework, problem sets, and case studies at all levels.

Freshman
- ethics, moral values, and professional responsibilities (humanities/social science)
- life cycle
- introduction to engineering (basic design)
- hazard recognition skills
- awareness of safety, health and environmental responsibilities
- team approach

Sophomore

→ general engineering fundamentals

→ safety, health and environmental examples

→ codes and standards

→ risk identification, quantification, and assessment

Junior

→ discuss specific engineering science and design

→ safety, health and environmental examples

→ hazard analysis

→ codes and standards

→ ergonomics

Senior

→ capstone design

→ risk assessment

→ application of above

Issues for faculty and industry to address and consider:

Faculty

→ Change reward structure to emphasize safety, health and the environment.

→ Encourage hiring faculty with industry experience.

Industry

→ Secure cooperation of recruiters and university of Board of Advisors members to ask questions about safety, health and environmental issues.

→ Guest lecturers from industry.

Consensus from the Symposium participants was as follows:

Safety, health, and environmental principles must be a way of life with emerging engineers, and that this can only be achieved by integrating it into existing courses. Integration must begin at the freshman level and continue into capstone design courses. Insights were offered.

Physical facilities were not seen as a problem. Faculty must become involved with industry to be convinced of the need for this knowledge.

→ Promote incorporation of safety, health, and environmental issues and a safety through design approach in design texts.

→ Must clarify expectations and express importance of safety, health, and the environment.

DISCUSSION
SAFETY EDUCATION AND TRAINING

Most engineers (especially faculty) receive little or no formal safety training. The most significant safety 'training' occurs through lectures or self study, and even 70% of the faculty and 40% of the remaining three population samples had not received such training. This is a predictable consequence of what design engineers are not taught about safety because the faculty themselves have received inadequate safety training and because the design literature omits formalized safety theory. These data offer empirical evidence for Hammer's[5] statement that "Because so many subjects and facts must be taught in engineering schools, instruction in safety and accident prevention is generally often omitted."

The education shortfall is especially pronounced in the engineering faculty, who had received the least formal safety training in nearly all categories. These results lend some support to statements made by Hammer, "Most engineering school faculty members who instruct students in safety matters have themselves been inadequately educated."

Currently most safety, health and environmental education will occur on the job rather than in University. This can be inferred from the data since safety training is not provided in school. The safety training engineers receive is evidently on-the-job based training or employer funded training. Given that safety is a fundamental canon of engineering practice and that certain basic safety tools and topics have broad application in engineering, the university would seem an appropriate setting for basic safety training.

Safety training occurs in industry to reduce the very real risks of injury, illness or property damage. There is an explicit need for safety training in industry. Conversely, the faculty work environment is relatively low risk. There is very little explicit need to train faculty in safety for their work environment and the faculty employer has little incentive to provide significant safety training. The faculty does not tend to receive significant on the job training with respect to safety, health and the environment. Therefore, resources for safety training are difficult to obtain and the faculty may be less sensitive to safety, health and environmental issues. Although a case could be made that faculty need and would benefit from safety training, an alternative argument could be made that without specific practical application, training faculty will be little more than an academic exercise resulting in minimal significant change to the safety education engineering students receive.

If faculty members are to receive safety training, the impetus for change will need to come from culture changes in university management, such as deans and department heads (who themselves probably have not received significant safety training). Resources for the training will need to be made available. Tools and techniques to move safety into design will need to be included.

Dembe noted that the limited availability of appropriate case studies remains a significant barrier to implementing this approach. Individual faculty members tend to write most of the case studies, problem sets, and homework assignments, which are used in the classroom. Since most faculty are removed from significant safety work, and their worksite is low risk/low hazard, it should come as no surprise that they wouldn't have the ability to develop such study materials. Conversely, most safety practitioners in industry do have access to multiple appropriate cases, which could be developed into study tools. However, industry doesn't have the time or practical application to devote to writing case studies. This is especially true in today's downsized world.

Having established that most engineering programs need improvements in safety, health and environmental issues, the follow up question becomes "how?"

"Empowering" design engineers with the fundamentals of safety theory and hazard identification techniques may be a beneficial approach to improving design safety. Specifically, engineering education and training should include the basics and tools of conducting hazard analyses and risk assessments.

The results of the survey indicate that motivating the design engineer is not a problem; engineers do not try to create unsafe designs. Therefore, if the hazard identification task is

explicit or formalized within the design process, the subsequent hazard evaluation and elimination/control will likely follow thereby increasing the overall level of safety. Engineering judgment would dictate how far the hazard evaluation and subsequent analyses should be carried. Intuitively, if hazard identification is implicit or subjective in more than the simplest systems, the designer is likely to address only the most obvious hazards and omit others. Once the hazards are identified, the design engineer would be empowered to make decisions and/or request additional safety expert advice as the need requires. Designs with complex or difficult hazards may require a quantitative hazard evaluation or other more sophisticated techniques available through safety practitioners.

This proposed approach focuses on identifying hazards and minimizing risks through hazard elimination and control. Under the proposed approach, a design team (for example, engineers, safety practitioners, end-users, insurance or legal advisors) would explicitly identify and document the hazards as best possible. As the design evolves, so too will the understanding of the hazards involved. The underlying hypothesis of this proposed approach is that the fundamental safety methods (specifically hazard identification techniques) can be learned and applied by designers. This approach is an adaptation of the more formalized approach within safety engineering.

In addition to the traditional Fault Tree Analysis (FTA), Failure Mode and Effects Analysis (FMEA), and Preliminary Hazard Analysis (PHA), which are tools developed over many years, there are new computer tools coming on line to aid engineers and safety practitioners through this process.

IMPLEMENTATION

As is readily apparent from the ISTD Symposium, the consensus opinion is that the most effective method to implement safety, health and environment into engineering education is to embed it. Dembe proffered:

In recent years, there has been a growing recognition that safety and production are not only compatible, but that safety is really just one essential aspect of production efficiency, in much the

*same way as is quality and reliability...
A prime method for highlighting this
commonality of purpose is to use safety-
related examples to illustrate basic
engineering concepts throughout the
engineering curriculum.*

Dembe has proposed that "...problem sets
and case studies can be selected that correspond
to most of the fundamental topics that are currently presented to engineering students." A summary of such examples is presented in Table 5-B.

To effectively implement safety through
design safety, health and environmental considerations must be integrated very early in the
process. For the engineering education process
the integration should begin with the freshman
year and continue throughout the program. For
industry, the integration should commence at the
writing of a project statement of scope or as far
upstream toward this ideal as possible. The design
should consider the life cycle of the product,
process or facility through decommissioning.

POCKETS OF CHANGE

INDUSTRY

Safety through design is neither a new nor a foreign concept to many companies. There are
leading companies who are beginning to implement safety through design in the design and
development processes and products. To highlight those companies and organizations leading
safety through design efforts, the ISTD convened a second Symposium held in 1997.
*Benchmarks for World Class Safety Through
Design* gathered together engineers, educators,
and safety, health and environmental professionals from diverse backgrounds across business, industry, labor, government and academia.
The Symposium-desired outcomes were to
establish benchmarks for World Class Safety
Through Design "best practices," and to determine information on the methodology for
implementation of such practices.

Jerry Scannell, president of the National
Safety Council noted that:

*The diverse and high level of
Symposium presenters and participants
indicates the significant strides being*

*taken by many organizations to incor-
porate safety through design principles
and practices into their operations and
thereby eliminate retrofitting.*

Two days of highly qualified speakers presenting an excellent cross section of papers
yielded interesting discussions and insights into
the thinking of attendees about safety through
design. First, it was clear that the use and understanding of the term "benchmarking" varied, but
what did not differ was the passion to address at
the earliest possible stage the safety, health and
environmental risks that affect employees, people in the community, and the environment.
Secondly, that opportunity is most frequently in
the designing of processes, whether it be the
equipment, tooling, product, work methods,
training, facilities or design of services.

The presentations and outcomes of the discussion groups provide a foundation for every
company and organization to build on. Benefits
of integrating decisions affecting safety, health
and environment in the early stages of the design
process include the following:

→ Significant reductions in injuries, illnesses,
  damage to the environment and attendant
  costs;
→ Productivity improvement;
→ Decreased operating costs; and
→ Avoidance of design shortcomings and
  expensive retrofitting.

James C. Rucker, Chair of the ISTD
Advisory Committee commented:

*The presentations and discussions of
this Symposium reinforced the fact that
there are pockets of knowledge about
safety through design principles and
practices that are old in concept but relatively new in dedicated practice. It is
also clear that there is a definite void in
technical books, case studies, checklists
and simple engineering tools to support
the process...thorough reading of the
presentations and summaries of the
round table discussions, will support
the conclusion that health, safety and
environmental requirements must be
considered during the early stages of
the design process.*

Table 5–B. Engineering Discipline Interest in Safety Course Topics.[2]

Engineering Concepts	Safety & Health Examples
Statics & Dynamics	Calculation of safety factors & performance limits Rated capacities of hoists, cranes, scaffolding, storage racks, etc Floor loading
Mechanics & Kinetics	Slip & fall protection Properties of floor surfaces and optimal coefficients of friction Biomechanical assessment of musculoskeletal system Health hazards of segmental & whole-body vibration
Fluid & Gas Dynamics	Ventilation of air contaminants Design & hydrostatic testing of sprinkler systems Safety properties of cryogenic fluids
Thermodynamics	Control of explosions and other unintended releases of energy Safe use of compresses gases Safety of boilers and pressure vessels
Electrical Theory & Systems	Protective and system grounding Lockout/tagout Zero energy state Prevention of fires and electrical shock
Strength of Materials	Fire safety in building design Storage and transport of corrosive and reactive substances Selection and testing of personal protective equipment (hard hats, safety shoes, etc)
Information Management	Safety assessment and inspection techniques Warnings and hazard communication Incident investigation and record keeping
Engineering Economics	Risk assessment Cost/benefit analysis Cost justification of safety projects
Engineering & Project Management	Establishment of safety programs and work teams Pre-operations safety planning Measuring safety performance Development of effective oral/written safety reports and management
Quality	Detection and Analysis of defects and system failures Hazard identification techniques System safety analysis (e.g. FMEA, Fault Tree)
Simulation & Modeling	Process hazard analysis ("what-if," use of checklists, etc) Material process flow analysis Ergonomics task assessment and use of anthropometric data
Productivity	Work physiology and fatigue Detrimental effect of shift work/overtime Optimization of ambient environmental conditions (e.g., lighting, temperature, etc)
Product Design	Product hazard assessment and control Product life cycle analysis (e.g., installation, repair, maintenance, disposal) Use of CPSC, ASTM, and other safety-related standards
Customer Relations	Handling complaints from public/users Responding to accidents/incidents Written communications (warnings, instructions, etc)

Table 5–B. Engineering Discipline Interest in Safety Course Topics.[2] *(continued)*

Engineering Concepts	Safety & Health Examples
Emerging Technologies	Risk assessment Job safety analysis Epidemiological analysis of new materials and substances
Process Design & Analysis	Product safety in acquisition and installation of new process equipment Toxic use reduction Formalized process hazard analysis
Layout & Facility Planning	Ergonomic design of workplaces Minimization of materials handling Facility traffic flow and vehicle safety Design for fire prevention and protection Life safety and evacuation planning
Electronic Data Processing	Safety data storage and retrieval Software safety Hazards of computers and VDTs
Professional & Engineering Ethics	Federal/state safety standards Familiarity with industry and consensus standards Risk management, insurance and liability
Automation	Robotics safety Use of automation in the prevention of materials handling hazards Assessment of human tolerance for speed
Control Systems	Selection and use of controls Human error Layout and positioning of controls

A complete description of the Symposium, results, and papers of leaders in safety through design implementation are contained in the *Proceedings.*[1]

ACADEME

Pockets of change are also beginning to appear in the academic community. To channel the lessons learned from the Symposia to engineering curricula, the Institute formed a coalition to develop and integrate safety, health and environmental concepts into undergraduate engineering curricula: NETWORC—A National Coalition of Engineering and Technology Institutions Working to Organize Relevant Curricular Changes. The Coalition was formed in 1997 to enhance curriculum development efforts. Coalition participants previously initiated changes in their curricula to enhance engineering student knowledge of safety, health and the environment.

The Institute and NETWORC will work together to facilitate development of curriculum materials (lecture modules, case studies, homework problems, and design problems) relating to the competency gaps. The target audience of this project is mechanical, manufacturing, industrial, chemical, civil, and where materials may be integrated, electrical engineering undergraduate students. Materials will not be presented as an added course, rather through utilization of existing presentations of course knowledge, with modifications to incorporate principles so they are fully integrated (embedded) in curricula and become a way of thinking for the graduate student.

Case studies and workshops will aid in the pursuit of continuous improvement and improving productivity and cost through safety through design. Current capstone design courses generally don't consider safety, health and environment, and if included would expect students to have prior knowledge which he or she generally would not have... it must be embedded.

ENGINEERS AND SAFETY PRACTITIONERS

To address the needs of the practicing engineer and safety practitioners, ISTD has teamed with the National Safety Council to sponsor Professional Development Seminars focusing on safety through design. The seminars are useful to increase the knowledge of design engineers, safety practitioners, educators, and managers of the safety through design concepts, and their consideration of safety, health and the environment in designs of facilities, operations and products. Seminar knowledge objectives are as follows:

1. Benefits of applying safety through design concepts.
2. Safety through design best practices.
3. Principles of task based risk assessment process.
4. Principles for creating an environment for continuous improvement toward global safety through design concepts.
5. Methodology for assuring best practices are used.
6. Principles to establish benchmarks for safety through design in an organization.
7. Techniques for minimizing fear and building trust and teamwork between management, engineering, safety and production

Students are not the only engineers requiring additional safety and technical knowledge. Practicing engineers who lack basic safety knowledge need to develop hazard identification/recognition skills for both short term and long term (acute and cumulative) hazards. They need to improve their awareness of the safety, health and environmental responsibilities in design. Engineers need to acquire the basic knowledge indicated earlier for undergraduate engineers. They need to become familiar with risk assessments, and with the financial impact of injuries and incidents. With current and future production demands in industry, there will be no time to retrofit for safety once the equipment/process arrives on the production floor. Safety needs to be included early in the design process. The engineers and safety practitioners responsible for process and product design need to work as a team to realize the productivity gains and cost efficiency opportunities of safety through design.

In order to contribute effectively to designs early in development, safety practitioners need to better understand the design process and what they can or should expect from engineers during the process. Upgrading their technical skills and knowledge of engineering design will permit them to know what educational efforts to support for company engineers, and the type of data to provide engineers so that safety, health and environmental factors are included in the design. With this knowledge, they will be able to participate in technical discussions with engineers regarding design solutions and ideas. In addition, safety practitioners will have to be skilled in conducting risk assessments, accessing the Internet to secure current safety information from international sources, and adept in using computer engineering design software.

Graduating engineers need to know more about how to include safety, health and the environment in design. From a process perspective, the "finished product" being produced by engineering university is greatly lacking in safety through design, an area which the students should grasp. As delivered, these "end products" require rework (safety, health and environmental training or re-training) before they can be fully used in the buyer's (employer's) processes. The desired end result is to increase the ability of graduating engineers to enter industry with a substantively greater knowledge of how to incorporate safety, health and the environment in design.

Considerable teamwork will be required to successfully implement safety through design methods. No one individual or community can affect such change alone. Engineering faculty and administration need to grasp the concepts and their application, and begin educating engineering students in the safety through design approach and tools. Engineers, safety practitioners and managers in industry should ask questions of new hires during the interview process and recruiting, and when serving on engineering department advisory boards. Engineering societies should join in promoting the safety through design approach and integrate it into the professional engineering exams. ISTD will work to promote safety through design tools, techniques, and educational and training materials for engineering educators, practicing engineers, and safety practitioners. A team of organizations and individuals working cooperatively stand a far better chance to move the need for knowledge of safety, health, and the environment from a concept to an imbedded practice.

SUMMARY

Safety through design is still evolving and improving. Currently there are different approaches and techniques to implementing the safety through design concept. This chapter pointed out that most engineers receive little formal safety training, and the lack of design safety training may limit an engineer's ability to identify safety concerns. Most engineering programs lack adequate coverage of safety, health and environmental issues and safety through design concepts. It was shared that the best method to introduce safety through design changes to curricula are via existing courses through case studies, problem sets, homework assignments, and other study tools beginning in freshman classes and infused throughout the degree program.

There is ample opportunity for improvement and gains in productivity, rework, costs, and losses by implementing the safety through design approach. Successfully implementing these concepts will require teamwork. Engineers, safety practitioners, and educators should be prepared for change as the methods undergo continuous improvement.

REFERENCES

1. *Benchmarks for World Class Safety Through Design, Proceedings 1997 Symposium.* Institute for Safety Through Design, Itasca, IL: National Safety Council, Aug 19–20, 1997.

2. Dembe AE: The future of safety and health in engineering education. *Journal of Engineering Education*, pp 163–167, Apr 1996.

3. Christensen WC, Main BW: *Compendium of the 1996 Integrating Safety Through Design Symposium.* Itasca, IL: Institute for Safety Through Design, National Safety Council, Sep 17–19, 1996.

4. *Engineering Criteria 2000: Criteria for Accrediting Programs in Engineering in the United States.* ASEE Prism, pp 41–42, Mar 1997.

5. Hammer W: *Occupational Safety Management and Engineering.* Prentice-Hall, 1989.

6. Main BW, Ward AC: What do engineers really know about safety? Implications for education, training and practice. *Mechanical Engineering,* 114, No. 8, Aug 1992.

Part II

INTEGRATION INTO BUSINESS PROCESSES

Chapter 6

RELATING PRINCIPLES TO QUALITY MANAGEMENT

by Tom Cecich
Mark Hembarsky

INTRODUCTION

The concept that there is a remarkable kinship between the principles of safety through design and total quality management was introduced in Chapter 1. This chapter will explore how the total quality management philosophy evolved over the past 20 years and its implication for adopting safety through design concepts. The management systems and tools that were developed as part of total quality management will be examined for their applicability in advancing safety through design as part of an organization's culture.

In the early 1980s many manufacturers were beginning to recognize that the United States was becoming non-competitive in the growing world marketplace. What started slowly as an evolutionary change in quality management became a revolution in the late 1980s and early 1990s through the introduction of total quality systems. Businesses discovered that to survive in the global economy all aspects of a business must be committed to being as competitive as possible.

It was clear that foreign competition, mostly from Japan, had convinced the American consumer that Japanese manufacturers could produce a better quality product than available in the United States. Automobiles, televisions, and computers for example were making significant gains in markets traditionally dominated by U.S. companies. Competition was defining the acceptable level of quality that must be designed and built into a product.

Old philosophies associated with the quality of a product were now unacceptable. A company could no longer afford to build and ship a product that didn't work the "first time, every time." Organizations that prided themselves on how quickly their customer service department could fix field problems quickly realized that customers didn't want fast repair services, they wanted the product "right the first time."

Complicating the picture for industry were profit improvement strategies such as "speed to market," where it was recognized that every day a new product is delayed from market introduction, sales are lost that will never be recovered. In addition, delays in product introductions allowed competitors time to gain market advantage. Other cost reduction techniques such as "just in time manufacturing" sought to reduce inventories and the associated carrying costs by transferring the burden of rapid delivery to suppliers.

Thus, American manufacturers were faced with the dilemma of needing a higher quality product, being brought to market in a shorter time frame, all the while producing a competitively priced product to strict customer delivery schedules. These multiple challenges were presented in the face of growing international competition emerging out of the rapidly expanding global marketplace. It became clear that a new philosophy of doing business was required.

EMERGENCE OF TOTAL QUALITY MANAGEMENT

Both business and the U.S. Government recognized that a new standard for quality management was required for the United States to be competitive in the growing global economy. Industry needed to make a significant positive change and government moved to facilitate that change through the creation of the Malcolm Baldrige National Quality Award (MBNQA)[1] instituted through the U.S. Department of Commerce. The MBNQA is designed to recognize American companies for business performance excellence and quality achievements. The criteria provide a framework to assess an organization's business processes and performance fundamental to business competitiveness and success.

Although the MBNQA award was not the beginning of the total quality revolution in the United States, it was its symbolic birth. Spurred on by fierce international competition organizations throughout the United States scrutinized the award and more importantly the award process for the benefits that could be reaped. Interestingly, although the award became highly coveted for what it represented, most organizations quickly recognized that the true value of the government's effort was not in the actual receipt of the award, but rather the close examination of the company's business processes required in order to compete for the award. In the end, the MBNQA award was a catalyst for American business to focus on defining, measuring and continuously improving internal processes.

TQM DEFINED

TQM is a business philosophy that defines an organization's management system in order to achieve the following:

- ➤ Seek to improve the business;
- ➤ Guarantee long-term survival through a consistent focus on improving customer satisfaction; and
- ➤ Meet the needs of all stakeholders (customers, employees, owners and suppliers).[2]

The ANSI/ISO/ASOC A8402-1994 standard, *Quality Management and Quality Assurance - Vocabulary*[3], describes TQM as "A management approach of an organization, centered on quality, based on the participation of all its members and aiming to long-term success through customer satisfaction, and benefits to all members of the organization and to society."

As a business philosophy, TQM cuts across and impacts all areas of an organization. It is important to understand that TQM does not just focus on the quality of the final product but rather is a complete realignment of a company's culture to focus on process improvement in every aspect of an organization's business. Thus, the complete process of a company's product life cycle comes under the TQM umbrella, including research, development, supply, manufacturing, distribution and sales.

It is said, that to achieve its full potential, TQM must be woven into the basic fiber of how an organization functions and become a core value for all staff to embrace.

TQM AND SAFETY

If TQM is an organization's overall philosophy of doing business, then to be successful the management of safety must be integrated into that culture. Traditionally, safety, along with quality control and assurance functions, were looked at as bolted on activities that were tolerated as a necessary, but relatively non-productive efforts. Under TQM some may think that safety now becomes a component of a quality assurance function. However, as is depicted in Figure 1, to achieve optimum results both quality control and safety are separate activities that are clearly integrated into the management processes of an organization, both seeking to advance their organizations toward meeting their business goals.

Within an organization, TQM should seek to achieve the following:

- ➤ Institutionalize a never-ending process of improvement;
- ➤ Emphasize and be driven by the need to meet and exceed customer needs and expectations;
- ➤ Work to eliminate waste and rework; and
- ➤ Harness the brainpower of all people in the organization (ASQC, 1997).[2]

Compare how safety aligns with the preceding TQM philosophy:

- ➤ No organization ever achieves complete "safety." Only through a process of continuous risk assessment and reduction does an organization approach its goal of zero accidents.
- ➤ All stakeholders (employees, management, stockholders, and government) expect that organizations will actively seek to eliminate accidents and injuries.

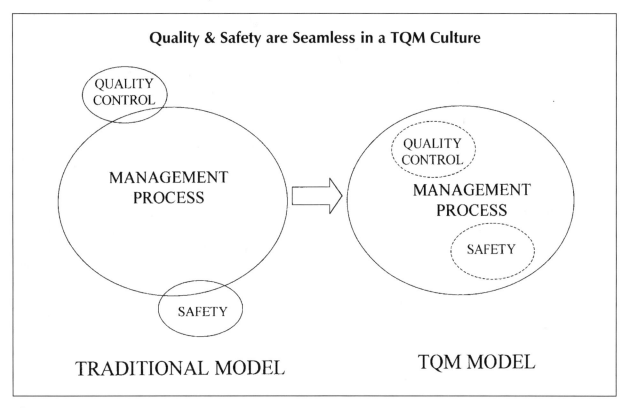

Quality & Safety are Seamless in a TQM Culture

TRADITIONAL MODEL

TQM MODEL

Figure 1.

➤ Accidents are a complete waste of an organization's assets such as people, property and time.

➤ To be successful safety must be a common value to be embraced by all staff.

Thus, from this comparison it should be apparent that in a TQM culture safety objectives do not stand alone but, rather, fit neatly into a company's overall business processes. In fact, many Malcolm Baldrige award winners have been leading companies in the prevention of employee injuries and illnesses. Their focus has not been on exhorting emotional appeals to employees to achieve injury free performance but by designing work processes so that the causes of accidents and other business interruptions are eliminated.

TQM AND SAFETY THROUGH DESIGN

It should be apparent from the previous discussion that the goals of safety through design and Total Quality Management are completely aligned. The quality focused rallying cry of "do it right the first time" has many lessons and applications for safety. The same processes that must be incorporated to ensure that a product

meets all quality expectations will also ensure that all safety related expectations are achieved both for the employees producing the product and for the product users. In fact a quality failure in many cases may be synonymous with a safety failure. In this regard safety and quality cannot be separated. The techniques used for quality improvement programs can be freely substituted to achieve safety improvement.

A recognized leader of the total quality movement was Dr. W. Edwards Deming. He focused on defining and improving processes as a means of achieving business success. Deming clearly advocated designing quality into every form of a product and stressed that designing in quality versus relying on inspecting in quality is always superior in terms of cost and customer service. His comparison of the value of design versus inspection could not have been a more pertinent principle to the practice of safety.

To achieve an organizational goal of superior quality, Deming presented a 14-point management approach in his book *Out of the Crisis*[4]. These points are listed below, along with each point's applicability to designing safety into management systems and products:

1. Create constancy of purpose—*strive to eliminate all inherent hazards in the design stage.*

2. Adopt the new philosophy—*create a culture change that focuses on removing hazards in the design stage.*

3. Cease dependence on inspection—*build safety into products and processes from the beginning.*

4. End the practice of awarding business on the basis of price tag—*review contractors past safety practices and performance.*

5. Improve constantly and forever—*consistently improve processes to remove hazards thus improving safety performance.*

6. Institute training—*training should reinforce that the right way to perform a job is also the safe way.*

7. Institute leadership—*true leaders manage safety the same as they do productivity, quality and human resources.*

8. Drive out fear—*safety through design should be viewed as a positive outcome.*

9. Break down barriers—*transform thinking so that people responsible for products and processes also accept responsibility for building in safety.*

10. Eliminate slogans, exhortations, and targets for the workforce—*safety is achieved by proper design, not through promotions or campaigns.*

11. Eliminate work standards; eliminate management by objective—*don't count injuries, substitute management leadership to implement proper processes.*

12. Remove barriers that rob employees of the right to pride or workmanship—*employee participation is a key to eliminating hazards.*

13. Institute a vigorous program of education—*incorporate safety through design principles in all training.*

14. Put everybody in the company to work to accomplish the transformation—*safety through design is everyone's responsibility.*

QUALITY STANDARDS AND SAFETY THROUGH DESIGN

Total quality management systems that are developed and implemented to ensure a quality product are the same as those necessary to ensure a safe product or process. As such, company standards that are developed to guarantee consistent and uniform products can also be utilized to ensure safety through design principles are fully incorporated.

In the *Encyclopedia of Quality Terms and Concepts,*[5] a quality standard is defined as "mandated quality performance criteria or requirements that must be adhered to in the manufacture of products or in the performance of a service." Such quality standards ensure that quality expectations are clearly defined and that consistent processes are utilized to achieve desired quality on a continuing basis.

Perhaps the most widely recognized set of quality standards is the ISO 9000 series of quality standards that were originally published in 1987 and revised in 1994. Although the original intent of the ISO 9000 standards was to provide a system that could be audited to ensure the standardization of quality of products and services, they also serve as a basis for developing management systems for the continuous improvement of quality processes. With these factors in mind, it is easy to accept that a management system for improving product or organizational quality should have no problem utilizing safety through design concepts that will enhance an organization's overall safety performance.

ISO 9000 APPLIED TO SAFETY THROUGH DESIGN

Since their publication, the ISO 9000 standards series have been widely accepted as the benchmark for implementing effective quality systems and establishing the baseline for the improvement of existing systems. The ISO standards were designed to be international in scope; with the initial support of the European Union countries, ISO 9000 registration has become a requirement for doing business in many markets.

In simple terms the goal of a management system in general and of the ISO 9000 series in particular is to require an organization to "say what it does and then to do what it says." Essentially, a management system requires an organization to define its processes to achieve its desired level of quality. By logical progression, if well documented processes are clearly and routinely followed, then the predetermined level of quality will be consistently built into the product. An example will help to illustrate the principle.

A manufacturer of bottled water had three geographically separated production facilities. Given the nature of their market it was vital that bottled water produced at each facility met the same quality specifications. To achieve this goal, a management system was developed that specifically defined the desired goal and clearly identified the processes that would be required to ensure that bottled water from each facility was interchangeable from the consumer's perspective. Thus, as long as each production facility adhered to their documented processes, they could be assured of a uniform and consistent product in their varied markets. With these specifications in place, customers purchasing their product anywhere in the country could be confident of obtaining bottled water of the same quality.

Management systems such as ISO 9000 have significant implications for the concepts of safety through design, which aims to include safety principles and practices throughout the entire life cycle of a product or service. The use of ISO 9000 systems or equivalent measures can ensure that processes can be designed to routinely include proper safety assessments and reviews. Once safety related activities are formally included in the product specification, failure to properly perform the required safety components would be viewed as a product non-conformity requiring management investigation and remedial action. At this point safety principles achieve equal status to product quality.

A word of caution, ISO 9000 and other management systems for quality and safety have limitations that must be clearly defined. Perhaps using the computer reference of "garbage in, garbage out" is most accurate. The outcomes of implementing a management system are only as good as the targets set. If an organization sets low targets for quality and safety then implementing a formal management system will only ensure that low performance will be achieved. Referring to the bottled water example used above, a management system will ensure consistency; if the target is a lower grade of water than the competition, the management system will ensure that the water produced by all three plants is consistently below that of the competition. Management systems can help support superior performance but only if the proper objectives are established.

APPLICATION OF TQM PRINCIPLES AND METHODS FOR SAFETY THROUGH DESIGN

All the principles and methodology of TQM apply to safety through design. The Baldrige model provides an excellent framework to reference for this discussion:

Leadership—Organizational culture and mindset starts at the top. For safety through design to become part of the operational fabric, leadership must be committed to incorporating it into the organization's way of doing business. Leadership must "walk the talk" by demonstrating safety through design in its decision-making, reporting and review, and reward and recognition processes.

Strategic Planning—The needs of the business must be clearly understood and the safety through design strategy and efforts must be aligned and contribute to this outcome. The strategy for safety through design must be integral to the overall strategy for the business. Resource allocations, organizational goals and objectives/ targets, and performance management systems must support the safety through design efforts.

Customer and Market Focus—For safety through design, the "customer" includes the people (consumer /user, employees, general population), the business (management and stockholders), and the regulators. These customer needs must be clearly understood and addressed throughout the safety through design process in a balanced and conscious manner.

Information and Analysis—Key data, ultimately translated into useable information, must be available and appropriately analyzed throughout the safety through design process. Environmental scans of business needs, industry trends, competitor efforts and results, plus internal performance measures must be visible to all parts of the organization.

Human Resource Development and Management—All employees in an organization embracing safety through design must have awareness of its focus and principles, and have the necessary skills and associated tool-kits to allow them to practice safety through design. These skill-sets are largely the same as in TQM, and include:

➤ Working collaboratively and participatively with others in formal and informal teams.

➤ Using facts and data in problem solving/ process improvement methodologies and processes.

➤ Identifying and addressing the root issues.

➤ Effectively and efficiently managing the implementation of these efforts.

➤ Appropriate training and development must support these skill-sets. Reward and recognition systems must reinforce the application of these skill-sets and the resulting outcomes.

Process Management—The safety through design effort must be managed as a process. It is not the unique responsibility of the Safety Department, bur rather the collective responsibility of the organization. Yes, there can and should be a part of the organization that "leads" the effort, but all parts of the organization must participate and collectively "own" the outcomes. The outcomes will reflect to overall effectiveness of the process, including how well all the groups in the organization work together.

The safety through design effort is however not a process onto itself. It is part of the overall business management processes and integral to achieving overall business outcomes. Key concepts in process management are "Systems Thinking" and "Getting it Right the First Time," as the impact of errors or poor decisions are compounded throughout the process in terms of quality, cost, speed and safety. "Systems Thinking" and "Getting it Right the First Time" require that safety through design considerations be factored into overall business decision making and management. All the right people need to be involved at the right time in the design and implementation processes, looking at the overall impact of actions and decisions.

Business Results—Ultimately, safety through design (and TQM) is about achieving better business results. The implementation of projects and initiatives are tasks. The beneficial changes in the business outcomes resulting from these actions are the true measure of success. Long term sustainability of these outcomes will be the result of the appropriate processes and organizational involvement in safety through design (and TQM) efforts, and focus on continuous improvement by management and employees.

SUMMARY

This chapter examines the evolution of total quality management and its impact on American business competitiveness. Also highlighted is the relationship that exists between TQM and safety through design. Since safety through design falls under the TQM umbrella, by adopting TQM methods, safety in the design stage can be positively impacted. Also examined were the benefits and limitations of quality management standards such as ISO 9000 and their value in enhancing the safety through design process.

REFERENCES

1. *Malcolm Baldrige National Quality Award Criteria.* U.S. Department of Commerce, 1998.

2. ASQC's *Foundations of Quality.* Milwaukee: ASQC, 1997.

3. ANSI/ISO/ASQC A8402-1994, *Quality Management and Quality Assurance – Vocabulary.* Milwaukee: ASQC, 1994.

4. Deming WE: *Out of the Crisis.* Cambridge, MA: Massachusetts Institute of Technology, Center for Advanced Engineering Study, 1986.

5. Cortada J, Woods J: *McGraw-Hill Encyclopedia of Quality Terms and Concepts,* New York: McGraw-Hill Inc, 1995.

Chapter 7

INTEGRATING CONCEPTS INTO THE DESIGN PROCESS

by Thomas A. Hunter

INTRODUCTION

The concept of safety through design set forth in Chapter 2 addresses risks inherent in a product, process, or facility and requires that such risks be reduced to an acceptable level. This level is difficult to define since it is a highly subjective concept, what may be acceptable to one person or group may be anathema to another. However, as a benchmark, it must be accepted that there is no such thing in the real world as absolute safety, where even risks from random events are ruled out. Random events have a certain small, elusive probability of occurring.

Acceptability of risk also brings the concern that the level is subject to frequent and drastic changes. What is acceptable today may be outlawed tomorrow, sometimes by government regulation, or by media emphasis on newsworthy incidents. These have produced a record of product horror stories, environmental disasters, and public health tragedies. All have a definite impact on the responsibility of companies and designers to be aware of the shifting perceptions of acceptable risk, and to continue their best efforts to reduce the risks inherent in their operations and products.

Safety through design is not and cannot be isolated from normal business planning considerations. This chapter will share information on the product design process, including several case histories. Then, since costs have a substantial impact on the ability to implement these concepts, a variety of cost factors and considerations will be reviewed. Finally, keys to understanding typical business practices and decisions are shared, since they have a significant impact on the ability to implement safety through design principles.

PRODUCT DESIGN PROCESS

While there are a few products which appear to be a solution looking for a problem, most are the result of a person or group of persons realizing that there is a need for some thing to perform some function which is either not being performed now, or is being done in a manner which cries out for improvement. This is the need-demand view of why new products come on the market.

Yes, there are cases where an organization comes up with a product or process almost by accident—the serendipity phenomenon—and then it is necessary to create the demand by selling the capabilities of the product to the marketplace. There are also people who are struck with the "flash of invention" and come up with products based on their special insight. But the huge majority of products start out with a problem statement.

STATEMENT OF THE PROBLEM

This statement is usually based on information developed in the marketing department of the organization. Marketing believes, for a variety of reasons, that there is a real, or perceived, need for new products or services. The product or service might not be available presently, and customers are asking for help with a problem; the R&D department has come up with some thrilling advance to give the company a competitive edge; sales personnel are reporting a threat from a product introduced by a competitor and demanding a response; the current line is growing stale and needs to be updated; maybe a little planned obsolescence is needed. There can be many reasons.

Whatever the source, the real or perceived need must be defined as precisely as possible. Any assumptions made in defining the need should be spelled out because no product is ever going to be any better that the assumptions on which it was based. Defining the need demands that marketing people know who is going to use the product and how they are supposed to use it. They must answer the following questions, which pretty much define the product performance parameters and cost objectives to be met:

a) Who needs it?
b) What are they going to do with it?
c) How are they going to do it?
d) How much will they pay for it?

After the marketers have defined the need, cost target and the performance requirements, all the other departments in the organization should be brought in to formulate the problem statement. Engineers will be called upon for several solutions; legal will need to spot opportunities for licensing, patent protection, or threats of product liability suits; manufacturing will provide input on how they will produce the product and what facilities will be needed; finance will figure out what the money needs will be for budgeting purposes. Inputs from all of the groups are needed to reflect concerns, and resolve any internal conflicts. External problems, particularly those related to the effect the product or process will have on the health of the community or the environment, must be reflected in the requirements included in the problem statement. Once the problem statement has been developed, normal procedure would be to send it to top management for information and approval.

Develop Problem Solutions

If the problem statement calls for reworking of an existing product to improve it, to make variations in order to extend a product line, or to adapt the existing product to fit a new market, then there is an established base of information and practice from which to work. The solution to the product design problem is "new" only in the sense that it has not previously been made in that exact form or style. While there may be rough spots along the road to production, prior experience and field reports provide feedback for application of safety through design concepts.

Guidance on hazard recognition, elimination, mitigation, warnings and any instructions or training that may be required are all on record. Of course the effect of any changes in the legal aspects must be taken care of, but generally "new" versions of old products do not make heavy demands on creativity.

Carrying Out the Design Process

The process begins with development of a preliminary design where for example, in the mechanical area literature is researched, energy forces and the strength of the materials are evaluated, to achieve a design solution that performs the intended function. The first design review usually produces a number of suggestions by the review team, based on the performance requirements established in the problem statement. The rule for hazard elimination is "The sooner the better."[1] It is also the most cost effective. The final design incorporates the changes and modifications that were generated in the review process and considers the cost objectives. In the second design review all the changes made are reviewed and it is determined if any additional hazards have been incorporated.

Then the test and evaluation of the product or service begins, followed by pilot production to determine if it is acceptable to the customer. Finally, a third design review is made to determine that all parameters in the problem statement have been met. After passing all of the foregoing successfully, the design is frozen and the product is released to production.

User Friendliness

In considering the foregoing cost aspects and design process, regardless of whether a given design effort is directed to a product, a process, or a facility, there is one primary factor in the design protocol which is highly variable, unavoidable, and practically uncontrollable. That factor is the person who is going to use the product, carry out the process, or staff the facility. While having considerable latitude in specifying materials, requiring certain processing methods, and arranging the components of a facility to suit personal preferences, the designer is more or less stuck with little choice regarding the ultimate characteristics of the person who resides at the end on his efforts.

Fortunately there is a great deal of highly detailed information available about the physical characteristics of human beings. Both government and private organizations have conducted large scale investigations to determine how strong people are, how far they can reach, how well they can distinguish between objects, how well they can hear, etc. This data is sufficiently well defined and is available in handbook reference form.[2]

Mental capabilities and psychological aspects of humans have also been studied extensively, but the available data is hard to quantify and is therefore of limited use to product designers. Current practice in those areas is for designers to use focus groups as a means of testing their products or procedures for validation or rejection by prospective users.

One of the primary objectives of human factors research has been to assist designers in their efforts to make the interface between the person and the product as nearly problem-free as possible. What is sometimes referred to as the "person-machine interface" should be designed to maximize the probability that the "man" component will be able to utilize the product, or equipment safely. Neither human failures (errors) nor machine failures (breakdowns) should have consequences which result in sickness or injury to persons, damage to property, or degradation of the environment.

To enhance the acceptability of the designer's product it should impose the least possible physical or mental demands on the user. In a couple of words, the designers should make their product "user friendly." The easier the product is to use, the more people will want to buy it, the more they will enjoy using it, the better its marketability will be, and the maker of the product will enjoy greater returns on the required investment.

As a corollary, a user friendly product is inherently safer than an "unfriendly" product simply because it is less prone to misuse, abuse, or erroneous use. The "inherently safer" concept has been developed by companies engaged in the chemical process industry and is covered elsewhere in this book. It is synonymous with the concept of "design it out" as a method of reducing hazards to an acceptable level. It is based on the belief that a process is inherently safer if safety considerations are designed into the process right from the start, rather than being tacked on at the end in the form of engineering controls, detailed procedures, or the inclusion of personal protective equipment as means of hazard mitigation. A philosophy is to design the product to fit the user rather than trying to get the user to fit the product. Similar approaches apply to industry facilities and processes.

HAZARD RECOGNITION AND MITIGATION

During the preliminary design and final design stages, the designer must give attention to a thorough study and identification of hazards and their mitigation. Valuable tools in these areas are Standards promulgated by consensus groups (American National Standards Institute [ANSI], American Society for Testing and Materials [ASTM], and the National Fire Protection Association [NFPA]) and numerous other bodies that are not consensus (Underwriters Laboratories, Inc [UL], Factory Mutual [FM]), as well as local, state, and federal governments which adopt regulations (OSHA, etc).

There is a long running argument regarding the question "How can you tell good art from bad art?" One common answer is "Well, I can't really tell you precisely, but I know good art when I see it." Wouldn't it be wonderful if product designers could say the same thing about hazards—"I know one when I see it." The problem is that too many designers can look a hazard right in the eye and never recognize it as such.

Fortunately, both formal and informal methods of hazard recognition are available. Their application helps designers see and evaluate the possibilities for harm or damage to persons, property, or the environment which may result from events which are unplanned, unforeseen, or unexpected. Application of these methods is known as hazard analysis. Recognition, identification, and evaluation of hazards are integral parts of the hazard analysis process.

Formal methods, such as Preliminary Hazard Analysis (PHA), Fault Tree Analysis (FTA), and Failure Mode and Effects Analysis (FMEA) have been available for many years. They are well described in the literature, and have proven their worth in the design of complex systems where the number of possible failure modes is very high and the need for reliability of performance is very great. Most of these systems are based on military applications where the mantra is "Failure is not an option."

The dictionary definition of "mitigate" is "to lessen" or "to make less severe." As applied to hazards to persons, property or the environment, the dictionary definition of the term "hazard mitigation" implies that the potential of hazards can, in fact, be made less severe. This means that both the probability of occurrence of a hazardous situation and the severity of its outcome are subject to modification. It is up to the product designers to develop and select the most cost-effective methods for achieving the goals of reducing hazards to their optimal minimum.

In addition to the mountain of information designers have available on human factors, an even larger amount has been collected on the subject of what constitutes a reasonably good way of carrying out a particular design assignment. This information generated over a substantial period of time, has filtered out the unworkable design approaches, and the core methods that remain have been recognized as what is called "best practices."

Years ago best practices of many companies were treated as trade secrets, often kept in "little black books" whose contents were closely guarded and known only to a few select insiders. In recent years, best practice information has become widely available and has been collected and published as industry norms or standards.

One of the leading contributors to standards formulation and publishing is ANSI. When a product or a service has been developed to the point where compatibility and interchangeability between and among competitors is thought to be desirable, members of the industry petition ANSI to set up a forum for the development of a standard. A sponsoring organization is selected and members of the industry, government, and other interested parties are invited to participate in a consensus process of developing a standard. This is a lengthy process, with many reviews, revisions, and compromises before the standard is approved and finally published. In contrast to the former practice of keeping good practices under wraps, ANSI standards are available for purchase.

With the availability of carefully developed consensus standards, one of the first things any designer should do when given a new assignment is consult the standards literature. In addition to providing insight into the nature of the design problem, standards often keep the designer from falling into the trap of reinventing the wheel. Another significant benefit is the possible avoidance of a products liability lawsuit based on the allegation that the designer failed to comply with the published standards. This aspect can be particularly important when the standard sets forth specific and detailed safety requirements for the product.

Many government bodies, acting under their general obligation to protect life and property from injury or harm, have adopted published standards into their laws or ordinances. This legal recognition (mandatory versus optional) adds considerable weight to the influence of standards in the design process.

In general, regulations or codes tell a designer what to do, when and under what circumstances to do it. Standards tell the designer how to do it, and are frequently regarded as recommendations, not requirements that have the force of law. Legally enacted codes, such as fire codes, building codes, and plumbing codes commonly refer to national or industry standards. When provisions of those standards are included in local codes, they become legally enforceable.

There are two basic types of codes; performance-based codes and specification or prescriptive codes. Performance-based codes state what a particular requirement is intended to achieve, but does not tell the designer what method is to be used to reach that objective. Specification-based codes state their requirements in specific and detailed terms, leaving the designer with little or no discretion.

Codes applied to what are called "skilled artisans" are classed as trade codes, and include building, plumbing, mechanical, and electrical codes. Trade codes are prepared by national, state, and local organizations which have responsibilities for the public welfare in their Charter. One widely used is the National Building Code prepared by the Building Officials & Code Administrators (BOCA). It has been published for many years as a model for building regulations intended to protect health, safety and welfare. The BOCA code is prepared, so by reference a municipality may adopt it as an ordinance, establishing minimum requirements for building construction.

Because there are so many one and two family dwellings, a separate code was established published by the Conference of American Building Officials (CABO). In addition, the Uniform Building Code, published by the International Conference of Building Officials (ICBO) is widely used in the western U.S., and the Standard Building Code, published by the Standard Building Code Congress (SBCC) has been adopted in many southern states. All of the codes have the same intent, which is the protection of life and property, and many of their provisions are similar. However, there are differences between them and the designer must still ascertain exactly which of the codes is applicable to the particular assignment.

Building trades related to plumbing are covered by the International Plumbing Codes developed in 1994 as a joint effort of BOCA, SEBC, and ICBO, and is based on a format established by CABO. It uses both performance and prescriptive provisions to establish minimum requirements for safeguarding public health and safety throughout the country. In 1996 a code for mechanical sections of the building trades was developed by BOCA, SBBC, and ICBO was published as the International Mechanical Code. It sets out minimum requirements for mechanical systems in buildings, and incorporates both performance and prescriptive provisions, with emphasis on performance. Another major trade code is the National Electrical Code has been in use since 1897, and has been sponsored by NFPA since 1911.

All of these trade codes, and several others, provide detailed guidance to designers of facilities and equipment that will be built, installed, operated, maintained or salvaged by persons skilled in those trades. It is important to note that all consensus standards and code organizations maintain a continuous review and updating process to ensure that the requirements reflect the latest developments in materials, equipment and methods. It is incumbent upon the designer to make certain that the applicable version is being used.

CASE STUDIES

1. The Food Vendor Cart[3]

It has been known for ages that heating water in a closed vessel will cause the pressure to rise in the container. If the pressure rises to a level beyond the strength of the container, it is an absolute certainty that the vessel will rupture and release the accumulated energy in a violent manner. Any designer who forgets those simple truths is in for trouble, but the designer of a food vending cart did exactly that.

Intended for use along the streets of a resort area, the cart was required by local sanitary regulations to have a hot water source on board. The designer met this requirement by putting in an 8-gallon tank for water and a small gas burner to heat it. A small faucet was provided to draw off hot water to wash utensils, or make hot beverages. There was no sight glass to check the water level, no thermometer to indicate water temperature, and the hole used to fill the tank with water was fitted with a closely fitting lid. No vent or safety valve. No food cart, either, after it blew up the first day it was in use. Two innocent passers-by were badly scalded, and sued the operators of the cart. It was a simple matter to prove the obvious gross design defects to the litigants. It was equally obvious that no hazard recognition or mitigation effort had been made by the designer of the cart.

2. Collapse of a Cherry Picker Crane[4]

An electrical utility lineman was working in an elevated bucket when it suddenly collapsed, dropping him to the ground, and severely injuring another workman when it landed on top of him. Eyewitnesses indicated that the hydraulic cylinder in the lower leg of the crane had failed. Examination of the failed cylinder showed that the threads on the end of the piston rod had been stripped off, permitting the piston to slide off the end of the rod and drop the crane boom. To find the threads stripped off was a surprise, since that mode of failure indicated that a strong tensile force had been present on the rod at the time of failure. Normally there would have been a compressive load present, so the investigation led into why there had been a reversal of the loading pattern.

The kinematic drawings of the crane linkage showed that the designer had called for the maximum piston travel to be identical to the maximum possible extension allowed by the cylinder. There was zero allowance for overrun. In addition, the drawings showed that the piston head would land directly on the inner surface of the piston rod packing gland in the maximum extension condition. No cushion volume was provided. It was obvious that the designer had overlooked the possibility of the piston bottoming on the end of the cylinder. That was goof number one.

But goof number one had a corollary—since the designer never figured the piston would hit bottom, no limit switches were provided to prevent that from happening. So when the operator drove the crane boom to its outer limit, there was nothing to stop the accident which was just waiting to happen. This was a clear instance of the designer failing to recognize a hazard, and also an example of an inadequate testing program which should have revealed the problem if carried out properly.

3. Failure in the Standard[5]

Several organizations publish standards with the intent of improving product safety through the establishment of minimum requirements to be met by designers. Some standard publishers, such as the American National Standards Institute (ANSI) use the consensus approach to formulating their requirements. All interested parties get into the act with the result that the safety level of some standards is lower than experience shows is necessary.

An example is the case of a construction foreman who needed a place to spread out his drawings. He was nowhere near his construction shanty, so he used the nearest available space which happened to be the crawler tracks on a large crane being used on the job. The tracks were just the right height for examining blueprints, and he was engrossed in that task when the signal man for the crane directed the operator to swing around to pick up a load. The designer of the crane had provided a 7-1/2 inch clearance between the bottom of the counterweight and the top of the crawler tracks, thus incorporating a brutal shear hazard at that location. Of course the foreman's head and chest were crushed between the two parts, killing him instantly.

The causes and remedies for this foreseeable fatal condition have been known for many years, but the ANSI standard did not include a requirement for placing barriers around the rear portion of the crane as a method of "guarding out" the inherent hazard. The Occupational Safety and Health Administration (OSHA) does require the installation of barrier guards in such a situation, and represents a distinct improvement in the level of safety.

4. Tippy Kitchen Stove[4]

Kitchens, in many locations with minimum space, have a compact four burner cooking top unit with an oven underneath for baking or roasting. The oven door is hinged at the bottom to pull down for access to the oven. If a vertical force is applied near the outer edge of the door when it is fully open, the moment of the force tends to tip the stove forward, using the lower front edge of the stove as a fulcrum. Anything cooking on the top burners will be dumped toward the front of the stove, and may cause burn injuries to anyone nearby.

This potentially serious hazard has been recognized for many years. In 1978 the question of stability was addressed in the Standard for Safety, Household Electric Ranges, ANSI/UL 858. Section 33, Stability, requires that a downward force of 75 pounds applied at the center of an open oven door shall not cause damage to or significant deflection of the door. This requirement can be met at minimal cost by using a clip on the splash plate of the stove to secure it to the wall, or by anchoring the rear feet to the floor.

Unfortunately, some older model stoves don't incorporate this obvious improvement. This case involved a seven-year-old girl who was scalded by a kettle of hot soup that spilled on her when she bumped into the open oven door. The subsequent investigation revealed that a force of only 29 pounds 3 inches from the edge of the door would cause the tip-over. Clearly the designer did not recognize the tipping hazard nor anticipate the foreseeable high probability that a vertical force would be applied to the open door during normal use.

COST FACTORS AND CONSIDERATIONS

In the usual approach to cost analysis three major factors are examined: labor, material, and overhead. In manufacturing, the cost of labor is often the single largest expense and therefore gets the most attention from management. For control purposes this cost is divided into direct labor and indirect labor. Direct labor includes the wages and benefits paid to everyone who works to produce the product or service that the company sells. Indirect labor costs cover the non-salaried people who support the direct labor force. Time keepers, tool crib attendants, and cafeteria employees are typical of people who fall into the indirect labor classifications.

Benefits are a major component in labor cost. Some benefits are mandatory, such as social security and workmen's compensation insurance, while others such as health plans, dental or child care are optional with the employer. The costs of the optional benefits are obviously under control of management. However, some of the costs of workmen's compensation insurance are subject to management control. Because the rate charged by the insurers is based in part on the number and size of incident claims experienced, anything management can do to reduce the frequency or severity of injuries in their work place will be reflected in a lower premium or cost for compensation coverage.

As in the case of products liability exposure, there is considerable bottom line leverage available to management from efforts to reduce the workmen's compensation cost by applying the principles of safety through design. That is, recognize work place hazards, then design them out of the production processes where possible. If they can't be designed out, then guard them, but if hazards still remain, provide suitable warnings, training, and education. In addition to generating measurable cost savings, providing a working environment driven by safety through design programs makes the employees aware that management is concerned with their safety and well being. That employee awareness improves the morale of the work force, with the intangible benefit of greater productivity, higher quality, and fewer rejects.

Material cost is usually the largest production cost factor after labor. Purchased materials are commonly ordered from vendors in accordance with specifications established by the product designers. It is therefore obligatory that the designers consider any real or suspected hazards that may be inherent in the specified materi-

al when making the material selection. The material call-out phase is one of the best and easiest places to recognize a potential hazard and eliminate it. It is the place where alternatives and substitutes can be selectively considered and carefully evaluated on a cost-benefit basis. Further, it is a place where management directives regarding the emphasis factors applied to safety considerations can be effectively brought into play.

OVERHEAD COSTS

Overhead is the term used to cover everything beyond the costs of labor and material. Like labor, it is broken into components such as fixed and variable expenses. Common fixed expenses include rent, certain taxes, or interest on any borrowed capital. Being fixed, they do not change with the level of production. On the other hand, variable overhead expenses are related to production level and vary directly with it. A common example is the cost of freight and insurance involved in receiving purchased materials and shipping out the finished products. Yes, there are overhead items that are partly fixed and partly variable, they don't stop completely when production shuts down. Utilities are an example— you still have the expense of providing heat or air conditioning, light, water, power, and phone services even on holidays.

It is common business practice to recover overhead expenses by adding them as a "burden" on the direct labor costs. This can lead to some incongruous situations where the overhead burden is several times the underlying direct labor costs. When this happens, management gets into the act and tries to come up with cost avoidance or cost reduction programs to reduce the burden rate to a more competitive level. At that point any overhead expense items which are attributable to safety through design efforts may be vulnerable to reduction or elimination. It is important that good cost-benefit analysis be prepared for use in justifying these expenses when they are called into question.

Variable overhead costs are subject to subdivisions generated internally by the enterprise and others come from external sources. The internal items are subject to monitoring, accounting, and corrective action if they become excessive. For instance, the costs of scrapping or reworking products which are found to be defective by the quality assurance team can be tracked, allowed for, and changes made to reduce this cost if it gets out of predicted control limits.

In contrast to the internal items, the external variable items show up outside the business, and sometimes are nearly impossible to predict or control. Among these are the costs attributed to defects in products which get through the quality assurance screening process, and find their way into the stream of commerce. In cases where the product fails in service, wears out prematurely, or does not perform its intended function, the costs are covered as warranty expenses which can be monitored and controlled. In other cases the product defect results in personal injury or property damage. A lawsuit alleging liability for the injury or damage may be the result. It is possible, for a price, to obtain insurance coverage to indemnify the company against any losses resulting from such legal actions. Again, application of safety through design principles can be used to reduce the price of this protection.

There are instances where the design of the product is poorly performed, with little or no attention given to hazard recognition, elimination or mitigation. The result can be a product in the marketplace which is so dangerous that it is considered an imminent hazard to persons or property. If the product is intended to be purchased and used by consumers, this situation can be brought to the attention of the U.S. Consumer Product Safety Commission (CPSC). If it agrees with the reported information, it has the power to order the product recalled from the market for repair, refund, or replacement. In extreme cases CPSC can ban the product from sale or distribution in the United States.

It should be clear that when CPSC actions are involved it has the attention of management. The financial impact of such recalls is often sufficient to cause the product to be removed from the market. For small companies which have only a few products in their line, such an outcome can result in financial ruin. Larger companies may survive financially, but their reputation suffers damage which is very difficult to assess. It is important to note that application of the safety through design principles can not only prevent the introduction of defectively designed products into the marketplace, but can also be used as a defense against unfounded allegations of defec-

tive design when the principles have been used in a carefully documented manner. The defensive value is another advantage which can often be used to impress management of the value of such efforts, and to enlist their support in implementing them throughout the company.

COST-BENEFIT EQUATIONS

Just as for any other behavior modification project, it is a formidable task to convince top management that adopting these principles is a good idea worthy of their enthusiastic support. Basically, it is only an example of the old marketing maxim "the only thing you really have to sell is advantages." Any successful salesman will regard it as a chance to "make a believer" out of the decision makers. Cost/benefit analysis is generally regarded as one of the most effective tools available for explaining the advantages of these concepts to all those managers who are focused on the bottom line.

SAFETY COSTS

Most safety costs can be determined quite accurately by application of conventional accounting techniques. During the hazard recognition and elimination phases of the design process, alternative solutions to the problem can be worked up and the direct production costs evaluated. The optimum design is then selected. Note the word optimum reflecting the fact that absolute safety is not achievable, and that many compromises and trade-offs must be made before the final configuration is determined. Also, only direct production costs are considered at this stage of the selection. Indirect costs such as possible adverse effects on the marketability of the product, costs of product liability insurance, and competitive positioning are more difficult to evaluate in monetary terms. Any values assigned to the indirect items must reflect the best judgment of all company departments: engineering, production, marketing, finance, and legal.

It is of great importance that careful, complete records be kept of design alternatives considered, their cost evaluations, and the methodology used in making the final selection. While this may appear to be an exercise in paper work, this information can be invaluable if a products liability lawsuit is filed which alleges defects in the design. One of the standard allegations is "it could have been done better" some other way. Having the background information available is of great assistance in the defense of such accusations.

If determination of indirect costs of safety features is vexing, the benefits realized from including them is even more troublesome because they can be elusive. Since many of the benefits of the incorporated safety features derive from personal injuries and property damage incidents that did not take place, and lawsuits that were not filed, the monetary benefits can only be estimated from past experience.

An additional complicating factor is that the benefits of these loss prevention efforts may take a long time to become apparent, they aren't a quick fix item. Peripheral values such as "public interest," "company image" and the influence of existing or pending regulations must also be considered, and are equally hard to relate to dollars. It is in these intangible areas that reference to company objectives, particularly the long range ones, is often useful when making the safety through design presentation to management.

HEALTH COSTS

The influence of operations, products and services on health costs has been receiving greater and closer attention in recent years. Increases in the cost of medications have priced many items out of the reach of some people, and the number of people without health insurance coverage has been made into a major national concern. This situation indicates that there is considerable leverage in any efforts made by designers to recognize and eliminate any health hazards inherent in their operations or products. This leverage can be used in making the presentations to management.

The classic case of not giving due consideration to health hazards of a product is the long battle between major tobacco companies and various government agencies. When individuals sued cigarette makers on the basis that their product was unreasonably dangerous and, therefore, defective, the individuals lost. The companies denied that nicotine in their product was addictive, and claimed that the victims used their product voluntarily. But when various states used the increases in cost of state funded medical care programs as a basis for claims of harm to their

taxpayers, then the shoe was on the other foot. The states could, and did, prove that smoking and chewing tobacco products were responsible for definable amounts of public health expenditures. The states sued to recover those costs and that caught management's attention.

Interestingly, alleged health hazards in a product have sometimes been used to extract settlements from the producers even though it was proven that the hazard did not exist. Such was the case of a major chemical company which made one component of a prosthetic device which was widely used by women for cosmetic reasons. Some women reported health problems following the implantation procedure, and sued for damages. Many studies failed to connect the implant material with the health problems, but various juries awarded huge verdicts. The company eventually filed for bankruptcy.

Health costs for production workers have long been the subject of regulations published by the Occupational Safety and Health Administration (OSHA). Management attention to these requirements has been obtained by selective enforcement against company officers who failed to observe them. Limits on worker's exposure to many process chemicals have been issued, and there is extensive reference material available regarding the numerous hazardous substances in use today. Material data sheets should be among the information resources used by designers in the hazard recognition stages of their project. That is when opportunities for possible substitution are most readily available.

ENVIRONMENTAL COSTS

The most widely distributed of the variable overhead cost considerations are environmental, since they can be spread far beyond the safety costs accrued by users of a product, the health costs to workers who produced it, and property losses incurred through incidents involving the product under consideration. Since the environment is everywhere, the cost of damage to the environment can be incurred everywhere. Because they are so diffuse, many environmental costs can also be extremely difficult to recognize and mitigate. However, warnings and extensive education campaigns have proven effective in reducing the harm inflicted on nature by humankind.

The general public had little awareness of the word ecology until Rachel Carson wrote *Silent Spring*.[6] Its best-remembered portions recounted the effects of the pesticide DDT on the thickness of the shells on the eggs of certain wild birds. A large drop in the bird populations was allegedly caused by DDT as an unintended disturbance in the food chain of the birds. With heightened public awareness of how all living things are some how related to each other, environmentalists began to press their agenda, and have had considerable success in their endeavors.

Some of the first targets for improvement were the common elements air and water. Air pollution in the form of sooty smoke from power plant stacks had long been regulated by local ordinances, but they soon came under the scrutiny of regulators, and damage to forested areas brought attention to the acid rain problem. Regulations were passed to restrict the amount of particulate matter that could be emitted in smoke, the amount of the dioxides of sulfur and carbon that could be vented in flue gasses, and levels of noxious or offensive odors were curtailed.

The Clean Air Act of 1962 set the limits nationwide which have been revised several times, always becoming more stringent. Similar legislation in 1965 was passed to improve water quality and has had substantial impact on both manufacturing and agricultural enterprises. Noise as a pollutant has been addressed by local ordinances, the Walsh Healey Act, and OSHA. Limits on noise generation have had major impact on the design of equipment, such as air compressors and jack hammers, used in the construction industry. Modification of management behavior to include safety through design principles for those products was obtained only by legislation.

The cost of the corrective measures was imposed on the entities generating the offending materials. Where the costs of abuse of the environment had previously been passed on to the general public, under the new regulations those costs had to be recognized by management. The level of capital expenditures required to accomplish the necessary corrective actions was substantial in many instances, and received much management attention. Legislation was what brought the environmental components of the safety through design concepts into focus, and forced management attention to the impact their decisions have on the environment.

CLEANUP COSTS

One of the aspects of the safety through design concept is that it considers products and operations from the concept phase to the decommissioning/recycling phase. In planning future projects, management must follow the requirements of the clean air and water acts to include any recognized and predictable environmental costs in their estimates of variable overhead. Another area, clean-up costs, is now being addressed. The chemical industry is under heavy pressure to remediate contamination resulting from the dumping of materials at various disposal sites. Correction of former poor habits is not restricted to the chemical industry. Many other companies have dumped unwanted waste in ways which avoided costs and improved the bottom line, but harmed the environment. Such delayed expenditures can be avoided by management application of the safety through design principles to include cost of proper disposal in their cost estimates.

The Environmental Protection Agency (EPA) has developed a hierarchy of waste management which can be widely applied in many industries. Since the principles are so similar, they can be applied in conjunction with safety through design principles. They are as follows:

1. Source Reduction: Don't make waste in the first place, but if you must, then minimize its volume and toxicity.
2. Recover, Recycle, Reuse or Reclaim It: See if you or somebody else can use it; if not as is, reclaim as much as possible economically.
3. Treat It: If it can't be reclaimed, treat it to make it safe.
4. Dump It: But only after it has been made safe.

Again, integration of these principles into management thinking has only been accomplished by legislation which forced the cost-benefit approach to include the environmental costs.

SOCIAL COSTS

So far as it is ever considered as a variable overhead item, the cost to society of products or services which reduce the quality of life are almost impossible to calculate, but they are generally regarded as being substantial. This is discussed by philosophers as "the tragedy of the commons." It occurs when a common resource which is available to anyone is exploited to the point of its exhaustion, simply because no one takes responsibility for looking after it. Over-fishing of sea food sources, destruction of animal habitats, and the possibility of global warming are obvious examples of reduction in quality of life features resulting from over-use of natural resources. So what is the corrective action for this situation? Conservation. And how does that get brought to management's attention? Cost-benefit analysis can help, but monetizing either the costs or the benefits is extremely difficult.

One commonly used tool which gives an approximate evaluation is the environmental impact statement. In some ways, these statements are just another application of the principles being discussed. Their intent is to reduce hazards to the environment to a minimum, and they do this by forcing attention to the realization that hazards do exist, that they must be recognized and evaluated, provisions made to eliminate them at their source if possible, and suitable protective measures must be taken to mitigate their adverse effects. Integration of the principles into management thinking has come through legislation which demanded the necessary behavior modification.

LIFE-CYCLE COSTING

A somewhat different method of analyzing product costs has recently come into vogue. It claims to be more comprehensive in scope than the usual labor, plus material, plus overhead approach and therefore gives a more accurate picture of the real cost of the product. This method tries to account for every cost item beginning with the production of required raw materials, through the acquisition process, manufacturing, distribution, use and ultimate disposal at the end of the article's service life. The only novel feature in this cost treatment is the inclusion of cost incurred after it is sold to the purchaser. Whether such costs should be allocated to the producer is subject to considerable debate. However, once the producer becomes aware of the after-use history of the article, any hazards which can be recognized and designed out of the product in accordance with safety through design

principles should be attended to as a matter of sound public policy.

A classic example of such a correctable residual hazard was the mechanical door latches used on household refrigerators. Discarded units were commonly left in places where young children play. Some played hide-and-seek by getting inside the box and pulling the door closed after themselves. Of course they were hard to find, and when found it was often under tragic circumstances. Because the mechanical latches could not be opened from the inside, the children were trapped and suffocated from lack of oxygen. Once this potential hazard was recognized, the corrective action required all latches to be removed from discarded units, and it was designed out of new units by using magnetic door seals.

RECYCLE COSTS

In terms of costs versus benefits, one of the best examples of the systems approach to improving the quality of life by using safety through design principles has been the program for drastically reducing the solid waste problem posed by discarded beverage cans and developing a program for recycling them. The first step was to design a can which used only one material. This avoided the problems of material contamination and resulting degradation of its properties. Tin coated sheet steel, used for years for canning fruits and vegetables, did not meet the contamination requirement. Pull rings used to open cans were a source of litter when discarded by the user. Uncoated sheet aluminum, however, could be formed into a pressure tight container, and a pop-tab which was secured to the lid by an aluminum rivet was developed. But the all aluminum can, as clever as the design was, wasn't enough to cure the littering problem. Something had to be done to make the user refrain from throwing the can away when it was empty.

Systems analysis to the rescue! Provide an incentive, and everyone knows that money talks. So require a deposit large enough to make it worthwhile for the users to return the container to get their money back. That approach was successfully used for years on glass bottles which were returned to the storekeeper, the empties picked up by the beverage distributor, returned to the bottler for washing, refilled, and reused several times. But non-refillable cans were a throw-away item and needed a stronger incentive. In addition, distributors wouldn't take the empties back, and shopkeepers didn't want the disposal job. So, more systems. Something to collect the cans and get them back to where they started, to the raw material stage. Then the material could be reused, either for more cans or for other applications involving aluminum of that type. Machines were developed to accept returned cans, read bar coded information on the cans to screen out non-conforming ones, compact the cans for collection, and print out a chit to redeem the deposit. Periodic collections got the crushed cans back into the metals market, completing the loop.

So with all the costs of those post-sale system elements to be recovered, where is the net benefit? The key is the high cost of the energy needed to produce primary aluminum from its ore. The recycling effort eliminates that cost, making the overall system cost effective. The improvement in quality of life from the reduction of litter is a freebie. Significantly, with the system in place for recycling aluminum cans, it has proven possible to handle glass and plastic containers in a similar manner since both materials can be re-processed economically.

Unfortunately, some high volume disposable products don't lend themselves well to recycling efforts. Newspapers are a prime example because of the difficulty of removing the ink from the paper, particularly with adoption of colored inks by many publishers. While recycling old papers into newsprint is not presently feasible, repulping the old paper yields a material which can be made into things other than newsprint. The cartons used to pack eggs, and certain kinds of box boards are examples of products made from this remanufactured material.

Office paper and other lightly inked or scrap materials can be successfully recycled into envelopes, wrapping paper, and similar products, each proudly bearing information on how much of its content is recycled. In each case, the cost-benefit equation has yielded a positive balance, otherwise there would be no incentive to use the process. Considerations of safety, health, or the environment play little part in decisions in this area other than the possible reduction in the number of trees that would have been needed to produce an equivalent amount of product.

Another attack on the waste reduction problem is based on the value reclamation method listed by the EPA. Reclaiming residual value of a product which has reached the end of its normal service life can be done in two different ways. One is by scrapping the unit and recouping the salvage value of the materials. This is the "junk yard" method, used worldwide on vehicles of many descriptions.

Another method is to dismantle the product, remove worn out, defective or obsolete components, and replace them with new, operable, updated parts. This is the remanufacturing way, and is widely used on high value capital equipment items which are then sold as "better than new" because they have all the latest modifications built into them. Frequently the modifications will include safety equipment which was developed to mitigate a hazard which was not recognized in the original design, or was not available or required when the equipment was originally sold. For it to be sold again legally, the rebuilt version must comply with the latest safety rules and regulations.

A variation of the remanufacturing technique has developed in the computer industry. The fast pace of development has made obsolescence an important cost factor, and it is common for system components to be replaced with higher performance models long before the components have worn out. With plenty of service life remaining, the replaced components are sold on the secondary market at heavily discounted prices. Compatibility rather than safety is the primary consideration in rebuilding computer systems which wind up with no brand names to identify them.

COST ALLOCATION PROBLEMS
In the discussion of life cycle costing, it was noted that there is a difference of opinion regarding the proper place to assign certain product costs if those costs are incurred after the producer has relinquished title to the item by selling it. In the cases of premature product failures, the manufacturer sets up a reserve fund to cover the delayed costs of warranties. Post-sale costs of injury and damage claims after the product has been in use for even extended periods of time can be covered by the purchase of product liability insurance. However, costs of disposing of a

worn-out product such as an automobile tire are common examples of charges levied against the user rather than the maker.

On a larger scale, how about the cost of dismantling a worn out production facility? Is it fair to the community as a whole for management to decide to just walk away from the facility? Or should there be an escrow account fund established when the permits are given for the construction of the facility, with the fund proceeds earmarked for the restoration of the plant site at the end of its useful life? This would be an example of using safety through design concepts to design safety, health and environmental protection features into the facility while it was still on the drawing board. While it sounds attractive, not many organizations have voluntarily integrated this approach into the design process at the present time.

BUSINESS PRACTICES
MANAGEMENT OBJECTIVES

Several years ago it became fashionable in business circles to take an introspective look and ask "What are we trying to do here?" A buzzword came out of that—objectives. Not only what are we trying to do here, but how are we going about doing it, and how will we know when we have arrived.[7]

The idea behind this effort was to get the people who were running the enterprise to stop putting out fires all day and take a look at where the business was really going. It took a while for this idea to filter through the ingrained habits fostered by hands-on management, and change the mind set of managers. Eventually most businesses began to formulate a set of goals that they wished to achieve.

SURVIVAL

The first objective of any business enterprise is obvious but often overlooked. That is to stay in business, be able to pay the bills, meet the payroll, satisfy customers; in other words, to survive. It is a matter of record that most new business enterprises fail within five years. The most common reasons for failure are lack of capital, inexperience, and lack of market. One of the best tools for enhancing the probabilities for survival is to prepare a business plan which sets forth the capital requirements of the enterprise for a spe-

cific period of time, usually a year or so, establishes marketing quotas, and makes a projection of costs, expenses, and incomes. If an enterprise is a start-up deal, and capital must be obtained from banks, they will surely ask for a business plan which justifies the need for the requested funds and shows how they will be repaid. Banks seek a return on their investment which is at least equal to other lending opportunities available in the marketplace at the time.

RETURN ON INVESTMENT (ROI)

While some enterprises are intended to operate on a break-even basis or at a loss (the non-profits), most intend to provide a product or service for which they receive compensation in return. The hope of the enterprise operators is that their return will be more than their outlay. In other words, that they will be better off after any transactions have taken place than they were before. This hope is what is called the profit motive, and drives the entrepreneurs to the risk that they may be wrong, and that their hopes are not in vain.

If the business is successful, and survives in the marketplace, the operators will derive a certain amount of profit from their efforts. When translated into money units, and compared with the amount of money invested in the business, the ratio of the profit obtained to the investment required is the Return On Investment (ROI). One common business objective is that the ROI should be a certain percentage, say ten percent, commensurate with the amount of risk the entrepreneurs had to assume when setting up the business. If the investment won't pay off enough, the players go somewhere else with their money. As an example, the minimum ROI to be expected from a business risk should certainly be more than an investor can get from buying U.S. Treasury bonds. Many businesses yield ROI in excess of 10%, and certain types of businesses have a typical ROI associated with them. Investors will want managers to achieve at least the ROI typical of their class of business.

So how do business managers meet their ROI objective? Since ROI is a calculation based on a fraction, there are only two things managers can do: work on the numerator (the return) or on the denominator (the investment). Efforts to improve the return usually focus on control of costs with the intent being to reduce them to the minimum possible. Efforts to improve the ROI by decreasing the investment are based on sharing the investment risk with others and involves capital management techniques which are outside the scope of this discussion.

COST CONTROL/REDUCTION

The first step in cost control is to identify all the business elements which contribute to the total cost. In making this identification, it will be discovered that costs naturally fall into two basic types: fixed and variable. Management has relatively little control over fixed costs, but has a lot of control over variable items. Variable costs include such things as the cost of direct labor, the cost of materials, cost of scrap and rework, and the cost of nonproduction expenses which are gathered into the umbrella group of variable overhead.

Included in variable overhead expenses is an item of great interest to the safety through design effort for products. That item is the cost of litigation and product liability insurance. It should be obvious that design procedures which stress hazard recognition, elimination, mitigation, and warnings will result in products and services with minimal risks, lower costs of litigation, and therefore lower premium costs for product liability insurance coverage. Clearly this is one cost item which is subject to control by management and is prime candidate for cost reduction results through the application of safety through design efforts. Since this cost reduction will increase the numerator of the ROI fraction, it will help management achieve that objective.

OPERATING MARGINS

Managers in line positions are directly responsible for using the assets of the organization in the most cost-effective manner. One of the tools used to accomplish this objective is to formulate budgets and cash flow projections to estimate what will be happening down the road. As time passes in an operating business, expenses require cash outflow, while sales of the product generate income. The difference between the direct costs of the product and the amount received for it is the gross operating margin. If things work out as planned, the amount received is greater than the cost, and the operating margin is positive (gross profit).

Based on experience, operating margins are set to recover fixed and indirect costs at achievable levels of production, and are often in the 30% to 40% range. Anything the managers can do to increase the contribution of their department to the paying off fixed overhead charges lets them reach the break-even operating point more quickly. This results in a net (as contrasted to gross) profit situation.

Without going into detail, it should be noted there is considerable leverage in operating margins. Small changes in operating margins can have large effects on net profit, particularly in products which are produced in large volumes. Any reductions in expenses charged to the product for products liability insurance, for instance, can have substantial beneficial results on operating margins. For that reason control of such expenses through the safety through design approach should be very attractive to line managers.

BOTTOM LINE

Line managers report to people in positions which carry over-all profit and loss responsibility for the business. From the Chief Executive Officer (CEO) on down, their attitude toward the implementation of safety through design proposals is colored by one item in particular. That one item is the bottom line, the amount left over after all revenues and expenses have been accounted for on the profit and loss statement. Many over-all management objectives are based on bottom line results, since they will be reflected in the earnings per share (EPS) of the stock of the corporation. The EPS figures are then used by other organizations external to the company to establish a price for the company's stock and the stock price may have an effect on the compensation of senior managers. Clearly, cost avoidance benefits generated by application of the safety through design principles have a pronounced ripple effect on how well management achieves its ROI and EPS objectives.

Make no mistake, the way the CEO regards any safety through design concepts will be reflected throughout the entire organization. If the CEO is presently a nonbeliever in their cost-effectiveness, a major effort at behavior modification will be necessary. One way of doing that is by consideration of the way the concepts can have a positive effect on the bottom line. By careful evaluation of the extra costs connected with not using safety through design principles, a convincing case can often be built for their adoption. The key argument is the way cost avoidance by using these concepts can drop to the bottom line and help management achieve its objectives.

SUMMARY

Integrating the safety through design concepts into the design process is an exercise in behavior modification on the part of management. The behavior pattern being sought by the safety through design process requires consideration of costs and benefits in a larger framework than the usual material, labor, and overhead approach, or short term objectives of ROI. By expanding the concept of costs to include losses incurred by injuries to persons or damage to property, the costs of deteriorating personal health attributable to the product, and the cost of adverse impacts on the environment caused by the product, a more comprehensive picture of true product costs can be obtained. Management attention can then be directed to reducing these presently unrecognized costs, and improving the real benefits from the product.

Managers already know that the best method of avoiding unnecessary costs is to stop them from being incurred in the first place. Thus the best way to achieve the desired cost reductions, safety enhancements, health and environmental improvements is right in the beginning of the product design process. With greater management awareness of true product costs, designers can give more emphasis toward integrating the safety through design concepts of hazard recognition, elimination, and mitigation.

REFERENCES

1. Hunter TA: *Engineering Design for Safety.* New York: McGraw-Hill Inc, 1992.

2. Woodson WE, Tiliman B, Tiliman P: *Human Factors Design Handbook,* 2nd ed. New York: McGraw-Hill, 1992.

3. Hunter TA: *Design Errors and Their Consequences.* ASME Paper 89-WA/DE-14, 1989.

4. Hunter TA, Ast PA, Wilson RN: *Analysis of Major Design Failures.* ASME Paper 85-WA/DE-2, 1985.

5. Hunter TA: *Product Failure Prevention.* ASME Paper 88-WA/DE-2, 1988.

6. Carson R: *Silent Spring.* Boston: Houghton Mifflen, 1962.

7. Olsson D: *Management by Objective.* Palo Alto, CA: Pacific Books, 1968.

Chapter 8

INFLUENCE IN CONTRACTING AND PURCHASING

by Thomas W. Piantek

In the United States, buying a building or a machine has varying amounts of risk. Safety, health, and environmental criteria must be designed in to protect people from experiencing any adverse effects while using the building or machine.

BUILDING CONSTRUCTION

Integrating safety criteria into a remodeling or new building project, even though highly regulated, varies widely across the United States depending on the location, the type and use of the building, the potential safety issues, the building's insurer, and the desires and direction of the owner. As an example, fire protection sprinkler systems have been around since the early 1900s, but not all buildings constructed today have sprinkler systems installed. Private homes rarely have sprinklers, but hotels and schools do. Office buildings may or may not have sprinklers, depending on the number of stories, occupancy, and location. One reason for this is that variances are sometimes granted to attract owners who will bring jobs to a community.

Typically, building codes are the first requirement that must be satisfied in the design of a new or remodeled building. They are mandated by federal, state, county or local city governments to protect the occupants and neighboring structures. They must be interpreted and implemented by a competent architect, who develops drawings and specifications for a building project. The local jurisdiction (city or county) may have special requirements in drafting specifications for a particular type of building construction or use on a specific site within its boundaries.

Finally, the code enforcement official (building inspector) approves the project for construction with certain recommendations. He inspects and audits the construction progress, and grants final approval to the contractor when the structure is completed. The final approval is in the form of a Certificate of Occupancy that allows the building to be occupied for its use as submitted and approved by local code enforcement authority. Thus, the building inspector controls the construction process, and determines the building's safety criteria. He can withhold the Certificate of Occupancy if the contractor fails to deliver the building to the purchaser as designed and approved.

A hotel built in downtown Los Angeles compared to one in the rural parts of Alaska varies greatly in the adherence to safety criteria, even though both are hotels in the United States. Fire sprinklers may not be designed into all hotels, and a disaster may occur because of their absence. One example is the fire in the DuPont Hotel in San Juan, Puerto Rico, a building with no sprinklers. That hotel was rebuilt with sprinklers.

Design criteria, such as structural strength, earthquake resistance, ADA (Americans for Disabilities Act) requirements, and other safety-related specifications—can vary depending on the safety criteria set. Those who influence the safety criteria designed into a building include the following:
- State or federal government;
- Local government (city, town or county);
- Organizations that develop building codes, such as Building Officials and Code Administration (BOCA), Southern Building Code, Uniform Building Code;

→ Insurance carriers and underwriters;

→ The architect and contractor who design and build the building, and select the design approach, materials, construction techniques, and workmanship; and

→ Owners who can specify safety criteria that they require in the specifications.

WHAT INFLUENCES VARIABILITY IN DESIGN SPECIFICATIONS

The purchaser really determines what is designed into a building. Simply satisfying the applicable code results in a building with the absolute minimum standards. In a small community, some architects or contractors will get business by only marginally satisfying the codes and using influence to get building documents approved for construction. If the owner is willing to pay, the architect or contractor will comply to get the business. So, it is the purchaser who is the absolute influence in what is included, what process is used, and what requirements are met in the specifications of a building.

As an example, Johnson & Johnson has a policy that all buildings—office, R&D, warehouse, and manufacturing—will be sprinklered. Therefore, no matter what the location is in the world, J&J buildings will be sprinklered to protect the people, contents, and continuity of production operations. That decision to meet set safety standards raises the cost of construction. The purchaser in a company can insist on what is important for its business, what location is chosen, what architectural criteria, and what total costs can be supported. The quality architect who interprets the owner's needs is the next most important influence in the purchasing process. Finally, the code enforcement officials and their attention to detail will influence the safety requirements that are built into a particular project.

Thus, economics determine if a hotel can be built: cost to build, and potential return at an assumed occupancy level. The lower the cost, and the quicker the payback, the better the business potential. However, a lower cost may exclude vital criteria for safety, like sprinklers, fire-resistant construction, and adequate slip-resistant materials on walking surfaces, unless mandated by local regulations or specified by the owner. In some instances, there are temporary modular trailer-type hotel units that meet few safety requirements when built for short term events, like a World's Fair or the construction of an oil pipe line.

The economics influenced by occupancy rates, estimated payback, what the owner is willing to pay, what the local jurisdiction will allow to be constructed or used, and what occupants are willing to pay as a room rate determines to a large extent what safety measures are the accepted practice. A hotel near Denali Park in Alaska has floors with visual elevation changes of six inches to eight inches caused by settling and foundations inadequate for the frost experienced in that region. That hotel would have been shut down as unsafe in most other locations.

What is accepted in a particular location may be determined by the need for the local economy to keep and attract business. If jobs are the most important issue, certain risks may be taken and some requirements glossed over to get the commitments for the long term construction. When a disaster happens, responsible parties sometimes plead ignorance and point fingers. Insurance carriers raise rates to cover potential losses, and this affects the consumer's purchase price.

Another way economics can be influenced is when, for instance, a city requires sprinklers in all hotels built within its boundaries. All hotels in that area will have sprinklers, likely making room rates higher than those in areas outside its jurisdiction where there are lower construction standards (and possibly lower room rates). Most people, when making reservations, do not inquire whether a hotel is sprinklered. But consumers do strongly influence hotel construction standards by what they are willing to pay in room rates, and demand in amenities. They decide whether the cheapest and lowest cost is acceptable no matter what the risk. While price is generally the driving force, consumers do consider location, security, and even earthquake protection in potentially seismic areas. Some requirements are mandated and strictly interpreted while others are ignored or glossed over.

BUYING MACHINERY

Buying and constructing machinery offers different design challenges than buildings. In the United States purchase orders for new machinery often specify adherence to OSHA (Occupational

Safety & Health Administration) regulations. OSHA does not regulate the designer or fabricator in the construction of new machines. OSHA regulates the *user*. Therefore, the user must select machinery fabricators and suppliers that build machinery which allow the user to satisfy OSHA requirements as well as other industry codes, national standards, and applicable company requirements. If criteria are not clearly defined and understood, and inspections are not made throughout the design and fabrication process, the purchaser may receive machines that do not satisfy OSHA or company requirements. The fabricator or machine supplier who provides the machine may be unaware of a specific ANSI or NFPA standard, or may not know what raw materials will be used, or how the machine will be used. There may not be a definitive standard for a specific criteria, it may be interpreted differently, or the supplier may not be reputable in adhering to standards.

Unlike buildings, there is no permit or approval authority to hold the fabricators or suppliers of industrial machinery accountable for what they are supplying. There are guidelines for constructing machinery such as ANSI (American National Standards Institute), NFPA (National Fire Protection Association) and ASME (American Society of Mechanical Engineers) standards. ANSI standards are voluntary consensus standards and some cover industrial machinery in the form of the B11 Standards on Machine Tools, the National Electric Code (NFPA 70), and other codes like the Electrical Standard for Industrial Machinery (NFPA 79).

In most jurisdictions, compliance to the National Electric Code is mandatory in the construction of new buildings, but loosely or not applied at all to machinery. This is determined by the local electrical code enforcement official. That official may not pay close attention if he is understaffed, not familiar with a particular machine type, or does not have intimate knowledge of the National Electric Code when it is applied to machinery. If he does look at machinery, he may only look at the incoming power to the machine to see if adequate circuit protection and grounding is installed.

Beyond the local electrical code enforcement official, no other outside agency except OSHA will inspect a machine for compliance to a safe-

ty standard or code. Compliance is largely due to the reputation and willingness of the manufacturer or design engineering firm. They may meet or go beyond compliance due to fear of litigation. Many machines are designed with easily bypassed interlock switches so that in the event of a lawsuit, the machine builder can cite bypassing practices by the user as an unsafe practice, and thus avoid personal liability. The inspection, knowledge of applicable codes, and acceptance of a machine relies on the purchaser's ability to recognize or hire experts to insure compliance. Even when the fabricator builds to his view of compliance, how the user plans to operate the machine may result in violations of a code.

"Buyer Beware" is the best strategy when ordering machines. There are usually production start-up dates and other pressures associated with the delivery of a machine. Not accepting a piece of equipment once it is near completion is very difficult, usually winds up in executive negotiations, and may lead to arbitration or possible lawsuits. Therefore, it is extremely important that the initial communications are detailed, the selection process for the manufacturer or fabricator is thorough, purchase agreements reflect safety requirements in detail, and that the design is reviewed before any prototype or construction is initiated. It is these written communications that determine who is financially liable when disagreements occur.

It is not likely that a purchaser can afford to walk away from a less than compliant purchase given the long lead time for machinery and the typical costs of a new product launch or a business startup. The purchaser may choose to fix the deficiency at his own expense to keep the machine delivery on schedule, or the manufacturer may expedite changes to facilitate acceptance and a quick final payment. Because purchases of new machinery may occur at irregular time intervals, many purchasers may not repeat the process until years in the future. People, companies, sales personnel, and manufacturers may change in succeeding years. Therefore, when purchasing machinery, "Buyer Beware." Design in, and document, safety requirements at the very beginning.

The machine manufacturer typically negotiates contracts with clients. In most cases, price and delivery are the key drivers in a purchase decision. It is only an enlightened buyer, experienced design engineering firm, or a machine fabricator with a concern for safety or a long history of litigation, that makes sure safety is designed into the machine from the very beginning. The machine supplier typically has experience in what is acceptable, what has been selling, what people will pay, what competitors supply and their legal responsibilities. They also have specific strategies to get people committed to the purchase of a machine while maintaining a profit. They have standard quotations and purchasing processes that require the purchaser to approve certain language in the transaction documents.

Prior to issuing a purchase order is the time to exercise due diligence, and make sure the fine print on the back of purchase documents expresses the details of the purchase from a legal standpoint. The purchase order details must be reviewed for each project to ensure they are legally valid. This is also the time for buyers to insist on implementing a safety through design strategy in the purchase of these machines. The buyer must maintain control of this process or be asked to accept something that may not meet company safety expectations. It is at the earliest discussions in the purchasing process when the safety details for design, fabrication, acceptance and performance criteria should be discussed. It may be appropriate to start the selection process by reviewing available technologies, prices, safety design features, and talking to previous purchasers before any firm plans are made to purchase new machinery. The earlier and more detailed the understanding of the safety criteria and applicable codes, the better the end product will be.

From the very start, the purchaser typically pursues the lowest price and shortest delivery time. The rush to proceed may cause codes and standards to be ignored in the order process. Everyone understands dollar differences between competing suppliers, but the adherence to established safety standards is more difficult to quantify. The machine manufacturer tries to get a commitment to purchase before the details are worked out. Furthermore, purchasers often assume their company safety standards are included when they are not.

The purchaser usually begins by getting a ballpark price so funding can be approved. If safety standards or other changes are determined as the project ensues, there are sure to be price increases. This is another reason to make expectations very clear, and in writing, before signing the contract. Who determines the safety requirements? The purchaser does by stating his requirements (safety included) in an invitation to bid or a request for quotation. This is more than a laundry list of standards or codes. The list may be legally all encompassing, but if a particular requirement is not clearly understood up front and reviewed, there is a very high likelihood that the final machine will not contain exactly what is required.

Another reason machines fail to meet expectations is that the purchaser chooses to omit important details for security reasons (e.g., the potential use of raw materials). Additionally, the fabricator must clearly understand how the purchaser will use the machine in order to understand the importance of incorporating the appropriate safety features. These specifics are important as engineering decisions and components are ordered and assembled into a machine. It is always more expensive to change parts after they have been installed, and it also causes delays. Therefore, it is imperative to develop specific requirements before requesting a price quotation. It is also necessary that fabricators incorporate these requirements into their price quotation.

REQUIREMENTS IN THE UNITED STATES VS. EUROPE

The European New Machinery Directives (EN 292, EN 60204, EN 1050) have an excellent risk assessment process where the designer is required by law to complete a risk assessment and reduction process for each new machine. This data must be documented and included in a technical file. The machine designer is required to go through a rigorous process (Figure 8-1) that requires the machine to be methodically evaluated for hazards. This process holds the designer responsible for a due diligence completion. The Directives list the designer's responsibilities, show the appropriate methods to be used (Figure 8-2), list applicable standards, and presents a risk assessment process for identifying safety hazards. There is also a step-by-step engineering approach to eliminate or control the hazard while

Designer's Responsibilities

European Std. EN 292 -1/2 Lists the strategy for selecting safety measures and states that these safety measures will be a combination of the measures incorporated at the design stage and those measures required to be implemented by the user.

It requires that designers should in all circumstances:

1. Specify the limits of the machine.
Determine the intended use of the machine, the performance limits, the space limits, range of movements, space requirements for installation and time limits to foreseeable life of the machine or if necessary some of the component parts (wear on faces, tools, or control components)

2. Identify the hazards and assess the risks.
This should be considered over all phases of the machine's life, in manufacture, transportation, installation, normal use, foreseeable misuse, dismantling and disposal. Again, the degree of injury and probability of occurrence must be assessed at this point.

3. Remove the hazards or limit the risk as far as possible.
This can be achieved by taking out traps, reducing speed and force, through good ergonomics and by applying fail-safe principles

4. Design in safeguards against remaining risks.
Where hazards cannot be designed out, safeguards must be designed in. These can include interlocked guards, light curtains, pressure mats, two hand controls, trip devices etc

5. Inform and warn the user about any residual risks.
This can take the form of signs, symbols (both visual and audible) for all personnel including operators, installers and maintenance etc.

6. Consider any other precautions.
At this stage the designer must determine whether additional requirements are necessary in view of emergency situations for all personnel.

The reference that requires designers to consider the hazards, risks and safety measures apply over all phases of the machines life:

e.g. Manufacture
Transportation
Assembly
Commissioning
Normal Use
Foreseeable misuse
Maintenance, setting, cleaning etc. Disposal
At all these stages, the hazards must be identified and the risks assessed.

Excerpt from : Pilz GmbH & Co. A guide to the Machinery Safety Standards
Vol 1: 5th Edition March, 1996   Page 24 & 25   Used with Permission

Figure 8-1. Designer's Responsibilities

protecting the operator and reducing the risk to an acceptable level.

If a test is required to verify compliance, it must be conducted, and all the data documented and assembled in a technical file. At the completion of the technical file, a Declaration of Conformity must be completed and signed by the fabricator to verify completion of the process and compliance of the equipment. This is truly a safety through design process, mandated by law (directive) in Europe for all new machinery put on the market since January 1, 1995.

Only when this process is completed, can the CE Mark be affixed to the machine (Figure 8-3). This mark assures the purchaser of compliance with the standards. Only when there is an injury will the authorities ask for the technical file and see if the proper methods have been used in protecting the user. The technical file must be produced within 48 hours of a request. An

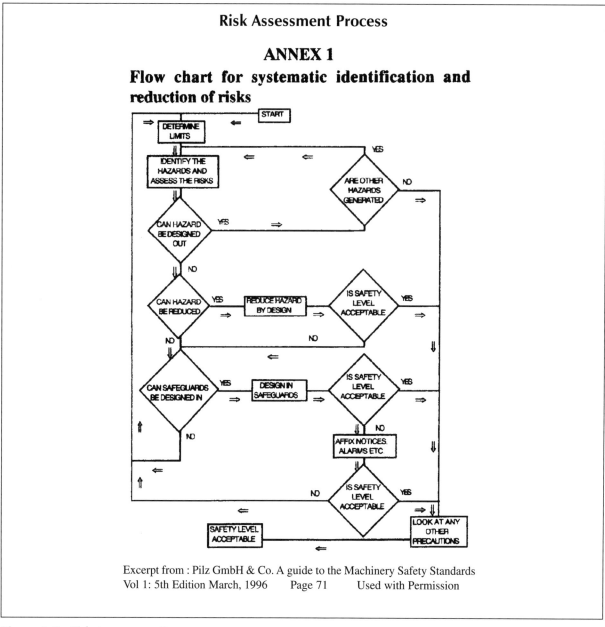

Risk Assessment Process

ANNEX 1

Flow chart for systematic identification and reduction of risks

Excerpt from : Pilz GmbH & Co. A guide to the Machinery Safety Standards
Vol 1: 5th Edition March, 1996   Page 71   Used with Permission

Figure 8-2. Risk Assessment Process

improperly conducted process can mean a fine or jail, depending on the degree of fraud or negligence involved.

These regulations place accountability on the manufacturer. This is lacking in the U.S. machine manufacturing industry. Some U.S. manufacturers build very safe machines, and many even comply with the European regulations. It can be a competitive advantage for the machine supplier who recognizes the higher level of attention to safety detail. Unfortunately, a European machine supplier shipping a machine to the United States has no legal obligation to build it to the European

Standards, or U.S. Voluntary Consensus codes, and can ship almost anything if the purchaser accepts it.

In the United States, the voluntary consensus ANSI standards are applicable in many situations, but no system of accountability exists to certify that a machine is compliant except for the purchaser's influence and review, the courts, the product liability system and the machine builder's own standards. Lawsuits for personal injury or product liability are often where standards are determined. An insurance company pays the claim and consequently may raise its

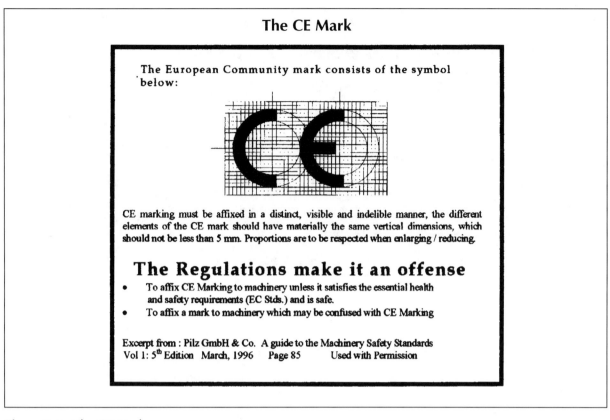

Figure 8-3. The CE Mark

premiums to the machine supplier. It is typically only after a serious injury and resulting lawsuit that a supplier raises his safety standards. As a result, his costs go up and he may have to become more cost competitive by incorporating higher safety standards and avoiding litigation. New companies often present the greatest risk because they focus on their technology, and meeting safety requirements becomes a lower priority.

In both building construction and machine fabrication, the parties involved need to clearly understand what the safety requirements are at the very beginning of a project. Providing clear definable specifications is necessary for a mutual understanding of the particular safety requirements and risks with the project. A company should have standardized specifications to present at the very beginning of the negotiating process, commonly called "Boiler Plate Specifications." An example, "Electrical Specifications," is reflected in Figure 8-4. They should not be turned over to a salesperson, but should be reviewed in detail with members of the machine builder's technical staff. The purchaser

should also request that the technical expert of the machine builder present how he will meet the requested safety requirements. Misinterpretation or poor executions should be determined very early in the negotiation process. It is too late after the purchase order is issued, progress payments have been made, the designs are complete and the machine is under construction. The fabrication schedule will drag, wasting time and money for both parties.

INTERNAL COMPANY CULTURE

Every company has its own values, priorities, and manner of conducting business. If safety is a high priority in a company, there will be a detailed process to guarantee that any upcoming purchases will comply with specified safety requirements. Many checkpoints set up within the buying process will ensure compliance at critical points, from beginning negotiations to delivery of the final product (machine or building). If the company is cost-driven with little regard for safety, it will get what the machine supplier or building contractor chooses to provide, meeting minimal standards for compliance

Machinery Boiler Plate Specifications

XYZ Facility **SPECIFICATIONS : Rev. March, 1998**

4.0 ELECTRICAL SPECIFICATIONS

4.1 PURPOSE AND SCOPE

4.1.1 This specification is to be used for the purchase of custom designed equipment for *XYZ facility*. It will also apply to any custom modifications purchased for standard equipment.

4.1.2 This specification is a site specific addendum to the "NFPA 79 **Electrical Standard for Industrial Machinery 1997 Edition**". This standard will be referred to as "NFPA 79" in this specification. Equipment purchased using this site specific addendum must comply with this specification unless specific exceptions are listed in this addendum or a written request for deviation is reviewed by *XYZ facility* Controls Group and approved in writing by the *XYZ facility* Purchasing Department.

4.1.3 This specification is intended to be used with a XYZ facility "EPR". The EPR (Equipment Procurement Requisition) is an overall machine technical specification which details the process the machine is to perform, tooling information, required cycle time, etc. Additional electrical specifications specific to a given machine type or department within the plant will be included in the EPR.

4.2 GENERAL

4.2.1 Nominal power is 480 volts ac, 60 Hz 3 Phase, 4 wire, Wye unless otherwise specified in the EPR.

4.2.2 Control voltage shall be 24 vdc. Control voltage of 120 vac, 60 Hz is optional and must be approved by the *XYZ facility* Controls Engineer.

4.3 DOCUMENTATION

4.3.1.1 Wiring diagrams shall be done using AutoCad 14 and plotted "D" size (36 in. by 24 in.). The minimum version acceptable will be AutoCad Release 12. The use of blocks rather than shape files within a drawing is preferred. If shape files are necessary, the *XYZ facility* Controls Engineer must be contacted for approval. If allowed, the shape files must be included on the disk with the .DWG files. Final drawings may be printed 11" x 17" for inclusion into training and service manuals.

Sample Section Only - Must be developed as site specific.

Figure 8-4. Machinery Boiler Plate Specifications

(for example, whatever the supplier judges to be necessary to get a certificate of occupancy for a new building or adequate in shipping a machine that satisfies the intent of the contract). Selecting a supplier based on cost may exclude many competent suppliers that would be considered if safety standards were included at the very beginning of the bidding process. What is left are those who may minimally comply with safety codes and requirements because the purchaser is not skilled or interested in the safety requirements. Cost and schedule are easily understood elements, whereas safety requirements may be more complex.

A project driven by marketing or research and development trying to gain a competitive advantage may force a supplier to provide a machine with poor safety standards. Using an entrepreneurial supplier presents risks and possible project delays in bringing the project to a safe operational and compliant state. It may require greater involvement of safety and engineering professionals, especially at the very beginning, to protect the user who is regulated by OSHA regulations and meeting company standards and priorities.

A company with a strong top-down leadership style may short-circuit the negotiating process by insisting on arbitrary costs or schedules. Sometimes the goals can be overzealous, narrowing the final selection process, and glossing over safety requirements. A high level manager insisting on a particular supplier or contractor can also dictate the selection of suppliers who may not have a strong safety culture or the desire to meet customer requirements. The supplier may ignore skilled engineering or safety professionals before all details are specified or fully understood. Legal issues and proprietary technology may also cloud the process of a detailed review. Any resulting cost increases can be passed on to the purchaser unless he is particularly skillful in the areas of project management, communication, and documentation.

Here is an example of a building project gone awry. A major new manufacturing facility of 500,000 sq. ft. was under construction. As winter snows, winds, ice, and mud began to the delay this project, the owner insisted on maintaining schedule. So the building contractor proceeded to incur overtime, building temporary enclosures, adding heaters to make conditions tolerable, removing mud and adding fresh soil, paying premiums for expedited material deliveries, and working weekends to make up for delays in shipment of vital components. When spring came, about $500,000 in extra costs had been incurred in keeping the project on schedule. The owner refused to pay the bill saying he never authorized spending the additional half million dollars. The builder demanded payment saying the costs were incurred because the owner directed him to stay on schedule. Needless to say, an ugly situation developed with threats and counter-threats. The final resolution was a fifty-fifty split at the completion of the project. Both parties felt the resolution was not to their benefit and careers were in jeopardy.

Fortunately this did not involve a safety situation, but does reflect the impact of poor communications and poor documentation. A change order at the very beginning of winter, and frequent updates on project cost increases, could have alerted both sides that inordinate costs were being incurred.

ROLES AND RESPONSIBILITIES

There are specific roles from a business and legal standpoint in the construction of a new building or machine. The architect, contractor and machine fabricators are the creators, and therefore, the responsible parties in bringing projects to life. The purchaser must state the requirements for the project and look to the creators to make it happen. This is done in conversations, drawings, sketches, specifications, e-mails, and other forms of communication. The contractors and machine

suppliers must interpret the inputs, use their technical skills to build as requested, control cost, and avoid scheduling delays that may impact the project outcome. The customer must not be tempted into doing the contractor's job or getting too involved in the process of managing the machine construction or building process. He must audit the project so that his requirements are being met, and refrain from changing decisions so as not to cause delays and cost overruns. These roles and responsibilities will influence the final product.

Sometimes the machine supplier has a better understanding of the applicable codes, and is especially true with fire sprinkler contractors, suppliers of radioactive or radiation generating equipment, and contractors working in highly regulated industries. But they must also be aware of the final use of the building and location of a machine which can affect its safe operation. An example is dust-tight electrical requirements for motors being integrated by the user into a production line where an adjacent machine is grinding material which produces ambient dust.

Owner and builder representatives for each company must recognize a single communication point. They must be directly involved in the project, generally serving as project managers. A recognized communication system and detailed project management chart must be developed so that the communications are clearly defined and controlled on the all sides of the process.

The participants in a negotiating process must have mutual respect. There must be trust, a good rapport, and a willingness to listen to the requirements of all individuals in a cross functional team specifying a building or machine. There are tradeoffs and conflicting goals, so a final specification that describes the expected result is needed. Also, the purchasing agent must maintain a balanced perspective in the purchasing process to ensure that what is delivered best fits the company's needs (cost, delivery, and the expected function of the building or machine including safety issues). Being a good listener, skillful at conflict resolution, paying close attention to documentation changes, and having excellent communication skills makes the purchasing process go smoothly. It only takes one person with a hidden agenda—a person trying to control the direction of the project or process—

to instigate adversarial discussions that put everyone on the defensive and yielding poor project results. Experience of the participants also helps avoid pitfalls that may occur in a new project. This is especially true of safety issues where experience is often the best teacher of anticipating trouble points.

The objective of having a win-win negotiating process with a construction firm or a machine builder insures making a fair profit. This minimizes rework, information delays, and the purchasing company gets a machine that meets production and safety requirements at the agreed upon cost, on schedule. This is the optimum result. If everyone works toward the goal of making it happen, all will be winners in the process. Instituting safety through design principles that include up front bid specifications, and a detailed review of the bid documents with the contractor or machine builder to avoid communication traps, will help the group to build a machine or building safety and efficiently.

HOW CORPORATE GOALS CAN ENHANCE THE PROCESS

A corporation that has made safety a value and incorporates that value into purchasing activities is very likely to be practicing the safety through design process. A company that is geared to react and fight fires as a way of conducting business will have a difficult time using safety through design principles. In reactive companies, as new priorities arise, they will interfere with consistently using a safety through design process.

A safety through design process involves having a clear understanding of the project requirements at the very beginning of the process. It requires checkpoints, milestones, checklists and safety sign-offs as the process moves forward. A reactive company will not consider safety criteria in the design. Rather, it will wait until after the machine has been delivered, or the building has been constructed—or worse yet, wait until after an incident occurs, a citation has been issued, or a major catastrophe has occurred. Then they will try to correct the problem, when they could have prevented it.

Many times, engineering projects have been observed where the focus has been on the technology and product, and not on delivering safety requirements. Cost, completion date, and project

goals were the priority. Machine guarding, an important safety necessity, was left until late in the machine assembly process. By then, the design and execution were left to make-shift improvements or expensive guarding in a crash effort to meet a target date. In most cases, the guarding was assembled and looked adequate, but was not consistent with the way the machines were operated or maintained. They become a barrier to producing the product efficiently. In one instance, 18 screws had to be removed from a panel to adjust something that needed frequent access. Then maybe 10 screws were replaced after a repair. Before long, only 2 screws were left holding the panel in place, providing ready access but poor compliance to machine safety.

The safety through design process requires early involvement of the designer to identify the many operating and maintenance points so that panels, doors, and safety tunnels have free access while complying with the Johnson & Johnson company policy of "Zero Access"™ machine guarding (a Johnson & Johnson worldwide program of Machine Design & Modification Engineering & Safety Requirements - 1996). A retrofit improvement fails to identify the requirements for access; it seeks only to meet guarding requirements per company policy. Whether the guarding efficiently meets operating requirements is not a priority to the engineering group. As long as the project is completed on schedule, on budget and fulfills the technology requirements, it is viewed a success. Complaints from operators and mechanics are viewed as "sour grapes" and the engineers are off to the next challenge. It is only after an involved plant manager holds the engineering group accountable for operation issues that the development process changes.

ROLE OF SAFETY IN THE CAPITAL APPROVAL PROCESS

Probably the single biggest problem with getting people involved in a new project is that safety professionals and other safety contributors from the operations group may not be aware that new machines are coming until they arrive in the building. Input from safety, operators and mechanics cannot be included in the procurement process if it is kept a secret. This is especially problematic when the project team is composed only of people from engineering, R&D, and marketing. The best way to ensure a safety through design process is to include safety, health and environment, quality, and operational sign-offs in the approval process for new machinery and buildings. A sign-off at the capital appropriations approval stage guarantees the inclusion of safety input. Management sends a clear message to the entire organization about its safety value when it will not allow a project to move forward unless safety has been included in project scope development. At Johnson & Johnson, there are three phases that define a major engineering project:

Phase O is the scope development effort where the business proposal, project worthiness, and return on investment are determined. Engineering develops a number of options to determine the most acceptable business alternatives.

Phase I is selecting one alternative from Phase O and creating engineering drawings and specifications to arrive at a quotable "Cost to Build" for the project at hand. Machinery or land purchase may be included in this portion of the approval process.

Phase II is the final approval to turn the engineering documents into a real building, machine or process for the purpose of achieving a specific business result.

Safety criteria need to be understood by the project engineer and managers at all three phases. However, the detail of safety requirements will increase as the project develops. In the procurement of machinery and the construction of buildings, the greatest involvement will be with the Phase I development of the specifications and drawings to translate the ideas into buildable documents. Previously developed criteria, standards, and applicable code excerpts should be used to provide engineering safety input. Catalogue selections, pictures, specifications of safety items, test results, and excerpts from technical journals may be used to provide input to the designers or architects. A final list of recommendations should be provided in a report to the designer or architect after a review of the in-process documents. The Phase II portion should have safety involvement when the subcontractors provide engineering detail not yet developed in Phase I, including, for instance, ergonomic inputs to select furniture.

GUIDELINES, CHECKLISTS, RECOMMENDED PURCHASE COMPONENTS LISTS

To assist the engineers and architects in developing detailed drawings and specifications, clear information must be communicated. Because there are infinite projects and unlimited potential safety issues, a series of checklists should be developed to cover areas of major concern.

BUILDING CONSTRUCTION

Johnson & Johnson has been constructing buildings since the 1920s. Until the late 1990s, no formal criteria existed for the prevention of slips, trips and falls. Yet, approximately 15% to 20% of J&J injuries each year are due to slips, trips and falls. This data is consistent with other parts of the world and other companies. Consequently "Site Assessment Guidelines" for existing facilities, and "Construction Guidelines" (Figure 8-5) for new facilities were created. These guidelines are not highly technical, but offer a straightforward approach to identifying and removing potentially hazardous risks for a slip or trip.

A trip results from surfaces that are not level due to poor design. An example is a curb, designed to channel water and provide a boundary for separating automobile from pedestrian traffic. However in high volume pedestrian walkways, a change in elevation caused by a curb can be a trip hazard. The trip risk is amplified if the curb and surrounding materials are all constructed from the same materials and/or the same color. The risk is even greater if a person is in a rush, has poor visual perception, or has difficulty discriminating the differences in elevations. One remedy is to lower the sidewalk or raise the road by creating a ramp. Either solution is acceptable for reducing the risk of trips at curbs. Another method with a slightly higher risk is to use a different color and texture of materials. (for example, asphalt roadway, gray stone curb and concrete walkway). The last option is to paint the curb yellow, which most building codes do not accept.

The ADA (Americans with Disabilities Act) has guidelines that indicate the requirements for transitions between dissimilar surfaces, but most architects use this criteria for wheelchair access only and not for the general public who may be handicapped in other ways, like visual acuity.

Slip, Trip and Fall Construction Guidelines

❑ *Canopies and Architectural Overhangs* are desirable features of a well designed employee and lobby entrance system, and minimize water accumulation during rain or snow. This minimizes the water load on the entrance mats and the distance water will be tracked into a facility. The shoe soles of the employee must be dry before encountering a walking surface with a low coefficient of friction.

❑ *Entrance Vestibule Mats* should be recessed into the floor to provide a trip free surface and provide a mechanism for removing excess moisture. Space for snowmelt should be accommodated within the mat structure. Exposed flooring that frames or borders the entrance mats should have a high slip resistant rating.

❑ *Lobby Floors* should be selected with a high slip resistant finish. A coefficient of friction equal to 0.6 or higher is required. Under no circumstances should glazed ceramic tile, smooth marble, Terrazzo® or other high gloss flooring products be selected for lobby entrances. Slip resistance and good aesthetics are available with many flooring materials today. ADA compliant (US only) or other locally available, high friction materials manufactured by reputable companies should be specified.

Figure 8-5. Slip, Trip and Fall Construction Guidelines

Only in the design of new retail establishments are these issues taken into consideration.

NEW MACHINERY CONSTRUCTION

The technical issues associated with production technology and new products are typically the most difficult and most challenging to design engineers. The safety issues concerning machine guarding, ergonomics requirements, and electrical codes are thought to be straightforward and not a technical challenge. What is found is that many new engineers are not educated in safety, nor are there mentors available to provide on-the-job training as in the past. As an example, emergency stop (E-Stop) buttons are a simple requirement for every machine. The purpose is quite clear: in the event of an emergency condition, the machine must be brought to a safe condition as rapidly as possible. The simple safety requirement of having an E-Stop button at each operating station in a consistent location should be clearly understood. However, in machine safety audits, it has been found that many E-Stop buttons are located only on the main operator console—not reachable from other operator stations—and sometimes not properly hardwired with an industrial relay disconnect of power.

In an effort to arrive at consistency, Johnson & Johnson has developed a machine-guarding checklist to use to evaluate a machine's compliance with adequate machine guarding. A simple checklist printed in a Scientific Technologies safety catalogue and developed by Joe Snopek of Allied Resources (Figure 8-6) helps a safety through design process comply with the regulatory standards.

As described earlier, Europe has regulations called the New Machinery Directives and the CE mark to support the safety through design process. This guarantees that the manufacturer has used a detailed safety evaluation process by placing the CE mark. However, machines manufactured in Europe and sold in the U.S. can provide any level of safety because of no regulatory oversight exits. European manufacturers typically do not CE mark machines sold outside the EU unless there is a request by the purchaser. Sometimes, protective devices are eliminated in order to save money and become more competitive on price in the U.S. Quotations may include these parts as an option, but if the decision is left to an unskilled or inexperienced person, frequently they are passed over because of the cost increase.

RECOMMENDED PARTS LIST

Another important document to ensure a safe machine is a list of recommended or approved components (Figure 8-7). There are many suppliers of safety equipment. Left to their own choices, purchasers within a manufacturing plant do not always have the knowledge to understand the full ramifications of safety components they may be purchasing. As an example, there are myriad choices for safety relays, safety mats, and machine safety circuit switches. Some are acceptable and some are not. Simplifying the

Machine Safety Evaluation Form

EVALUATED BY:	**ALLIED RESOURCES CORPORATION** 111 Founders Plaza, 10th Floor East Hartford, CT 06108 860 290-6665 fax 860 290-6673	SURVEY DATE:

Machine Safeguarding Evaluation Form

Plant:_____ Bldg.:_____ Dept:_____Location
_____

Machine Type: _____ Inv. #:_____ Model:_____ Date Built _____
Equipment Photographed: Date_____By: _____
_____

Assessment Categories

Circle, check, or fill in items

I Mechanical Hazards
A. Point of Operation
1. Boring / drilling ()
2. Cutting / turning ()
3. Forming ()
4. Grinding ()
5. Milling ()
6. Punching ()

7. Shaping ()
8. Machine center ()
9 Other-( ) ()
B. Power Transmission
1. Belts / chains / pulley ()
2. Brakes / clutches ()
3. Connecting rods ()
4. Couplings ()
5. Cams ()
6. Cranks ()
7. Flywheels ()
8. Gears ()
9. Shafts ()

10. Spindles ()
11. Other-( ) ()
II Non-Mechanical Hazards
A. Guarding Considerations
1. Air systems
2. Pneumatics
3. Coolants
4. Fire control

5. Fluids/water-( )
6. Nat. gas - ( )
7. Hydraulics
8. Noise

9. Stored energy
10. Vibration
11. Temperature ( )

12. Electrical

III. Machine Safeguarding
1. Barriers ☐
2. Location & distance ☐
3. Feeding/ejection ☐
4. Enclosure ☐
5. Pers. Prot. Equip. (PPE) ☐
6. Interlocks: yes ☐ no ☐
   Control reliable: yes ☐ no ☐
   limit switch: yes ☐ no ☐
7. Presence Sensing: (PSD)
   a-Mat type: Captive ☐ Active ☐
   Size: Length_____
   b-Photo optical type:
   Single beam: yes ☐ no ☐
   Multiple beam: yes ☐ no ☐
   Horizontal: yes ☐ no ☐
   Vertical: yes ☐ no ☐
   Both: yes ☐ no ☐
   Length: ____ Height:___
   Adequate cover :yes ☐ no ☐
   c. Point of operation:yes ☐ no ☐
   d. Danger zone: yes ☐ no ☐
   e. Perimeter guard: yes ☐ no ☐
   f. Control reliable: yes ☐ no ☐
8. Safety Controls:
   Two Hand Control: yes ☐ no ☐
   Two Hand Trips: yes ☐ no ☐
   Concurrent: yes ☐ no ☐
   Restraint/pullback: yes ☐ no ☐
9. Other ( )
IV. Lockout/Tagout
1. Policy/Procedures: yes ☐ no ☐
2. Devices/Blocks: yes ☐ no ☐
3. Zero Energy: yes ☐ no ☐
4. Locks/Tags: yes ☐ no ☐
5. Power disconnects: yes ☐ no ☐
6 Other ( )

V Ergonomic Safeguarding
1. Workstation design: OK ☐ modify ☐
2. Guard design: OK ☐ modify ☐
3. Guard application: OK ☐ modify ☐
4 .Proper tools: OK ☐ modify ☐
5. Process Improvement: yes ☐ no ☐ modi
VI Electrical
Schematics available: Yes ☐ no ☐

Motor HP __ Full load amps __ Phase _
Service factor _____ Voltage _____
Operator control voltage ____ ac___ dc
Electrical disconnect: yes ☐ no ☐
Readily accessible: yes ☐ no ☐

Less than 6½ ft. high: yes ☐ no ☐
Disconnect type: magnetic ☐ mechanic
VII Emergency Stop Controls
Pull cord type: slack line ☐ tensioned ☐
Push button __ Mushroom ___Red__
Recessed ____ On/off ___ **No E-Stop**
More than one _____ How Many: ___
Control Reliable: yes ☐ no ☐

Clearly Identified: yes ☐ no ☐
Yellow background: yes ☐ no ☐
Readily Accessible: yes ☐ no ☐
1st more than 26": yes ☐ no ☐
VIII Power Failure/Restart

Manual Restart: yes ☐ no ☐
Auto Restart: yes ☐ no ☐
Brake: Power on only yes ☐ no ☐
     Power off only yes ☐ no ☐
     None : ☐
Auto Retraction : yes ☐ no ☐
   How Far? _____

IX Hazard Classification (See note 1)
   Class ____ Division
X Special Observations or conditions
   (note below in comments)

1-Hazard classification and division per NFPA 70; this information must come from client property insurance carrier and be signed by client.

Dimensions and Sketches on other side: yes ☐ no ☐	Photographs attached? yes ☐ no
Additional comments on other side yes ☐ no ☐ **Document** Evalform Rey G 10/09/98	**This May Be A Multiple Sheet** **J R SNOPEK CSP PE**

Figure 8-6. Machine Safety Evaluation Form.

Recommended Parts

XYZ Company Inc.

XYZ **ELECTRICAL SPECIFICATIONS : Rev. March 1998**

4.12   APPROVED ELECTRICAL COMPONENTS LIST

4.12.1 Only the listed items shall be used for electrical components. Any additions or substitutions will require written approval from the *XYZ* Co. Controls Engineer on an individual application basis. Non -Safety rated & none approved equipment is not acceptable for safety applications.

Annunciators	Allen-Bradley
Batch Counters	Red Lion, Veeder Root
Circuit Breakers	Sq. D, ITE, Westinghouse, Allen-Bradley
Clutch A Brake Control	Warner, Posidyne
Control Stations	Allen-Bradley
Control Station Devices	Allen-Bradley

Stop Cycle (red, mushroom head, maintained contact, illuminated)
> A-B #800T-FXQ24RA5

Start Cycle (green, guarded, illuminated)

E-Stop (red, mushroom head, maintained contact, illuminated)
> A-B #800T-FXTQ24RA5
> A-B #800T-X647 legend
> A-B #800-XA aux. contact

Drive Stop (red, mushroom head, maintained contact)
> A-B #800T-FX6RA5

Pilot lights (push-to-test)

Selector Switch (Std. Operator with required contact blocks)
> *Note: On 2 position selector switches having an "Off" position, the "Off" is to the left. On 3 position "Hand-Off-Auto" selector switches, the "Off" is the center position. Illuminated Selector Switches may be used to indicate an "On" condition for xyz type equipment, etc.*

Control Relays	Potter Brumfield or equivalent, A-B type 700-F "IEC" style.
DC Power Supplies	Sola CVDC Rack Mount, Lambda
Disconnect Switch	Sq. D 9422, A-B 1494F
Enclosures	Hoffman, McKinstry
Encoders	BEI, A-B
Fuses	Bussman, Gould Shawmut
Limit Switches	A-B, Sq. D, Microswitch all plug-in type
Machine Status Lights	Telemechanique
Motor Control Center	A-B
Motor Starters	A-B "IEC" style
Operator Interface	Panel View
Photoelectric Switches	Tritronic, Banner
Programmable Controller	A-B check with *XYZ Co*. Controls Engineer for type
Proximity Switches	Balluff 8 mm
Rate Indicators	Red Lion
Safety Relays	Pilz, Schmersal, STI,
Safety Switches	Schmersal, STI,
Servos	Pacific Scientific
Solid State Relays	Crydom, Opto22, Entrelec
Steppers	Pacific Scientific
Temperature Controls	Eurotherm, Honeywell
Terminal Blocks	A-B 1492-W4 and / or 1492-W6
Transformers	Jefferson, GE, Heavy-Duty Electric
Ultrasonic Welders	Branson

Figure 8-7. (Companies are just an example and not a recommendation.)

components list, limits the amount and variability of spare parts a company may need to stock to keep a facility safe and efficient. It also ensures a more consistent operation of the safety circuits, and keeps them operating as their designers originally intended them to operate. Sometimes, electricians under pressure to get a machine up and running may replace a component with an unequal part and, therefore, destroy some of the safety features originally designed into the machine. Immediate response may overrule an investigative process or doing the job right if the correct parts do not exist.

RECOMMENDED PARTS

Availability of supply is the other key issue to be considered when looking at global locations and the need to keep machines safe as well as continuously operating. Not all manufacturers will have supply points at all locations, so a number of manufacturers and representatives may have to be included. Cost is another issue, where poor countries undergoing economic hardship must look for suppliers internal to their country for affordable parts. Importing a safety component from the U.S. or Europe may not be economically feasible. Therefore, equivalent home grown suppliers may be the alternative that greatly influences the safety of the machinery by being immediately available.

Machine fabricators will have their own list of vendor supplied parts. It is extremely important to specify the components from the purchaser's recommended safety components list. Commonality with other machines and spare parts is paramount for the running of an efficient manufacturing operation.

GENERIC SAFETY CIRCUITS

A cross-functional team of design, maintenance, safety, and electrical engineers should develop a Generic Safety Circuit to be used in the purchasing process. Not all machinery is purchased with engineering input. Sometimes, a print shop, R&D facility, or warehousing operation will purchase machines that do not go through the engineering specification system. The people purchasing the equipment have good intentions, but are unaware of the possibilities for purchasing equipment that does not meet preferred standards. A process must be

developed, and Boiler Plate Specifications used along with the Generic Safety Circuits to insure a high level of consistency.

Generic Safety Circuits and Boiler Plate Specifications are needed to tell the electrical designers at a machine supplier how equipment is to be wired, where E-Stops are to be located and safety gates interlocked. This becomes quite complicated when unrelated machines from different manufacturers are integrated together to create a production line. A standardized philosophy must be developed so that machines may function to suit the user's production and maintenance requirements, as well as meet OSHA regulations. For instance, an E-Stop circuit must function at all times. Yet, some machines may be locked out for maintenance service while others are used to repack damaged product, rendering parts of the E-Stop circuit useless. In-plant electricians on third shift may temporarily rewire the circuits, at management request, which could make the operation unsafe when the machines are working together. These operational alternatives must be considered when the generic circuits are designed, and the E-Stop circuits must be operational when machines are energized.

Designers also have a legal requirement to incorporate a lockout/tagout function. Often times, multiple disconnect set-ups may be required. An example is where electrical heaters for plastic parts, glue systems or heated rolls must not be turned off while the main disconnect is locked out. The machine in this case should be designed with two disconnect switches: One that puts the machine motion producing parts at zero energy with the exception of the heating elements, other support utilities, and necessary control systems. The other is the main electrical supply disconnect that puts the user into a full shutdown while isolating all energy within a machine. With this setup, there is no impediment to the mechanic turning off the main disconnect. The auxiliary disconnect turns off machine motive power while keeping the support systems energized and in a state of readiness. The mechanic may be working on the machine and replacing a part requiring a 10- to 15-minute outage. If the glue systems and plastic heaters were shutdown, the start-up time may be extended to 30 or more minutes to get all systems to their correct operating temperatures, whereas with the auxiliary breaker, the startup can be immediately after the 15-minute repair. When this is done many times in a facility, the additional production time eliminates the possibility for equipment damage caused by a premature start-up. Typically, the equipment supplier, not knowing this potential scenario, will only supply the machine with a single disconnect.

To properly execute a dual or triple disconnect setup and be compliant with the National Electric Code and OSHA requirements, certain criteria in the electrical design must be met (such as isolating the energized wiring, correct color coding of the wires). This can only be done cost effectively at the supplier's initial design phase. However, most suppliers would not be aware of this requirement unless it is specified in the Boiler Plate Specifications or Generic Safety Circuit schematics.

As an example, recently it was discovered that a U.S. machine supplier wired the E-Stop and guard door interlocks to a common safety circuit. When a guard door is opened, the machine is completely shutdown, incurring an involved restart of all support equipment components and some auxiliary machine-related high inertia components. This will result in unacceptable delays during production. This setup is allowed by the NFPA 79 Standard for Industrial Machinery. However, this machine with many heating systems and large horsepower motors will never be operated as designed and cannot withstand the rigors of a production situation. The purchaser specified nothing about the E-Stop and guard door circuits or how the machine was to be operated. The machine supplier was supplying the machine in an expedient, safe, code compliant way—yet unrealistic for actual operation. Therefore, the purchaser is required to rewire the machine at additional cost and provide separate safety circuits for the E-Stop and guard door switches. Also, special configurations will be required at raw material changes, packaging, and support equipment installations. Considerable cost and project delays will be incurred while this work is done at the final location.

This situation could have been prevented if a safety through design process was used, where both parties discussed the operating criteria, and developed a realistic safety package at the very beginning of the project. The machine supplier, having a customer focus, could have had a safety through design system in place. The purchaser having Boiler Plate Specifications, Generic Safety Circuit information, and a Recommended Parts List could have also prevented this situation from occurring. Unfortunately, neither did, resulting in an unhappy customer incurring additional costs and delays.

The Boiler Plate Specifications (Figure 8-8), Generic Control Schematics (Figure 8-9), and Recommended Parts List (Figure 8-7) should specify and refer to the appropriate safety standards (NFPA 70, NFPA 79, and company standards), provide guidance in the design of the safety circuits, recommend specific components, cover other issues relating to the operational intent and compatibility with existing equipment. Even if the person ordering the equipment is not technically versed, the supplier can often understand what he can and cannot readily supply by reading these documents. This initiates a dialogue that would have never occurred had the documents not been developed.

PREQUALIFYING SUPPLIERS

Prequalifying suppliers may not be practical for all situations, but it does help minimize problems. In considering potential suppliers, a purchaser develops a checklist of requirements including more than technology, price and delivery schedule. When using a safety through design process, minimal risk—as identified by a risk assessment process—is also a requirement. Pre-qualifying the supplier can give the purchaser a lower overall project cost, on schedule, and an end product that more thoroughly meets the purchaser's safety needs. The project mentioned in the previous section, did not have a process in place, and the purchaser did not pre-qualify the supplier.

A supplier using a system modeled after Europe's (using risk assessment and standardized safety circuits, as well as questioning operator access, use of the equipment, and the correct application of proven safety components) indicates capability and willingness to meet requirements. A supplier who demonstrates an unwillingness to change, is defensive and secretive about the risk assessment process used, suggests he does not have a safety process. The

Boiler Plate Specification

Attachment 1

Page 3 of 12

2.6   Normal Operating Mode Safety Requirements:

No pinch point or other hazardous area can be reached by the operator when reaching OVER, UNDER, AROUND or THROUGH the equipment. The guard opening scale contained in Table 0-10 of OSHA's Federal Register 1910.217 shall be strictly adhered to.

2.7   Labeling: All panel doors, junction boxes, and power sources must be clearly labeled as per ANSI & NEC/ NFPA 70.

2.8   Moving components and Pinch Points that operators can access during operation shall be guarded following the Zero-Access Guarding Concept. Any area where a person could enter an interlocked area and close the interlock behind them requires either physical barriers prohibiting this from occurring or an HECP documented procedure using a lockable device on the entry interlock which prevents the interlock from being reset shall be incorporated.

2.9   Moving components and Pinch Points which are located inside the guard and stop immediately after the guard is opened will not have to be guarded.

Pinch Points which are located inside the guard but do not stop immediately when the guard is opened shall be guarded consistent with Table 0-10 of OSHA's Federal Register 1910.217.

2.10   Non moving parts such as knives, heaters and hot-melt nozzles located inside the guards which may potentially cause operator injury when touched by bare hands shall be guarded as much as possible. All hot surfaces above 145 degrees Fahrenheit will be insulated if possible. If not possible, appropriate personal protective equipment requirements will be implemented. Warning signs shall also be attached very close to the above parts.

2.11   For ease of adjustment and minimum equipment downtime, adjustment points for any device located inside an interlocked safety enclosure (i.e., amplifier for sensor sensitivity) should be mounted outside the safety enclosure. Where impractical, exceptions shall be reviewed and receive advance approval of *XYZ company*. Adjustment points should be located in a separate junction box or under the enclosure in a locally grouped manner and should be guarded as required per the general guarding rules per Section 2.1.

Figure 8-8. Boiler Plate Specification

company that is willing to share, explains processes in detail, describes expected results, and demonstrates an openness is using its safety evaluation process as a marketing tool.

MANAGING THE DETAILS

New materials, new product configurations, different operational strategies, and new technologies will present challenges to the safety through design process. Sharing test data, product performance attributes, and open concerns may eliminate delays at delivery of the final product.

During the purchase of a packaging machine it became apparent that Johnson & Johnson was operating numerous generations of this equipment throughout the corporation and had become somewhat complacent with the ordering process. The packaging machine had a few added features to accommodate new technology that required the operator to load materials and service the machine at three points rather than the usual one. One of these points was on the opposite side of the machine and a conveyor system interfered with ready access. The E-Stop buttons were not

Generic Safety Control Schematic

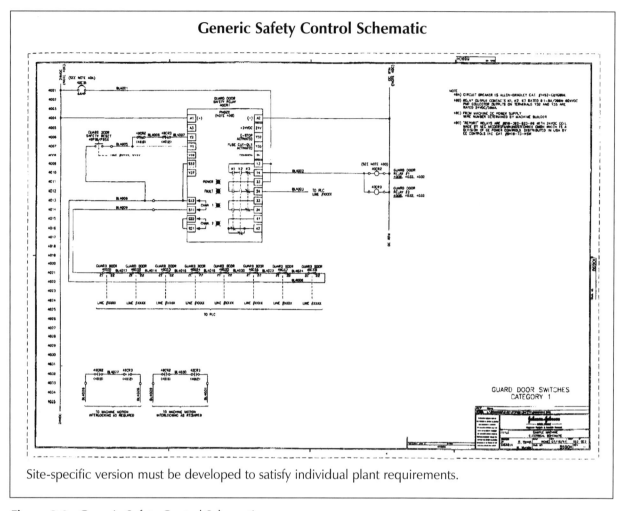

Site-specific version must be developed to satisfy individual plant requirements.

Figure 8-9. Generic Safety Control Schematic

at each operating point. When further critiquing the requirements, a safety reset and stop/start button needed to be added so that the operator did not have to jump over or under conveyors to get to the single control station containing the original E-Stop to restart the machine. A step in the safety through design process could have easily identified all operating points and the necessity for E-Stops and restart equipment at three locations rather than the usual single operating station. It was missed because the requirements did not include a clear definition of adequate E-Stops.

Lockout/tagout equipment is mandated by OSHA to put equipment at zero energy. However in a production situation, certain sections may need to be locked out while other support utilities are kept at operational readiness. This multiple lockout requirement will be satisfied by a machine supplier only if it is specified. Typically,

the machine will be supplied with a single lockout, which can become a barrier to the operator locking out the machine. The operator may rationalize that a five-minute outage to disassemble and replace a part is not worth the effort to lockout the machine, a violation of the OSHA regulation.

Global E-Stops are necessary where few people patrol a long, integrated production process (for example, a product manufactured on one machine goes to a collating device, onto a bagging machine and finally to be automatically case packer). Typically the E-Stop circuit is wired to the largest machine. If that machine is locked out for repair, the power in the E-Stop circuit will not be available, and therefore, the packaging machines cannot run with the E-Stop circuits de-energized. Sometimes, there is a management directive to electricians to get the machine to run in order to reprocess defective

Validation Process

Mutual E-Stop Check-out procedure

1 Turn on Card Power cabinet and reset Guards and E-Stop circuits
2 Turn on Calender Power cabinet and reset Guards and E-Stop circuits
3 Turn on Laymaster Power cabinet and reset Guards and E-Stop circuits
4 Turn on Fiber Feed Power cabinet and reset Guards and E-Stop circuits

Start ALL Fiber Equipment in any order and include:
Card
Calender
Laymaster
Fiber Feeder

Push Card E-stop Button(s)
Verify that Card, Calender, Laymaster and Fiber Feeder shut down
Reset Card, Calender, Laymaster and Fiber Equipment E-stop circuit

Push Calender E-stop button
Verify that Card, Calender, Laymaster and Fiber Feeder shut down
Reset Card, Calender, Laymaster and Fiber Equipment E-stop circuit

Push Laymaster E-stop button
Verify that Card, Calender, Laymaster and Fiber Feeder shut down
Reset Card, Calender, Laymaster and Fiber Equipment E-stop circuit

Push Fiber Panel E-stop button
Verify that Card, Calender, Laymaster and Fiber Feeder shut down
Reset Card, Calender, Laymaster and Fiber Equipment E-stop circuit

Signed By

Date

Figure 8-10. Validation Process

packages. The electrician being unaware of codes or E-Stop design philosophy may rewire the machine to allow the bagging and casing machines to run. Depending on the decisions he makes and whether the machines are returned to their normal operating condition, this rewiring can result in an unsafe condition. The safety through design process should include operational alternatives for these machines, including whether a global, zone and individual machine E-Stop is the correct design choice along with the locations and type.

LESSONS LEARNED

After the project is completed, representative engineers, safety professionals, operators, supervisors, and managers should get together to discuss what was done well, areas for improvement, and what needs to change for the next project. An open company with a good safety culture will welcome this discussion in the spirit of continuous improvement. A poorly managed cost driven company where there is finger-pointing, blame, and high turnover will not be willing, doesn't have the time, or is unable to share this kind of learning. The ability to learn from what went right and wrong will make the next effort much easier. Companies should seek to improve their process for machine fabrication and building construction so that it incorporates the latest safety through design process, and moves the workplace closer to becoming injury-free.

INSTITUTIONALIZING THE SAFETY THROUGH DESIGN PROCESS

When implementing a safety through design process, it is best to start with a single project or single facility. A complete turnabout of an entire corporation will not happen in a day, week, or month. It will take several projects and several years. It will take the dedicated commitment of a group of people willing to try the safety through design approach. It requires ownership from all involved: the machine supplier, the engineers, the R&D people, the purchasing group, and the operators. All stakeholders must be clear about the expected outcome, and know their role in achieving it. This approach takes a project manager who is not involved with the technological development, can objectively facilitate the project, and keep the process on target. It takes continuous monitoring of schedules and progress made to ensure adequate safety input. It requires planning ahead so that information is provided when needed to make the transition from the traditional retrofit approach to the safety through design process.

Standards, codes, and directives must be simplified so that meaningful input is provided to the appropriate suppliers. Project specific safety requirements must be developed, negotiated, and agreed to with machine suppliers, contractors or architects. They must also be updated as needed during the project to capture any newly identified safety requirements. A validation or certification process (Figure 8-10) must be implemented as part of the final acceptance so that all systems perform as specified and meet the original requirements.

After the pilot is launched, monitored, and completed, a "lessons learned" document must be developed for future projects. The stakeholders must analyze the project, and compare the process and results to another project that did not use a safety through design process. As much as possible, data should be gathered to factually quantify the results. A presentation should be developed publicizing the results and justifying further implementation. A proposal should be developed with appropriate project write-up (in report or video form) to sell the concept across the organization.

A project champion and an implementation team representing the appropriate cross functional contributors should be assembled and a project plan developed. The plan should include communications and phasing in the safety through design process to future projects. With the many differences between organizations, it is difficult to create a template for this plan. It needs to be customized for each company.

SUMMARY

In summary, the most critical requirements for using a safety through design process in the purchase of machinery are as follows:

- Commitment and support of management group;
- Project champion and cross-functional team
- Clear project criteria;
- Pre-selection of machine builder(s) with safety through design capability;
- Boiler plate specifications;
- Operational requirements/product specifications;
- Recommended parts list;
- Generic safety circuits;
- Generic lockout/tagout design requirements;
- Review safety through design requirements and process with machine builder;
- Safety validation process at final machine acceptance;
- Final acceptance upon completion of all requirements.

Chapter 9

DESIGNING FOR MAINTAINABILITY, RELIABILITY, AND SAFETY

by Tom J. Janicik

INTRODUCTION

This chapter describes representative types of maintenance work (planned, unplanned, and common hazards), general design control strategies to minimize risks (with examples), basic maintainability/serviceability and reliability concepts, and design control strategies to minimize risks and maximize productivity.

Most people intuitively think that maintenance work is risky due to the nature of the work (such as non-routine activity, working around high energy sources, the influence of production pressure). An interesting study documented by the UAW looked at 252 work related deaths over a 14-year period[1] and indicated that the risk of being killed on the job was 3.6 times greater for skilled trades (for example, maintenance) workers compared to all other workers. This emphasizes the significant risks associated with maintenance work and the importance of finding methods to reduce these risks during the design process.

Guidance will be provided on safety design considerations, which can help to minimize the risks posed to maintenance employees. It also applies to set-up and operations personnel who perform maintenance related functions.

MAINTENANCE WORK PROCESS AND RELATED HAZARDS

The Department of Industry, in British Standard 3811, Maintenance Aspects of Terotechnology, 1, Planned Maintenance[2] provides a decision tree, which illustrates the relationship between the different types of maintenance activities (see Figure 9-1). The two basic types of maintenance shown include planned and unplanned. The types of maintenance performed include servicing, repairing, and overhauling.

The philosophy of many companies on maintenance practices will be either to fix something only when it's broken (break down maintenance) or performing planned preventive maintenance in addition to breakdown maintenance. The National Safety Council strongly endorses preventive maintenance because it

→ reduces employee exposure to hazards;
→ decreases equipment downtime; and
→ optimizes maintenance expenditures.

An illustration of how effective predictive maintenance can minimize failures, optimize maintenance costs and thereby improve employee safety is provided in Figure 9-2. It shows that by reducing costs due to equipment being out of service and repair costs, an effective preventive maintenance program can help to minimize total controllable maintenance costs.

UNPLANNED MAINTENANCE

Unplanned maintenance needs to be evaluated/reviewed from a safety standpoint to ensure critical hazards are identified and appropriate hazard control measures are implemented prior to performing the maintenance work. Some of the typical hazards of concern include the following:

→ Inadequate removal/isolation of hazardous energy sources (for example, kinetic, potential, electrical, chemical, thermal, toxicity);
→ Inert atmospheres (asphyxiation);
→ Poor/difficult access;
→ Improper tool selection/availability;
→ Inadequate machine guarding;

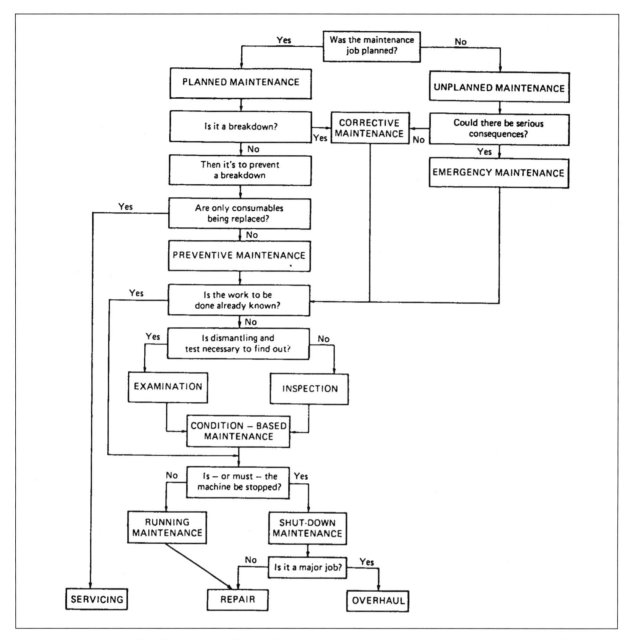

Figure 9-1. Decision Tree Illustrating Different Types of Maintenance. Source: British Department of Industry.[2]

→ Ergonomic risks; and

→ Hazardous material exposures.

Formal procedures such as job safety analysis and safe work practices (such as confined space permit, lockout/tagout) are effective means of understanding and managing unplanned maintenance risks. However, production pressure can have a strong influence on how effectively these types of safety procedures are implemented. These types of procedures should be thoroughly evaluated not just to meet the regulatory minimum, but also to meet good incident prevention practices.

PLANNED MAINTENANCE

Planned maintenance has the advantage of having more developed/focused management systems (such as knowing which equipment/parts are critical and basing inspection/testing on accepted industry practices or failure rate data). This provides the opportunity for additional safety considerations to be integrated into procedures and training efforts for these maintenance activities.

Investing in planned maintenance helps to reduce the time spent on unplanned maintenance, which benefits the safety performance of maintenance personnel. Similar hazards exist for

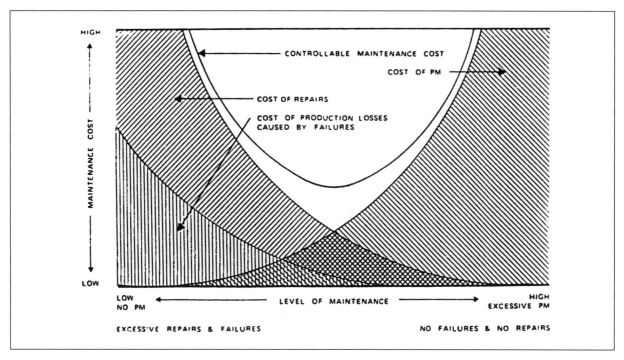

Figure 9-2. Controlling Maintenance Costs Using Preventive Maintenance. Source: National Safety Council.[3]

planned versus unplanned maintenance. However, the planned activities (by the nature of being well thought-out/established) provide a more rigorous method of minimizing risk and are less likely to be affected by production pressure (by the nature of being part of the production scheduling process).

GENERAL DESIGN CONSIDERATIONS

Designers should ensure that they have a good understanding of maintenance requirements for a product or process during the design phase. The Center for Chemical Process Safety (CCPS) published *Guidelines for Safe Process Operations and Maintenance*[4], which provide information on how to reduce the risks associated with maintenance work, in chemical plants, but it is equally applicable to all industry. The *Guidelines* suggest that designers of chemical process plants can eliminate or reduce hazards by engineering them out of their designs by considering the following principles:

➤ Ensure operations/maintenance departments provide input on maintenance design requirements, and solicit their ideas on improving safety, productivity, efficiency;

➤ Provide sufficient access for an operating area to handle maintenance needs;

➤ Use checklists which address maintenance related issues; and

➤ Consider design reliability/availability, levels of redundancy, diversity of redundant systems, and proof testing requirements.

This CCPS guide provides several examples, which demonstrate the application of these principles. One example specific to design considerations for maintaining pumps includes

➤ grouping, so they can be easily accessed and handled;

➤ locating outdoors whenever possible; and

➤ selecting optimal location, including sufficient clearance space.

When a designer effectively obtains the input of the most knowledgeable operations/maintenance personnel, the safety and overall effectiveness of the process or product is significantly enhanced.

SPECIAL MAINTENANCE DESIGN CONSIDERATIONS

Key maintenance design considerations regarding the following areas are described from an engineering perspective:

➤ Lockout/tagout;

➤ Confined space; and

➤ Fall protection.

111

LOCKOUT/TAGOUT DESIGN CONSIDERATIONS

In 1983, the National Institute of Occupational Safety & Health (NIOSH) published a study[5] which looked at incidents that could be attributed to the presence of uncontrolled energy during maintenance activities. This study was a precursor to the eventual Occupational Safety and Health Administration (OSHA) 29 *CFR* 1910.147 Control of Hazardous Energy (Lockout/Tagout). Much of the information is still valuable today, since fatalities from contact with electric current (over 300 per year) are still a leading cause of deaths in industry. The study focused on a detail review of 59 incidents which were categorized into the following:

➤ *Maintenance activities were initiated without attempting to de-energize the equipment/system or control the hazards with the energy present—27 incidents.*

One fatal incident in this category was a case in which an employee was lubricating the chain drive links in a conveyer belt system through a 10-inch x 12-inch opening between the bins and the metal guide post of the unstacker while the machinery was running. As the bins moved forward, his head caught between the bin and the guide post.

➤ *Energy isolation was attempted but inadequate—six incidents.*

A fatal incident in this category was a case in which an employee was attempting to clear a jam on a garnett machine while it was in operation. He crawled inside the machine through an unguarded hole where he became entangled in moving parts, was drawn into the roller and was crushed.

➤ *Residual energy was not dissipated—one incident.*

The injury incident in this category was a case where an employee removed a jam from a packaging machine with the power turned off. Residual hydraulic pressure activated the holding device.

➤ *Accidental activation of energy—25 incidents.*

A fatal incident in this category is a case where a maintenance employee inside a large mixing drum making repairs was struck by the beater blades when they were inadvertently activated.

In his book, *Lockout/Tagout: The Process of Controlling Hazardous Energy*,[6] Ed Grund defines an energy-release incident as any unwanted transfer of energy (electrical, mechanical, hydraulic, pneumatic, chemical, or thermal) that produces injury/damage to persons, property, or processes, or otherwise interrupts, interferes with, or degrades the activity in progress. This definition clearly shows the importance of understanding all types of energy, beyond the narrow view that lockout/tagout is for electrical energy sources.

Grund suggests that in incorporating energy isolating devices (such as breakers, disconnects, valves) designers have often failed to consider accessibility, ease of use, and clear identification. Some of the examples of energy isolating device design improvements he suggests include the following:

➤ Convert manual power press die block placement to automatic die block insertion;

➤ Replace simple pneumatic gate valves with lockable, pressure indicating, self-relieving valves;

➤ Modify gate or globe valves with permanent locking hardware;

➤ Operate automatic valves where appropriate;

➤ Install devices for each machine/equipment rather than for group services;

➤ Install pressure-relief features in piping systems; and

➤ Relocate or position devices to make their function more apparent and provide easier access.

CONFINED SPACE DESIGN CONSIDERATIONS

OSHA considers a confined space as having limited or restricted means of entry or exit, is large enough for an employee to enter and perform assigned work, and is not designed for continuous occupancy by the employee.[7] There are also requirements to assure employee(s) are not exposed to other potential hazards such as engulfment, operating equipment, hot liquids or surfaces, electrical shock, slippery surfaces, and so forth.

In 1994, NIOSH completed a detailed study on workers' deaths in confined spaces.[8] The study reviewed 10 years of incident information including 70 cases in which 109 people died. In 25 of the incidents, there were multiple fatalities, including deaths involving persons attempting rescue. Key points from this study (which is still applicable today, as reports continue to reflect similar tragedies) indicate that confined spaces can be categorized as follows:

➤ Open-topped enclosures with depths which restrict the natural movement of air (for example, degreasers, pits, selected type of tanks, and excavations); and

➤ Enclosures with limited openings for entry and exit (e.g., sewers, tanks, silos).

Typical hazards are atmospheric (oxygen deficiency, asphyxiants, flammable atmospheres, toxic gases) and/or physical (engulfment, failure to isolate energy sources, falling objects, thermal extremes, wet/slick surfaces, noise levels). Figure 9-3 illustrates that repair/maintenance type work was the number one reason for fatality related entries (40.4%) followed closely by rescue related fatalities (35.8%).

When designing operations, there are many critical considerations. The primary focus should be toward eliminating confined spaces altogether. If it is not possible to eliminate the space, consideration should be given to elimination of the need for entry. At this point the designer must perform a task based hazard analysis and risk assessment. Attention must be given to all tasks that might, or could conceivably be performed by production and maintenance employees, and others, including extraordinary (emergency) needs.

Once all required tasks and attendant or potential hazards are identified, it becomes easier to address them one by one and determine which can be relocated to the exterior of the space, or might be accomplished in another manner. For instance, valves might be motorized so they can be operated from outside, or the space/tank might have built-in cleaning nozzles to eliminate the need to enter and clean; valves, gauges, flow meters, and similar measuring devices could have their metrics moved outside. Thus, if entry is not required the potential of injury or death is substantially reduced.

If after analysis and evaluation, it is still deemed necessary to have a confined space, accessibility and ventilation should be addressed. Standards and codes should be reviewed as guidelines, but whenever possible the largest opening should be designed to permit easy access with personal protective equipment, including breathing apparatus, or emergency access with self-contained breathing gear. Do not be satisfied with a 16- or 18-inch opening; the goal should be at least 30 inches. Other design considerations should include equipment for continuous monitoring, personnel entry and removal, and protection of interior danger points.

Proper ventilation design and monitoring is crucial to controlling atmospheric hazards in a confined space. Don't be deluded by one time readings, concerning oxygen, flammable substances, toxic contaminants, and so on. The literature is replete with anecdotal information on cases where readings were taken and subsequently a delayed entry was made with the conviction that the area was safe, resulting in fatal consequences. There should be adequate protocol of testing to assure that a space deemed initially to be safe (free of toxic, flammable and other agents, and with sufficient oxygen) remains safe.

John Rekus in his *Complete Confined Spaces Handbook*[9] explains the key distinction between ventilation and purging. Purging is the process by which a space is initially cleared of contaminants by displacing the hazardous atmosphere with air, steam or an inert gas. Ventilation is the process of continuously moving fresh, uncontaminated air through a space.

During the design review of a process, if the confined space cannot be eliminated or entry requirements eliminated by moving controls to the exterior, then key design considerations should be discussed (such as purge/ventilation capability, accessibility including rescue, energy dissipation/isolation capability). It is very important to stress evaluation of all potential reasons for entry and determine if they can be eliminated.

FALL PROTECTION DESIGN CONSIDERATIONS

Fall protection is also an important design consideration for maintenance work. The NIOSH study on worker deaths in confined spaces[8] cited a case where inadequate fall protection contributed to a confined space related fatality. In this case, a maintenance worker suffocated from engulfment after falling into sawdust. NIOSH investigators specified several recommendations, however, with one specific to the design. Employers and manufacturers should consider retrofitting silos and other similar facilities with

Type	Reason for Entry							Total
	Const.	Insp.	Repair/ Maint.	Rescue	Retrieve Object	Dislodge Material	Unknown	
Tank	0	5	14	11	1	0	0	31
Pipeline/Tunnel	1	0	1	1	0	0	0	3
Tanker Truck	0	0	3	0	0	0	0	3
Utility Vault	0	1	3	0	0	0	0	4
Vat/Pit Digester	0	0	10	14	2	0	0	26
Silo/Bin	0	1	0	0	0	5	1	7
Sewer Manhole	4	3	10	10	0	0	0	27
Well	0	1	3	3	1	0	0	8
Total	5	11	44	39	4	5	1	109
(% of Total)	4.6	10.1	40.4	35.8	3.6	4.6	0.9	100.0

Figure 9-3. Confined-Space-Related Fatalities Investigated by the Fatality Assessment and Control Evaluation (FACE), by Confined Space Type and Reason for Entry, 1983–1993 ($N=109$). Source: NIOSH.[8]

mechanical leveling/raking devices, or other means to minimize the need for workers to climb or enter silos.

By considering these issues in the design process costly retrofitting solutions could be eliminated. J. Nigel Ellis in his book *Introduction to Fall Protection*[10] provides guidance on fall protection design considerations. One example specifically related to anchorage points suggests that an engineer consider the following questions:

→ What forces are present fall protection systems seeing?

→ What forces must you design for in horizontal lifeline systems?

→ What must be done to prepare a worksite for installing fall arrest equipment?

→ What fall protection is outdated?

MAINTAINABILITY/SERVICEABILITY DESIGN CONSIDERATIONS
BASIC MAINTAINABILITY CONCEPTS
Maintainability is defined by MIL-STD-721C[11] as the measure of the ability of an item to be retained in or restored to specified condition when maintenance is performed by personnel having specified skill levels, using prescribed procedures and resources, at each prescribed

level of maintenance and repair. In his book *Loss Prevention in the Process Industries*,[12] Frank Lees indicates some of the principles and key considerations in optimizing diagnosis/repairs including the following:

BASIC MAINTAINABILITY PRINCIPLES
1. Providing good access
2. Minimization of the complexity of the task, tools, and test equipment
3. Providing good maintenance manuals
4. Clear criteria for recognition of faults or marginal performance
5. Optimization of the diagnosis and repair task

KEY CONSIDERATIONS IN OPTIMIZING DIAGNOSIS/REPAIRS
1. Preparation
2. Malfunction verification
3. Fault location
4. Fault isolation
5. Disassembly
6. Part procurement
7. Part interchange
8. Re-assembly
9. Alignment
10. Checkout

MIL-STD-470[13] describes the details of a maintainability analysis. Figure 9-4 summarizes the process for performing a maintainability analysis. Each design drawing for a system is evaluated to identify the type of equipment being used and foreseeing potential failure modes including identifying potential causes.

This systematic process provides a rigorous review of the design of a system from a maintainability engineering viewpoint. This information is helpful when making design related decisions such as

➤ determining actions required to fix identified failure modes;

➤ identifying which parts/items are anticipated to fail and for what cause;

➤ estimating actions required to fix identified failure modes;

➤ determining optimal preventative maintenance approach; and

➤ determining best method for completing a repair.

Some critical safety design considerations include the following:

➤ Using standardized tools and provide adequate clearance;

➤ Providing ready access with supporting aids such as handles, rails, hoists and handling aids;

➤ Providing adequate visibility/lighting;

➤ Determining optimal fault detection/isolation design requirements (specifically for safety critical functions/equipment);

➤ Providing effective equipment lock-out protection (for example, electrical, hydraulic, mechanically actuated device) during maintenance activities;

➤ Determining effectiveness of labels/warning;

➤ Determining if planned design provisions for preventive maintenance are adequate; and

➤ Determining impact of maintenance activities on operational activities.

MAINTAINABILITY DESIGN CRITERIA

In addition to maintainability analysis, maintainability design criteria are an effective means of impacting design considerations with respect to maintainability issues and operational constraints. Key design criteria include

➤ specifying servicing/access provisions based on size, location, type of attachment, and time for opening.

➤ defining quantitative maintainability performance requirements for impacted equipment (i.e., time, rate, complexity);

➤ specifying requirements for color coding, type part, and access door labeling;

➤ defining which parts are interchangeable and are strictly replaceable; and

➤ defining scheduled maintenance type and frequency planned and methods of repair, accessibility requirements, and level of repair of the user.

EXAMPLE—INHERENTLY SAFER DESIGN IMPACT ON MAINTAINABILITY

Inherently safer design strategies described in the CCPS book *Inherently Safer Chemical Processes - A Life Cycle Approach*[14] include the following:

➤ Minimize—reduce the quantity of material or energy contained in a manufacturing process or product;

➤ Substitute—replace a hazardous material or process with an alternative that reduces or eliminates the hazard;

➤ Moderate—using materials under less hazardous physical (for example, lower temperatures, dilution) or chemical (development of a reaction chemistry which operates at less severe conditions) conditions; and

➤ Simplify—designing to eliminate unnecessary complexity, reducing the opportunities for error and mis-operation.

This book also provides a good example of how inherently safer design can contribute to maintainability safety design considerations when trying to reduce the risk of confined space entry. The example provided is:

Rail cars, tank trucks, and some reactors and storage tanks were cleaned manually by personnel who entered the vessel: fatalities occurred from unexpected or undetected low oxygen content or toxicity. An inherently safer system is a rotating pressurized water spray head that does the cleaning without vessel entry.

Inherently safer design considerations are a very effective means of reducing overall process or product risk and minimizing their

---

Maintainability Engineering Analysis (Task 205)

1. For each layout, major installation, and/or schematic drawing
   A. Identify
      - Anticipated failure modes
      - Anticipated actions to correct problems
      - Anticipated preventive maintenance
      - Preferred method of repair for each anticipated failure mode
   B. Parts list drawing — identify proposed/logical LRUs/WRAs to correct failures
   C. Observe/evaluate method of access & attachment for each repair
   D. List non-replaceable item repair requirements
   E. Document results of analysis on maintainability analysis forms
   F. Evaluate
      - Tool(s) needed & tool use access
      - Handling requirements/access
      - Visibility of work area (remove/replace/adjust)
      - Fault detection/isolation (effectiveness)
      - Safety lockout requirements & method
      - Potential maintenance hazards
      - Need for labels and placards
      - Preferential arrangement (function-failure rates)
      - Provisions for preventive maintenance/servicing
      - Potential operations—maintenance interference
   G. Identify desired LRU configuration (if not the same as drawing)
   H. Make first estimate of maintenance time (gross task elements)
2. Judge the design
   A. Satisfactory?
      - Sign off drawing(s) or
      - Log drawing number as completed
   B. Unsatisfactory?
      - Document/justify reasons (e.g., need, spec., quantitative)
      - Coordinate with others about options
      - Develop suggested solution/position based on cost effectiveness concepts
      - Talk to responsible personnel
      - Generate change request

Figure 9-4. Maintainability Engineering Analysis (Task 205). Source: MIL-STD-470.13

life cycle costs. The earlier inherently safer design considerations are discussed during the design development process, the more effective they are.

SERVICEABILITY CONSIDERATIONS

In a special report from *Plant Engineering and Design News*,[15] the editors described how design serviceability simplifies machine disassembly and repair. Key serviceability design factors included the following:

- Standardization;
- Assembly, packaging, and modularity of the system;
- Component selection, which affects maintenance time and frequency, as well as training requirements for special assembly systems;
- Accessibility;
- Mounting and fastening methods;
- Human factors;
- Warning systems;
- Assembly repairable or disposable; and
- Level of reliability specified by customer.

RELIABILITY DESIGN CONSIDERATIONS
BASIC RELIABILITY CONCEPTS

In a *Basic Reliability Tutorial*[16] Augustus Constantinides, provides an overview of key reliability concepts. He indicates reliability can be defined as the probability of successful operation for a specified period of time under specified conditions and environments of operation. Reliability considerations are very important from a safety through design perspective when evaluating safety critical functions of a particular product or process.

Three key reliability concepts include the following:

1. *Successful operation*—requires understanding what successful performance means and what is the intended use of the product;

2. *Period of time*—some specified interval of time or a specified number of cycles of operation; and

3. *Stated conditions of operation*—include environmental considerations (for example, temperature, pressure, vibration) and operating conditions (voltage, current, corrosive atmosphere).

Reliability can be specified as

➤ *probability of survival*—likelihood that a product or process performs for a period of time given that it is operating properly at the start of the time period;

➤ *failure rate*—number of failures per unit measure of life;

➤ *mean time-between-failures*—where mean time is the average time that an item functions successfully before a failure occurs; and

➤ *mean time-to-failure*—often used for the mean life of nonrepairable items.

Reliability can be enhanced by simplifying the product or process design, part derating (reduce the stress on the part or increase the strength of the part), minimizing environmental effects and operational stress, and minimizing single point failures. Several reliability analysis techniques which can affect design decisions from a safety standpoint include the following:

➤ *Failure Modes and Effects Analysis (FMEA)* considers potential failures and the effects of these failures upon the system, and

➤ *Fault Tree Analysis* is a deductive approach that models the system conditions that can result in a failure.

FUTURE TRENDS

The continued increase of automation throughout industry will create new challenges and risks for maintenance employees who are responsible for servicing and maintaining these evolving machinery and control system designs. Efforts to fully understand and standardize risk assessment and safety design approaches for control systems, that are likely to evolve across multiple industries (e.g., safety interlock systems), will be necessary.

Advanced quantitative based reliability and maintainability concepts such as Reliability Centered Maintenance (RCM), which began approximately 30 years ago in the airline industry, are likely to spread in application to other industries. RCM is a systematic process of analyzing a product or process to identify efficient and effective maintenance tasks. At the 1996 CCPS International Conference and Workshop on Process Safety Management and Inherently Safer Processes, a paper[17] presented a strategy for modifying hazard analysis techniques to integrate RCM type concepts for chemical process applications.

Based on further successful RCM applications, additional companies will likely gain interest in capturing failure rate data specific to their product or process in order to truly optimize performance and minimize overall life cycle costs. CCPS has published *Guidelines for Improving Plant Reliability through Data Collection and Analysis*[18], which provides future direction for applications in the chemical industry.

SUMMARY

This chapter offers guidance on safety design considerations, which can help to minimize the risk posed to maintenance employees. Both general safety design guidance and special maintenance design considerations (i.e., lockout/tagout, confined space, and fall protection) are presented. In addition, basic maintainability and reliability design concepts are reviewed along with design considerations to minimize potential risks and losses and maximize productivity. Future trends regarding safety design improvements (i.e., advanced reliability and maintainability techniques) expanding to additional industries also are discussed.

REFERENCES

1. Health and Safety Department of the UAW. *Occupational Fatalities Among UAW Members: A Fourteen Year Study*, 1987.

2. Department of Industry (DoI), BS 3811, Maintenance Aspects of Terotechnology, 1, Planned Maintenance, Apr 1975.

3. National Safety Council. *Accident Prevention Manual for Business and Industry, Engineering & Technology,* 11th ed, Itasca, IL: National Safety Council, 1997, p 104.

4. Center for Chemical Process Safety. *Guidelines for Safe Process Operations and Maintenance.* American Institute of Chemical Engineers, New York, 1995.

5. National Institute for Occupational Safety and Health (NIOSH), *Guidelines for Controlling Hazardous Energy during Maintenance and Servicing,* Sep 1983.

6. Grund E: *Lockout/Tagout The Process of Controlling Hazardous Energy.* Itasca, IL: National Safety Council, 1995.

7. Occupational Safety & Health Administration, 29 *CFR* 1910.146 Permit-required Confined Spaces.

8. National Institute for Occupational Safety and Health (NIOSH). Worker Deaths in Confined Spaces - A Summary of Surveillance Findings and Investigative Case Reports, Jan 1994.

9. Rekus JF: *Complete Confined Spaces Handbook.* Boca Raton, FL: CRC/Lewis/ National Safety Council, 1994.

10. Ellis JN: *Introduction to Fall Protection,* 2nd ed, Des Plaines, IL: American Society of Safety Engineers, 1993.

11. MIL-STD-721C, Definition of Effectiveness Terms for Reliability, Maintainability, Human Factors, and Safety.

12. Lees FP: *Loss Prevention in the Process Industries, Hazard Identification, Assessment and Control,* 2nd ed. Butterworth-Heinemann, 1996.

13. MIL-STD-470, Maintainability Programs for Systems and Equipment.

14. Center for Chemical Process Safety. *Inherently Safer Chemical Processes - A Life Cycle Approach.* New York: American Institute of Chemical Engineers, 1996.

15. Foszc JL, Colucci D, Puttre M: Machine maintainability should be designed in. *Plant Engineering,* May 1997, pp 94–96.

16. Constantinides A: Basic Reliability Tutorial. 1990 Annual Reliability and Maintainability Symposium.

17. Remson AC, King CS, Mitchell CM, et al: Reliability-Centered Maintenance Makes Sense for PSM-Covered Facilities. International Conference and Workshop on Process Safety Management and Inherently Safer Processes, Oct 8–11, 1996, Orlando, FL, published by Center for Chemical Process Safety of the American Institute of Chemical Engineers, New York.

18. Center for Chemical Process Safety. Guidelines for Improving Plant Reliability through Data Collection and Analysis. American Institute of Chemical Engineers, New York, 1998.

Chapter 10

PROACTIVE ERGONOMICS AND DESIGNING FOR ERROR-FREE WORK

by Donald S. Bloswick
Bradley S. Joseph

INTRODUCTION

This chapter will provide design engineers with an understanding of the need for consideration of ergonomics and human factors issues early in the design process. After an initial discussion of the engineering design process and engineering design team composition, poka-yoke and Design for Assembly[1] principles are presented and the importance of ergonomics and human factors in the design of manufacturing processes and end products is reviewed.

ENGINEERING DESIGN LIFE CYCLE

The engineering design process is the sequence of events resulting in an end product or process. The National Institute for Occupational Safety and Health (Talty)[2] presents a version of the engineering design cycle which starts with an establishment of performance criteria and ends with an evaluation of the resulting prototype.

1. Establish performance criteria (economics, safety, reliability, aesthetics, ethics, social).
2. Define problem.
3. Generate concept.
4. Select concept.
5. Analyze and optimize concept.
6. Construct prototype.
7. Evaluate prototype.

Hyman[3] presents a more inclusive eight-step engineering design life cycle, which begins with a "needs analysis" and ends with "product retirement."

1. Needs analysis

2. Feasibility study
3. Preliminary design
4. Detailed design
5. Production
6. Distribution
7. Consumption
8. Retirement

Ford Motor Company[4] uses a design process specific to automobiles. A summary of the major milestones included in this process is presented below.

➤ General corporate strategy
➤ Program definition
➤ Interior and exterior theme decision
➤ Prototype readiness
➤ Engineering and manufacturing sign-off on prototype
➤ Confirmation that production parts meet design and quality specifications
➤ Production (noted as "product launch" or "Job 1")
➤ Feedback from customers on performance and quality

While the above versions of the engineering design life cycle are not identical, each presents a sequence of logical events, which guide the designer from a concept to an end product. In each case designers have more freedom to make design choices early in the process and as the design process proceeds changes become more expensive. Figure 10-1 illustrates how Ford Motor Company perceives this increase in change cost as the design cycle proceeds where PD indicates

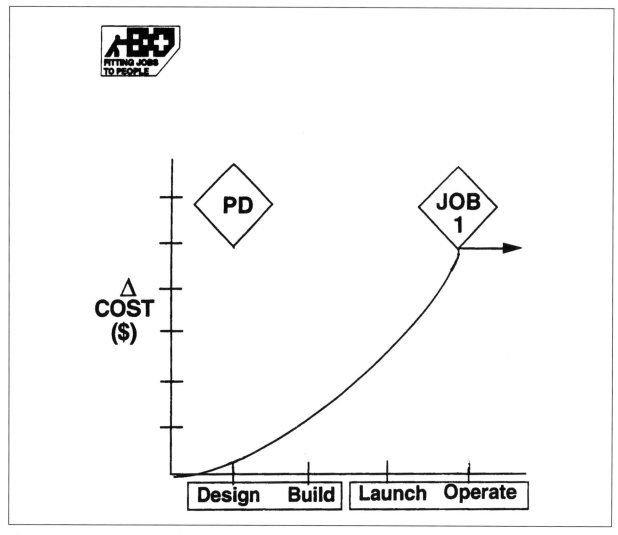

Figure 10-1. Increased cost of changes as design cycle proceeds. (From *Design for Ergonomics Participant's Guide* Version 1.0 by For Motor company. Reprinted with permission.)

Program Definition.[4] This same concept is presented by Hyman.[3]

Unfortunately, while change cost is lowest early in the design process, knowledge about the design problem is also generally low. Designers are faced with the dilemma that they have the most freedom to make decisions when they have the least knowledge about the product or process they are designing! If designers are to consider ergonomic and safety issues early, when design parameters can be established or changes can be made with a minimum of cost, it is important that they be provided with data on the ergonomic and safety implications of their design decisions. They must also have design "tools" which incorporate these issues as early as possible in this process.

ENGINEERING DESIGN TEAMS

Engineering design teams will vary in composition depending on whether the team is to design a product or process and will even vary depending on the type of product or process. Ullman[5] proposes that the following positions/capabilities must exist within a general product design team but notes that in a small project one person may assume more than one role:

➤ Product design engineer
➤ Product manager
➤ Manufacturing engineer
➤ Detailer/designer
➤ Drafter
➤ Technician
➤ Materials specialist
➤ Quality assurance specialist

➤ Industrial designer
➤ Assembly manager
➤ Vendor/supplier representative

Ulrich and Eppinger[6] note that the core product development team for an electromechanical product of modest complexity would consist of a team leader, manufacturing engineer, purchasing specialist, electronics designer, mechanical designer, industrial designer, and marketing professional. They would have an extended "support team" composed of representatives from finance, sales, and legal.

These recommended design teams, as can be seen, do not include a specific team member to represent safety, health, and ergonomic considerations, which often tend to be viewed as secondary. Safety, health, and ergonomic issues are often viewed as common sense items and the responsibility of all team members. One significant exception is Ford Motor Company[7] which has developed a formal Design for Ergonomics (DFE) System that is recommended for all new processes. The DFE process is discussed later but Ford recommends that DFE teams consist of representation from production, maintenance, service, program management, facility management, product design, process design, industrial engineering, material handling, medical, plant/union ergonomics, safety, management ergonomics, training, and vendors.

DESIGN FOR ERROR-FREE WORK AND DESIGN FOR ASSEMBLY

To design for error-free work is a concept developed by Japanese engineer Shigo Shingo who developed the concept as a means to achieve zero defects and eliminate the need for quality control inspections. He proposed the term "poka-yoke" [*poka* (inadvertent errors), *yokeru* (to avoid)]. Magrab[8] notes that defects often result from the following human errors (safeguards identified in parentheses):

➤ Forgetfulness (alert operator in advance, check at regular intervals);
➤ Misunderstanding (train operator, check in advance, standardize work practice);
➤ Identification (train operator, be attentive, be vigilant);
➤ Inexperience (build skill basc, standardize work); and

➤ Inattentiveness (instill discipline, standardize work, provide good work instructions).

A key aspect of poka-yoke is to design the product and/or process so that errors cannot happen as a part of the production process, an example is shown in Figure 10-2.

Boothroyd and Dewhurst[1] suggest that the incorrect installation of parts can be minimized by

➤ obstructions which prevent incorrect assembly;
➤ asymmetrical mating parts;
➤ symmetrical parts if orientation is unimportan;t
➤ prevention of subsequent operations if two parts are assembled incorrectly;
➤ marking of parts with words, arrows, or colors; and
➤ elimination of flexible parts, which are easy to install incorrectly.

Design for Assembly or DFA is similar to poka-yoke but also considers the ease of, and time required for assembly, as well as error potential. Helander[9] recommends the following design features to simplify assembly:

1. Use piece of the part as a fixture or base for the assembly operation.
2. Minimize the number of parts or components in the assembly.
   a. Integrate or combine parts (Figure 10-3).
   b. Minimize the number of, or even eliminate need for, different types and sizes of fasteners.
   c. Minimize the need for small parts such as washers or spacers (Figure 10-4).
3. Facilitate the handling of parts.
   a. Use parts that are easy to grip (Figure 10-5).
   b. Minimize use of flexible parts such as wires, cables and belts.
   c. Minimize use of parts that have a tendency to nest or tangle.
4. Facilitate the orientation of parts.
   a. Use symmetrical parts (Figure 10-6).
   b. Color or shape code asymmetrical parts when they are required.
   c. Use automatic part feeders when possible.
5. Facilitate assembly.
   a. Use self locating parts with chamfers, notches, or guides.
   b. Minimize tolerances in part mating (while maintaining quality).

121

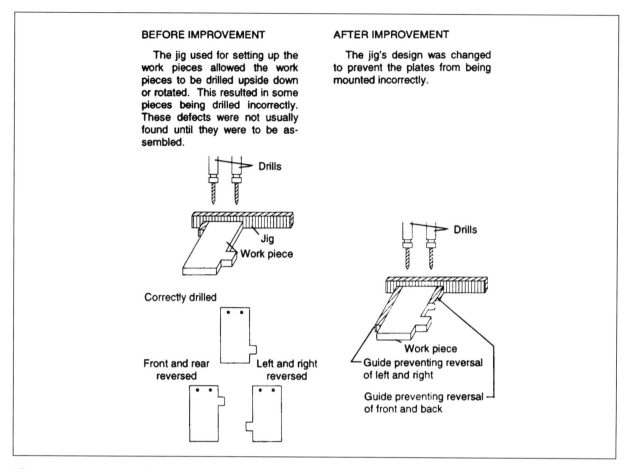

BEFORE IMPROVEMENT

The jig used for setting up the work pieces allowed the work pieces to be drilled upside down or rotated. This resulted in some pieces being drilled incorrectly. These defects were not usually found until they were to be assembled.

AFTER IMPROVEMENT

The jig's design was changed to prevent the plates from being mounted incorrectly.

Drills

Jig

Work piece

Correctly drilled

Drills

Work piece

Guide preventing reversal of left and right

Guide preventing reversal of front and back

Front and rear reversed

Left and right reversed

Figure 10-2. An example of preventing a mounting error of a jig for the drilling of several holes simultaneously. (From Poka-Yoke: Improving product quality by preventing defects, edited by NKS/*Factory Magazine*. English translation copyright © 1988 by Productivity Press, Inc. PO Box 13390, Portland, OR 97213-0390. Reprinted with permission.

6. Consider stability and durability of parts and assemblies.

Choices made in the product design stage can affect the types of processes which are available to the process engineer later during the manufacturing stage. For example the specification of a particular product shape in the product design process might necessitate hand assembly and prohibit machine assembly. This, in turn, may require the implementation of a potentially ergonomically stressful manufacturing process.

The choice of a particular material for a product might necessitate that the product be assembled with screws or rivets with potentially high ergonomic stresses. The choice of a different material could allow assembly using a spot weld or chemical bond, which would likely be less ergonomically stressful. The assembly tolerances specified in the design stage can also affect the ergonomic stresses during the manufacturing

process. For example, if two parts are to be mated with a manual "snap fit" or push-type connector, the mating tolerance specified during the product design stage determines the hand/finger force and resulting ergonomic stress during the assembly process.

DESIGN FOR MANUFACTURING ERGONOMICS

While the study of ergonomics deals with the relationship between the human and his or her total living environment, the term "ergonomics" is actually derived from the Greek words *ergon* meaning "work" and *nomos*, meaning "natural laws of" or "study of". When addressing manufacturing ergonomics it can be defined as the study of the natural laws of work or the relationship between the worker and the work environment. Ergonomics is concerned with work methods, equipment, facilities, and tool design.

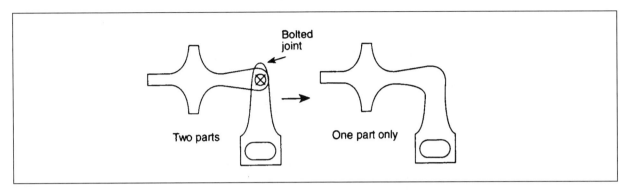

Figure 10-3. Combine or integrate parts to reduce assembly requirements. (From *A guide to the Ergonomics of Manufacturing* by Martin Helander. Copyright © 1995 by Martin Helander. Reprinted with permission.)

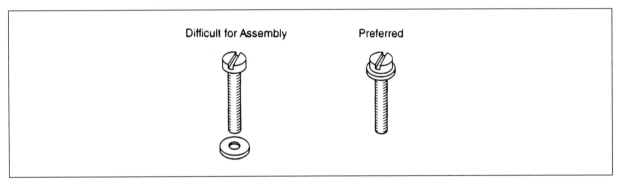

Figure 10-4. Design parts so that separate washers are not required. (From *A guide to the Ergonomics of Manufacturing* by Martin Helander. Copyright © 1995 by Martin Helander. Reprinted with permission.)

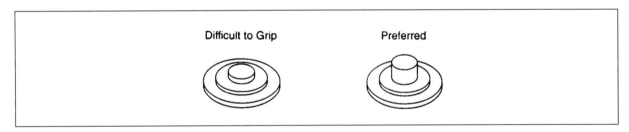

Figure 10-5. Improve parts handling by making parts easy to grip. (From *A guide to the Ergonomics of Manufacturing* by Martin Helander. Copyright © 1995 by Martin Helander. Reprinted with permission.)

At the most fundamental level the design engineer must deal with the relationship between the worker and the work environment to optimize the "fit" between the worker and the job (Figure 10-7). This fit may be pictured as the overlap between the capabilities of the individual and the requirements of the task.

In the manufacturing environment a poor fit can cause unnecessary stress to the operator and may adversely affect the worker through job related injuries or illnesses or may adversely affect the product through reduced quantity,

quality, or efficiency of production. When the task requirements match the capabilities of the individual the job related stresses are minimum. When the task requirements exceed, or do not match, the capabilities of the individual and the job related stresses increase. A proper fit between the worker and the workplace can

1. reduce occupational injury and illness;
2. reduce workers' compensation, and sickness and incident costs;
3. reduce medical visits;
4. reduce absenteeism;

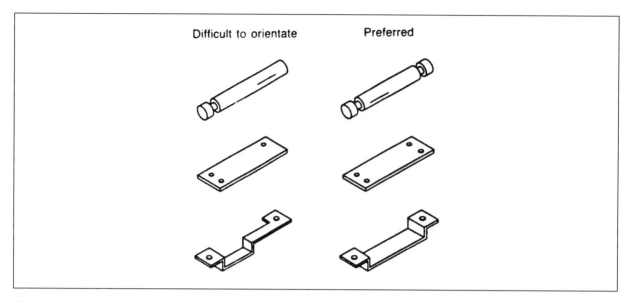

Figure 10-6. Symmetric parts are easy to orient during assembly. (From *A guide to the Ergonomics of Manufacturing* by Martin Helander. Copyright © 1995 by Martin Helander. Reprinted with permission.)

5. improve productivity;
6. improve quality and reduce scrap; and
7. improve worker comfort on the job.

Notice that items 1 through 6 above directly relate to the profitability of the enterprise. Even item 7, "improve worker comfort on the job," actually relates to profitability since worker comfort will affect items 1 through 6.

ERGONOMIC RISK FACTORS

Consideration of ergonomic issues in product and process design can greatly reduce the number and severity of ergonomic related stresses during the manufacturing or assembly stage of product development. Product and process designers must be familiar with the general types of risk factors associated with the development of musculoskeletal disorders on the plant floor. These general risk factors are summarized below.

→ *High Force.* The forces resulting from external loading must be resisted by the muscles in the body and are transmitted through tendons connecting the muscles to the bones. High forces can cause tendonitis (inflammation of the tendons) or tenosynovitis (inflammation of the tendons and surrounding tendon sheaths), high bone-to-bone compressive forces or decrease blood circulation to the muscle. The force applied to an object may not directly relate to the weight of the object. For example the pinch forces

required to assemble two parts are dependent on the type of connector not on the weights of the objects themselves.

→ *Awkward Postures.* Awkward posture accentuates the effect of the external forces noted above. They may overload the musculoskeletal system through increased external moments or load the joints or surrounding structure in an uneven or asymmetrical manner. Static postures maintained for long periods are also hazardous.

→ *High Frequency or Repetition.* When a task must be performed repetitively the muscles and tendons are stressed frequently. The precise relationship between force, posture and repetition is not fully understood. Jobs with short cycle times are generally more repetitive than jobs with longer cycle times because they require the operator to repeat the operation more often. In some cases, jobs with longer cycle times require the operator to make many similar repeated motions within the cycle so the number of cycles per shift may not be an adequate measure of job repetitiveness. A job where the same basic motion is performed within a cycle (running down several screws during one cycle) may be as repetitive as a job with a much shorter cycle time.

→ *Inadequate Rest (Lack of Recovery Time).* The lack of adequate rest or recovery time

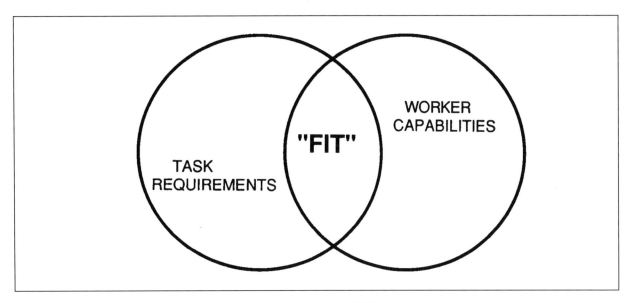

Figure 10-7. Fit between task requirements and worker capabilities.

between exertions may also result in high stress. For example a job with a cycle time of ten seconds, with a nine-second exertion and a one-second recovery time, is more stressful than a job with a cycle time of ten seconds, with a one-second exertion and a nine-second recovery time.

➤ *Vibration.* Vibrating tools can cause mechanical stresses, which result in constriction of the blood vessels in the hands. Vibrating tools may also desensitize the receptors in the hands and cause the worker to grip the tool harder than necessary. This increases the force hazard noted above.

➤ *Environmental Factors.* Cold temperatures may present a direct hazard to the tissues or desensitize the receptors in the hands and cause the worker to grip the tool harder than necessary. The use of gloves may decrease the effect of the cold but may require additional force to flex, may reduce the coefficient of friction between the hand/glove and the work-piece or decrease the pressure sensitivity of the hand. Hot temperatures can increase the metabolic load on the body.

➤ *Direct Contact Trauma.* Musculoskeletal or nerve disorders may also be caused by direct contact with the work-piece, tool, or work surface. Mechanical stresses can be generated on the tendons and nerves in the hands through contact with the sharp edges of work-pieces or tools. This is especially haz-

ardous when the hand is used repeatedly to pound or push on parts.

Very little research has been completed showing which risk factors or interaction of factors contributes most to the development of musculoskeletal disorders in the workplace. It is generally more cost effective to deal with the posture and force risk factors first, since a reduction in frequency/repetition will directly affect production rates. A task analysis checklist, which may assist the process designer is presented in Figure 10-8 (Cohen).[10]

UAW-Ford Design for Ergonomics Process

Ford Motor Company,[7] in conjunction with the United Auto Workers, has developed a method to integrate the consideration of ergonomic issues into the design of manufacturing processes for new products. This Design for Ergonomics (DFE) Process consists of three basic components as shown on Figure 10-9.

The DFE process starts with *Process Start Up* through which the DFE team is assembled and trained. This component consists of five basic steps.

1. Secure the commitment of key management and employee representatives.

2. Select the DFE team. The team should have representation from production, maintenance, service, program management, facility management, product design, process

"No" responses indicate potential problem areas which should receive further investigation.

1. Does the design of the primary task reduce or eliminate

    bending or twisting of the back or trunk?   ❑ yes   ❑ no
    crouching? .   ❑ yes   ❑ no
    bending or twisting the wrist?   ❑ yes   ❑ no
    extending the arms?   ❑ yes   ❑ no
    raised elbows?   ❑ yes   ❑ no
    static muscle loading?   ❑ yes   ❑ no
    clothes wringing motions?   ❑ yes   ❑ no
    finger pinch grip?   ❑ yes   ❑ no

2. Are mechanical devices used when necessary?   ❑ yes   ❑ no

3. Can the task be done with either hand?   ❑ yes   ❑ no

4. Can the task be done with two hands?   ❑ yes   ❑ no

5. Are pushing or pulling forces kept minimal?   ❑ yes   ❑ no

6. Are required forces judged acceptable by the workers?   ❑ yes   ❑ no

7. Are the materials

    able to be held without slipping?   ❑ yes   ❑ no
    easy to grasp?   ❑ yes   ❑ no
    free from sharp edges and corners?   ❑ yes   ❑ no

8. Do containers have good handholds?   ❑ yes   ❑ no

9. Are jigs, fixtures, and vises used where needed?   ❑ yes   ❑ no

10. As needed, do gloves fit properly and are they made of the proper fabric?   ❑ yes   ❑ no

11. Does the worker avoid contact with sharp edges when performing the task?   ❑ yes   ❑ no

12. When needed, are push buttons designed properly?   ❑ yes   ❑ no

13. Do the job tasks allow for ready use of personal equipment that may be required?   ❑ yes   ❑ no

14. Are high rates of repetitive motion avoided by

    job rotation?   ❑ yes   ❑ no
    self-pacing?   ❑ yes   ❑ no
    sufficient pauses?   ❑ yes   ❑ no
    adjusting the job skill level of the worker?   ❑ yes   ❑ no

15. Is the employee trained in

    proper work practices?   ❑ yes   ❑ no
    when and how to make adjustments?   ❑ yes   ❑ no
    recognizing signs and symptoms of potential problems?   ❑ yes   ❑ no

Figure 10-8. Task analysis checklist.

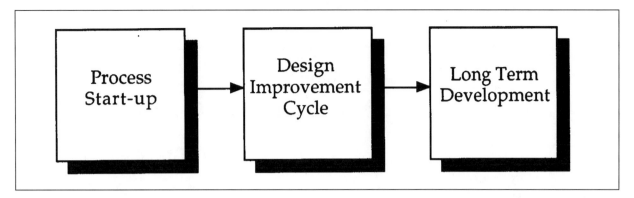

Figure 10-9. The UAW-FORD design for Ergonomic process. (From *Design for Ergonomics Participant's Guide* Version 1.0 by For Motor company. Reprinted with permission.)

design, industrial engineering, material handling, medical, plant/union ergonomics, safety, management ergonomics, training, and vendors.

3. Train the DFE team in ergonomics, project tracking and recordkeeping, and how to function as a team.

4. Develop a team mission statement, which defines the purpose of the team in terms of simple, measurable, consistent, realistic, understandable objectives with a defined time frame.

5. Develop the teamwork process.

The *Design Improvement Cycle* is the core of the DFE process. This cycle starts after the DFE team is organized and trained. It is within this cycle that the DFE team identifies potential ergonomic stresses in conceptual jobs, when the hazards can be abated with a minimum of cost and in a reasonable time frame. This process of identifying and correcting potential ergonomic hazards includes the six steps shown in Figure 10-10 (Ford Motor Company).[7]

1. The identification of priority jobs is accomplished through a development of the conceptual workstation and identification of the tasks expected to be performed by the operator.

2. Job stresses are predicted using the informed judgments of the DFE team members, ergonomic analysis methods, operator judgments, and group discussion. Potential stresses during both operation and maintenance/service must be identified.

3. Solutions are developed with consideration given to cost, benefit, implementation time, complexity, and effect on other workstations.

4. The implementation of solutions requires the

organization of resources to effect change. This might involve working with skilled trades, engineers, operators and vendors and, training of operators and supervisors on new equipment or methods.

5. Thorough documentation of projects is necessary to transfer experience to future projects and assemble cost/payback information.

6. Project follow-up is necessary to determine the long-term success or failure of the project and to determine if the process needs further ergonomic analysis during the design cycle.

Long Term Development assures that the results of the DFE process will be institutionalized and become a regular part of the overall product design process. It is during this stage that the results of the DFE process are communicated to other groups outside of the DFE team so that successful practices can be adapted to other design processes and unsuccessful practices can be avoided. The long-term development stage deals with the following three items:

1. Specialized training may be required in advanced ergonomic analysis techniques.

2. The results of the DFE process must be disseminated throughout the organization so that all parties understand the value of the process. This includes
   - managers and supervisors so they will approve and release their people for future efforts.
   - production workers so they will participate and accept changes resulting from the process.
   - employee representatives so they will support the process;

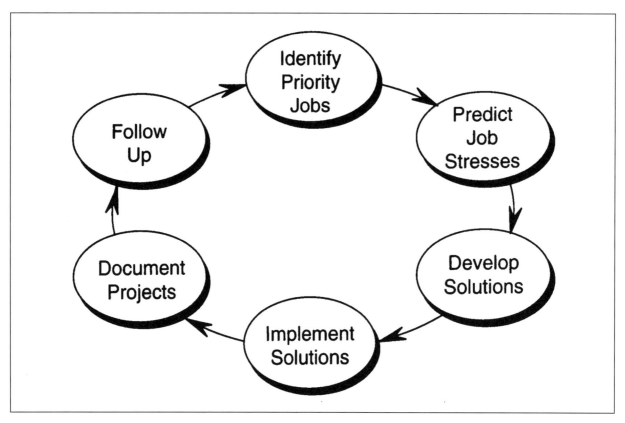

Figure 10-10. The UAW-FORD design improvement cycle within the design for ergonomics process. (From *Design for Ergonomics Participant's Guide* Version 1.0 by For Motor company. Reprinted with permission.)

- engineers so they will contribute to future projects;
- accounting so they will assist with cost/benefit analyses; and
- medical staff so they will provide feedback on potentially stressful jobs identified by medical records.
3. The overall progress of the DFE effort must be periodically reviewed to assure the following:
   - Ergonomic efforts are effective and appropriately prioritized.
   - Implemented designs and design changes continue to provide the desired benefits.
   - The DFE teams are functioning in an effective and efficient manner.
   - Documentation is complete and informative.
   - Key management and employee representatives are involved and satisfied with the DFE process.

DESIGN FOR ERGONOMICS IN PRODUCT USE

Ergonomic considerations in product use can be best understood by considering the human as a component in the simple closed loop system model shown in Figure 10-11. Information about system status is provided to the user in the form of some type of system output or display. This "display" may be visual, auditory, or tactile. The user perceives the display, processes this information, and takes action to modify system status through some type of system input or control. Information about this modified system status is again provided to the user through the system output or display. This process continues through this closed loop system. The effectiveness of the display (how it is perceived) is affected by the environment (lighting, noise, etc.) and display design, including such issues as compatibility with the type and detail of information needed by the user.

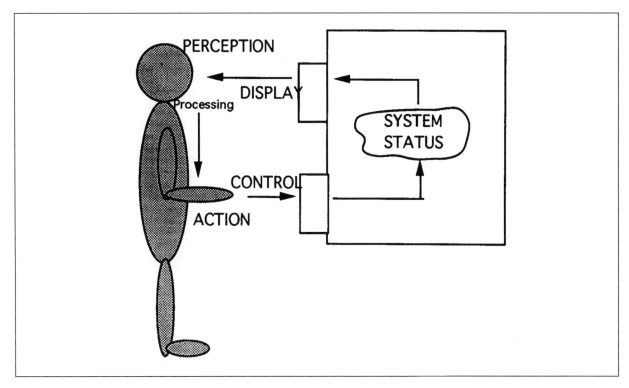

Figure 10-11. Human as part of a closed-loop system.

The processing of this information is influenced by relatively "permanent" user characteristics such as stereotypes of expected control/display relationships, training, experience, etc. and more transient characteristics such as fatigue, motivation, or emotional state. The effectiveness of the user action on the control or system input is determined by the type of control, and the user size, strength, dexterity, etc.

Lewis and Samuel[11] note that the human in such a closed loop system can function at a variety of levels. The human acts as the power source (jack up a car so that the wheels are two inches off the ground), sensor/transducer (push a button in response to a signal), processor/monitor of information (observe displays in a power plant control room), or tracker/controller (drive a car).

Magrab[8] proposes that one goal of ergonomics is to create user-friendly products. This includes the following design principles, which tend to optimize perception, processing, and action as shown in Figure 10-11.

➤ Fit the product to the physical and mental capabilities and expectations of the user. Minimize the necessity of awkward postures and extreme forces and use standard conventions, arrangements and systems.

➤ Simplify the number and type of tasks required to operate the system/product, make controls and control functions obvious, and display operating information clearly and unambiguously.

➤ Anticipate and prevent incorrect user actions and provide adequate feedback to the user about system status.

Ulrich and Eppinger[6] contend that the ease of use of a product is related to the following:

1. Do the product's features communicate their correct operation to the user?
2. Is the use of the product intuitive?
3. Are all of the features of the product safe?
4. Have all of the potential users and uses of the product been identified?

With respect to item 4 above it should also be recommended that foreseeable misuses of the product be identified so that the hazards involved can be anticipated and minimized. Products and processes must be maintained and serviced, often in field conditions so the ease-of-use issues noted by Magrab[8] and Ulrich and Eppinger[6] must also be considered when designing and specifying maintenance procedures for equipment and systems.

SUMMARY

In order to minimize the stresses associated with product manufacture and use, and optimize product performance, product and process designers must consider human physical and mental capabilities and expectations when designing systems with which humans must interact. They must realize the importance of, and have access to, information about ergonomics and human factors including human size, strength, range of motion, and control/display stereotypes. Information sources particularly appropriate for product and process designers are included at the end of the reference section under "Suggested Readings."

REFERENCES

1. Boothroyd G, Dewhurst P: *Product Design for Assembly.* Wakefield, RI: Boothroyd Dewhurst, 1991.

2. Talty JT: Memorandum: Visual aids-NIOSH and Project SHAPE. Cincinnati: Nov 25, 1987.

3. Hyman B: *Fundamentals of Engineering Design.* Upper Saddle River, NJ: Prentice-Hall, 1998.

4. Ford Motor Company, *Design for Ergonomics Participant's Guide* Version 1.0. Dearborn, MI: Ford Motor Company Human Resources Development Center, 1994.

5. Ullman DG: *The Mechanical Design Process.* New York: McGraw-Hill, 1997.

6. Ulrich KT, Eppinger S.D: *Product Design and Development.* New York: McGraw-Hill, 1995.

7. Ford Motor Company, *Design for Ergonomics Implementation Guide.* Dearborn, MI: Ford Motor Company Human Resources Development Center, 1994.

8. Magrab EB: *Integrated Product and Process Design and Development: The Product Realization Process.* Boca Raton, FL: CRC Press, 1997.

9. Helander MA: *Guide to the Ergonomics of Manufacturing.* Bristol, PA: Taylor & Francis, 1995.

10. Cohen AL, Gjessing CC, Fine LJ, et al: Elements of Ergonomics Programs: *A Primer Based on Workplace Evaluations of Musculoskeletal Disorders* [DHHS (NIOSH) Publication No. 97-117]. Cincinnati, OH: NIOSH Publications Dissemination, Mar 1997.

11. Lewis W, Samuel A: *Fundamentals of Engineering Design.* Sydney (Australia): Prentice-Hall, 1989.

SUGGESTED READING

Corlett EN, Clark TS: *The Ergonomics of Workspaces and Machines: A Design Manual.* New York: Taylor & Francis, 1995.

Eastman Kodak Company, The Ergonomics Group, Health and Environment Laboratories: *Ergonomic Design for People at Work.* New York: Van Nostrand Reinhold, 1989.

ErgoWeb (1995–1998), *ErgoWeb, Inc Home Page* [on-line]. Available: http//www.ergoweb.com.

Helander M: *Guide to the Ergonomics of Manufacturing.* New York: Taylor & Francis, 1995.

Kroemer KHE, Grandjean E: *Fitting the Task to the Human: A Textbook of Occupational Ergonomics.* New York: Taylor & Francis, 1997.

Pheasant S: *Bodyspace: Anthropometry, Ergonomics and the Design of Work.* New York: Taylor & Francis, 1996.

Salvendy G: *Handbook of Human Factors and Ergonomics.* New York: John Wiley, 1997.

Woodson WE: *Human Factors Design Handbook.* New York: McGraw-Hill, 1991.

Chapter 11

USING CONCEPTS IN RETROFITTING EXISTING OPERATIONS

by Wayne C. Loomis

INTRODUCTION

The need to apply safety through design techniques and concepts to existing operations is called *retrofitting*, the process of correcting errors in design after a product, equipment or process is out of the final design phase. Specifically, this chapter will deal with design errors that affect the overall safety of the product, equipment or process. Those affected include the consumer, the public, pilot plant employees, assemblers, maintenance personnel, service technicians, and many others.

Safety through design, when properly conducted during the initial stages of product, equipment or process development is a proactive activity. Retrofitting is, in contrast, a reactive process and much more costly. This high cost is highlighted in Chapter 1. Even though retrofitting is much more costly than correcting errors in the initial design, retrofitting does have its place in safety through design in existing operations.

Understanding and applying the safety through design techniques for risk elimination and control to existing operations is good business. The thought of designing out errors is not new. The authors of *Safety Management*,[1] in their original edition (1956), emphasized the importance of correcting physical hazards, thus making the "unsafe act" impossible. The practice, however, has been to design for functionality, and that leaves safety to be dealt with after the fact. As a result, there are situations that require retrofitting to correct *error-provocative*[2] products, equipment, and processes that already exist.

ERROR-PROVOCATIVE SITUATIONS

It is critical in retrofitting to understand the contribution of performance errors to the occurrence of incidents (accidents) and the significant gains to be made by designing to avoid them when retrofitting. Chapanis introduced the concept of *Error-Provocative Situations*. He states:

> *In their work human factors engineers find many man-machine systems are error-provocative. Other people have sometimes used the term "error-inducing" or "error-producing." Whatever it is called, an error-provocative situation is one that almost literally invites people to commit error.*

Chapanis provides some interesting insights into the concept that no single common factor or error provides the key to accident (incident) prevention. In fact, he established four axioms around this point:

AXIOM 1: *Accidents are multiply determined. Any particular accident can be characterized by the combined existence or coincidence of a number of events and circumstances.*

It has been a fallacy among design engineers in the past that safety is the responsibility of the user. If an incident occurred it was not necessarily the fault of the design but was caused instead by the inappropriate actions of the individual injured. In fact, the reader can find any number of studies that put the user fault level around 90%. Chapanis, in his axiom asks us to consider

Figure 11-1. Microsoft Windows 95.

looking at a much broader spectrum than just the user.

AXIOM 2: *Given a population of human beings with known characteristics, it is possible to design tools, appliances and equipment that best match their capacities, limitations and weaknesses.*

When reviewing incidents that have resulted in injuries and property damage, it requires a much deeper analysis than "what did the user do wrong." Chapanis challenges us to also look carefully at the design. When a situation is created where users must occasionally put themselves or something in harms way, then eventually an incident will occur.

AXIOM 3: *The improvement in system performance that can be realized from the redesign of equipment is usually greater than the gains that can be realized from the selection and training of personnel.*

The value received from improved design will outweigh, in Chapanis' mind, the benefits received from employee selection and training. Think of the times you take a totally unintended action and say to yourself "Why did I do that? I fully knew it would result in an unintended action but I did it anyway." An example that comes to mind is the little X that appears in the upper right corner of a Windows 95 (or NT) and later versions.

It is common practice to click the X only to find that the document closed when you really

wanted to do something else. Because of the close proximity of the close (represented by the X) and minimize buttons (represented by the _ or ❐) it is easy to make the wrong decision. (In reviewing this situation with many veteran PC users they all report that they have made this error.) There are two simple design changes that would eliminate this problem. One, move the X to the left hand side, or, two, open a dialog box that would say "Do you really want to close this item?" Chapanis infers that in situations of this type selection and training is not the solution to eliminating this type of error. Redesign is the answer to eliminating unwanted and unintended actions.

AXIOM 4: *For purposes of man-machine systems design there is no essential difference between an error and an accident. The important thing is that both an error and an accident identify a troublesome situation.*

Referring to the scenario described above when one hits the X the end result is frustration and self-incrimination (you dummy) but generally no harm is done. This is called an error. If, however, the X triggered an action that could result in property damage or physical harm, then an incident (accident) occurred. The goal in retrofitting is to uncover and correct as many of the errors as possible so the unfavorable incidents do not occur.

Chapanis discusses the human error situation in much more detail in the written transcript of

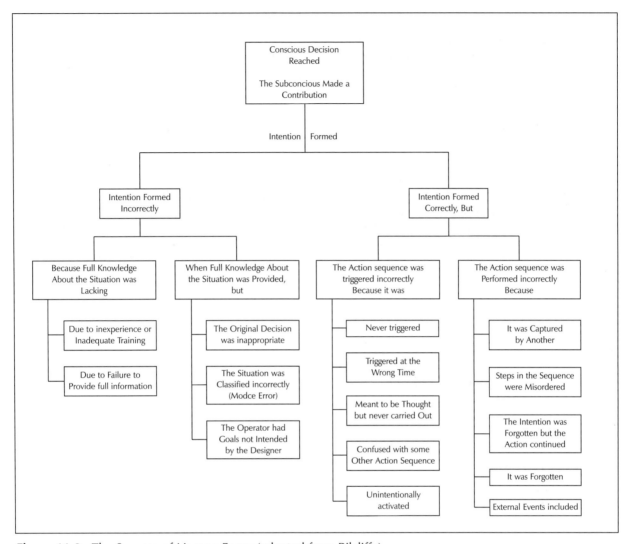

Figure 11-2. The Sources of Human Errors (adapted from Bilcliffe).

his presentation "To Error is Human To Forgive, Design."[3] He states:

> *Human actions, errors included among them, consist of two phases: First there is an intention to do something. Second, there is an action sequence that carries out the intention. Errors can occur either because intentions were formed incorrectly, or because action sequences were incorrect.*

Chapanis shows in diagrammatic form, in Figure 11-2,[4] the ways in which these errors can happen. The only part of error identification that deals with lack of experience and training is on the far left. The challenge to the designer is to identify all the other potential error scenarios that could occur and design around these errors. If the logic in Figure 11-2 is followed, it can be seen that the error in using Microsoft Windows is attributed to an action that was *unintentionally activated*. So, again, this error does not lie on the left side of the diagram (*inexperience* or *inadequate training*) and, therefore, the correction does not lie so much with the user as it does with the designer.

IDENTIFICATION OF RETROFITTING NEEDS

It is important to recognize the type of circumstances where retrofitting can come into play. While the techniques of safety through design can be applied in a variety of circumstances, there are four major categories identified and discussed in this chapter.

First, since the safety through design concepts and techniques have not matured it would be expected that there will be many instances where an existing product, equipment, or process needs to be reviewed because of a high potential to create an unwanted incident.

Second, through incident investigation and analysis, situations may be encountered that require application of the concepts of safety through design to identify error-provocative components of a design that were not noticed in the past. Ergonomic redesign is a good example.

Third, good engineering practice dictates that when there are major changes in existing products, equipment or processes and the safety through design concepts be applied to the redesign.

Forth, changing norms and standards may require that specific actions similar to safety through design be undertaken. An example of this is OSHA's Rule For Process Safety Management of Highly Hazardous Chemicals. For existing operations this is a retrofitting process and in new installations it is a true safety through design initiative.

EVALUATING EXISTING PRODUCTS, EQUIPMENT, AND PROCESSES

Once engineers and safety professionals have accepted the concept of error-provocative situations they are in a good position to look at all existing products, equipment, and processes with a different perspective. Safe job procedures are a good place to start. Where a procedure places the responsibility on the operator to take a particular action, the steps in the procedure need to be reviewed to assure that the requirements are realistic. For instance, the procedure could direct the individual to "lift safely." Even though the operator has been thoroughly trained in safe lifting, if the object presented is too heavy or too large then they are prohibited from "lifting safely." Therefore, in Figure 11-2, there is a situation where the "intention was formed incorrectly" because "the original decision was inappropriate."

It was once said that asking a person to lift safely under these circumstances is like trying to control noise exposure by saying "don't listen." Engineers need to be completely familiar with the requirements for safe lifting. The NIOSH Lifting Equation[5] provides a good starting point for two handed lifts. Engineers need to be very familiar with the equation and its application.

Another source of identification of error-provocative situations is through formal or informal discussions with operators. Formally interviews can be done, surveys conducted and group meetings held to identify issues. Informally, there is a need to be alert to situations that are observed or that employees identify. The results could reveal situations where employees feel it is inappropriate to follow procedures or safety rules because they feel it would be more hazardous to do so. An example would be a rule requiring the wearing of gloves to prevent cuts when working around sheet metal. If high dexterity is required for the employee to perform a task, then gloves would not be the answer. A redesign of the process to eliminate or protect the sharp edges would be more appropriate.

In reviewing processes, the consequences of operator error must be taken into consideration. If steps are performed out of sequence, left out, or added, what would be the result? Do instructions leave room for misinterpretation? There are many situations where intentions of operators were formed correctly, but circumstances intervened that resulted in disastrous miscues. The engineer needs to look at all existing processes under their control and perform a hazard analysis and risk assessment (see Chapter 2) to identify major error-provocative situations.

INCIDENT INVESTIGATION AND ANALYSIS

While incident reports provide valuable data regarding causal factors for injuries, illnesses, and property damage they are, in effect, a measure of failure. Therefore, to get maximum value from incident investigations, the inappropriateness of the often applied concept established by Heinrich[6] in the early 1950s that 88% of incidents are the result of "unsafe acts of persons" must be reconsidered thereby placing an emphasis on improving employee performance to prevent hazards related incidents. In contrast Manuele[7] states:

Heinrich's premises, and several causation models that are based on them, are still the foundation of the work of many safety practitioners.

Indeed, most causation models have focused on the behavior of the individual presumed to have acted unsafely, rather than on the design of the work environment and on the design of work methods. . .

An incident analysis, based on a causal model that has unsafe acts of the individual performer as the focus will often result in the wrong advice being given to decision makers. Such analyses miss the fundamental question-what aspects of the workplace and work methods designs are involved. They most often result principally in recommending some sort of behavioral modification to correct "man failure."

Manuele concludes "Safe practice, then, commences with design and engineering considerations." Incident reports, therefore, should be reviewed with a focus on "design of the work environment and on the design of work methods." These reports then become a valuable tool to be used in retrofitting product, equipment or processes.

Understanding the difference between "unsafe acts of employees" and "error-provocative situations" is essential to reducing errors by engineering methods. A review of a few typical incident scenarios may be helpful in illustrating the point.

CASE 1.

An employee, while hurrying to a meeting, slipped on the floor and injured her knee. The corrective action reported initially states "employee cautioned not to hurry." What's missing here is a full understanding of the walking surface involved. Most slips occur when people are not walking normally. If the surface has a coefficient of friction of .5 or greater, then slipping does not usually occur even when the person is not walking normally.[8] Rather than focus on the individual, the action should include assurance that all surfaces meet or exceed the .5 coefficient. (What did the original design specifications for the floor surface require?) Design specifications should be an essential consideration in analyzing an incident but would be

totally overlooked if the investigation only focuses on the individual.

CASE 2.

An employee was injured while lubricating a piece of rotating equipment. He removed a section of the guard and placed his hand and grease gun inside without locking out the equipment. The report stated that the employee "violated the lock-out procedure." While this is true, it was a practice often observed by the engineering and management staff assigned to this area. A simple redesign would be to extend the grease fixture outside the hazardous area. Again, by focusing on the individual, opportunities to eliminate the hazard from this time forward are lost.

CASE 3.

An employee was mixing the ingredients for a hydrogen peroxide mixture when a serious explosion occurred severely injuring the employee and two co-workers. The immediate investigation revealed the employee mixed the ingredients in the wrong order causing the violent exothermic reaction. In designing the process, no fail-safe steps were taken to assure the ingredients could not be entered into the batch in the wrong order. Because of the potential severity of this reaction, the procedures established should not have depended on humans to respond correctly 100% of the time. It is imperative in processes of this type that the design precludes human errors through the use of good engineering techniques.

CASE 4.

This incident involved extensive property damage and cleanup costs resulting from a ruptured bag on a central vacuum system used to collect toxic metals. This was a classic case where the initial design called for an expensive primary filter bag (three times the cost of a plain cloth filter) followed by a hepa filter as backup. When this process was moved to a new location in a different state it was determined by the design engineers that they could meet that state's emission criteria with a simple cloth filter.

When the initial process was installed a HAZOP (hazards and operability study) was performed. It was determined that even with the high initial cost, a higher priced primary filter and hepa backup would be required to prevent a high level exposure if the primary filters should fail. The subsequent redesign at the new location assumed that the more expensive system was originally required to meet state emission requirements. Based on this assumption and with no thought (HAZOP) given to what would happen if the cheaper cloth filter ruptured, the cheaper filter was installed. Needless to say, after the filter bag ruptured the redesigned system was retrofitted in accordance with the original design *after* nearly $500,000 was spent on clean up.

In addition to review of specific incident reports, data analysis can also be used in determining the need to retrofit. The data to be reviewed includes workers' compensation loss reports, product claims, "near miss" reports, first aid reports, parking lot incidents, and vehicle incidents to name a few. Good data analysis will detect trends that could indicate a thorough engineering review may be in order. This is often the case in evaluating ergonomic disorders. A single cumulative trauma incident may occur because of the variation in humans. If, however, a trend toward a problem is identified, then consideration of redesign of the work activity may be a solution in addition to dealing with the individual.

In accident data analysis it is critical that the corrective actions focus on the design and not the individual. This will allow the thought process to be open to the elimination of error-provocative situations and be more effective in preventing recurrence of these types of injuries and incidents. Keep in mind that in error-provocative situations the aspects of the situation are the principal casual factors, not the lack of training of the individual involved.

MODIFICATION OF EXISTING PRODUCTS, EQUIPMENT, AND PROCESSES

The modification (such as upgrading, expanding, major repair, relocation) of existing products, equipment, and processes provides an opportunity to conduct a risk assessment of the original design. An important consideration is to evaluate the current state of technology from a safety point of view. The National Safety Council's publication *Product Safety Management Guidelines*[9] encourages designers to analyze the application of technical developments to their particular industry to determine if they face any of the following situations:

- ➤ New technology may eliminate a hazard;
- ➤ New technology may eliminate tasks associated with incidents;
- ➤ New technology may enhance reliability of a safety critical assembly;
- ➤ New technology may be "inherently" safer (CO_2 abrasive cleaning vs. solvent cleaning); and
- ➤ New technology may make a formerly unusable safety device or feature feasible. Examples include magnetic position sensors to provide the capability to interlock guards located in hazardous environments and the advent of reliable "easy start" engines for lawn mowers, which made it practical to install a "dead man switch."

Engineers and safety practitioners are encouraged to look at the incident history of the products, equipment, and processes prior to modification for clues to where problems can occur that could be eliminated by redesign.

Following a good analyses of the situation the engineer should then determine if a full hazard analysis is appropriate. A description of the process to follow in arriving at this decision can be found in Chapter 2.

CHANGING NORMS AND STANDARDS

Engineers, safety practitioners and others in most progressive companies are aware of the need to keep abreast of what is happening in the world of regulations and standards. For example, many companies have engaged in an ergonomics program prior to standards being issued by OSHA or ANSI. These programs usually include in-depth training for the engineering personnel so they can fully understand their role in reducing the hazards associated with a poor ergonomic environment.

Recently, OSHA's Rule for Process Safety Management of Highly Hazardous Chemicals places a requirement on industry to thoroughly evaluate certain existing and modified processes and perform a hazard analysis. Engineers and safety managers may wish to use the hazard analysis requirements of this standard as a blueprint for *all* existing processes and equipment installations and for future modifications.

CONCLUSION

It is incumbent upon the engineer and safety practitioner to be schooled well enough in the principles of error-free design to identify and correct existing situations that could lead to injury or property losses. In retrofitting, the engineer must work closely with the safety engineer, operations personnel, and employees to assure that error-provocative and inherently hazardous situations are properly identified. The engineer and safety practitioner must assess whether a hazard analysis is appropriate for the situation at hand and then carry out the analysis as necessary. Necessary improvement must then be incorporated in the final redesign.

Retrofitting, while inherently more costly than good initial design, is an important element in achieving error and injury free operations.

REFERENCES

1. Grimaldi JV, Simonds RH: *Safety Management.* Homewood IL: Irwin, 1975.

2. Chapanis A: The error-provocative situation. In Tarrants WE (ed). *The Measurement of Safety Performance.* New York: Garland Publishing, 1980.

3. Chapanis A: To Err is Human To Forgive, Design. Presented at ASSE 25th Professional Development Conference, American Society of Safety Engineers, 1986.

4. Bilcliffe DSC: Human error causal factors in man-machine systems. *Hazard Prevention,* Jan/Feb 1986, Vol. 22, No. 1.

5. *Applications Manual for the Revised NIOSH Lifting Equation.* Cincinnati: NIOSH, 1991.

6. Heinrich HW: *Industrial Accident Prevention.* New York: McGraw-Hill, 1950.

7. Manuele FA: *On the Practice of Safety.* New York: Van Nostrand Reinhold, 1993.

8. Sherman R: Slip and fall accident prevention simplified. *Professional Safety,* Feb 1986.

9. *Product Safety Management Guidelines,* 2nd ed. Itasca, IL: National Safety Council, 1997.

10. Process Safety Management of Highly Hazardous Chemicals, OSHA Standard 1910.119, Feb 1992.

Chapter 12

APPLYING CONCEPTS TO PRODUCT LIABILITY PREVENTION

by Bruce W. Main

OBJECTIVE

This chapter presents an engineer's overview of the product liability system and discusses safety through design as related to product liability. It demonstrates the cost of product liability to a manufacturer using several cases, and discusses how safety through design can minimize these costs, prevent injuries, and reduce product liability exposures. Information resources are presented to ensure all pertinent data is used in design decisions to minimize product liability exposure.

INTRODUCTION

With all too regular frequency in the United States, people are injured and subsequently sue a product manufacturer. In many of the cases reported in the general media, juries assign large monetary awards in product liability cases. Given the award sizes and the resulting media attention that they receive, one would expect that product liability influences designers. It does.

Main and Ward[1] surveyed engineers as part of an investigation into what engineers know about safety. Respondents were asked about the impact of product liability on their design decisions. The Figure shows the responses. The skewing toward the right and the relatively high means indicate that product liability is a significant factor in design.

These results demonstrate that most engineers recognize the impact of product liability and are motivated to include safety in their designs. The issue becomes not one of whether engineers *can* easily include safety in their work, but rather do they know *how* and do they have the *tools* to do so?

Most engineers and persons in our society today are at least generally familiar with the U.S. product liability system. Much of this knowledge likely comes from the general media rather than formal study. This chapter shares an engineer's view of the product liability system in hopes of providing additional depth to the general knowledge, and to discuss a few shortcomings and how engineers can prepare for them. The discussion is not intended to substitute for sound legal advice. Readers should seek appropriate legal counsel as their situations require.

This chapter addresses safety through design and the product liability forces pushing it. Three cases are presented to illustrate the significant costs of this liability. One key element in reducing liability exposure is using current information in design. With the exploding availability of information, an engineer has a difficult task of staying current with the state of the art. Information sources potentially useful to an engineer are therefore identified to aid in avoiding product liability difficulties.

ENGINEER'S VIEW OF THE PRODUCT LIABILITY SYSTEM
LEGAL THEORIES

Product liability centers around whether the manufacturer of a product took adequate and appropriate steps to ensure the safety of the product users. Such cases raise issues of adequacy of design, manufacture, warnings , and others. There are several legal theories under which a plaintiff can sue a manufacturer (only three are discussed here):

➤ negligence;

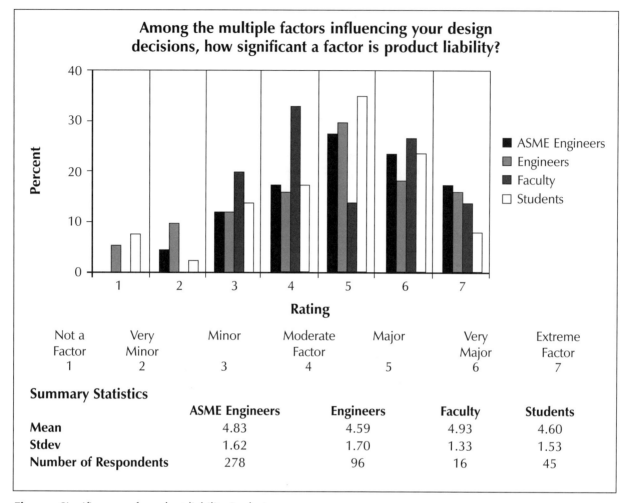

Among the multiple factors influencing your design decisions, how significant a factor is product liability?

| Not a
Factor
1 | Very
Minor
2 | Minor

3 | Moderate
Factor
4 | Major

5 | Very
Major
6 | Extreme
Factor
7 |

Summary Statistics

	ASME Engineers	Engineers	Faculty	Students
Mean	4.83	4.59	4.93	4.60
Stdev	1.62	1.70	1.33	1.53
Number of Respondents	278	96	16	45

Figure. Significance of product liability in design

➤ implied warranty; and
➤ express warranty.

The warranty theories involve the "contractual" relationship between the plaintiff and the product manufacturer, seller, and distributor. The primary claim against a manufacturer is negligence.

The negligence theory of liability is based on the defendant's lack of reasonable care in developing a product in which negligence causes harm to the plaintiff. This theory explicitly addresses the manufacturer's behavior and whether such behavior was reasonable. More specifically, product liability negligence claims have been brought for alleged improper, or inadequate, product or product components of the following:

➤ Manufacture
➤ Construction
➤ Design
➤ Formula
➤ Development of standards
➤ Preparation
➤ Processing
➤ Assembly
➤ Inspection
➤ Testing
➤ Listing
➤ Certifying
➤ Warning
➤ Instructing
➤ Marketing
➤ Advertising
➤ Packaging
➤ Labeling

ELEMENTS OF PROOF

There are four necessary elements for a plaintiff to prevail in a product liability case: duty, breach of duty, proximate cause, and damages.

There must be a legal duty owed by the defendant to the plaintiff. A reasonably foreseeable user of a product meets this criteria; for example, a user the manufacturer can expect to use its product.

1. There must have been a breach of the duty owed; e.g., the manufacturer did something wrong to violate the duty.
2. The wrong which the manufacturer committed must have been a "proximate cause" of the loss suffered by the plaintiff; e.g. the proximate cause is a primary cause which produces the injury without which the incident could not have happened. If the manufacturer's error is not found to be a proximate cause of the plaintiff's loss, the defendant will prevail.
3. There must be damages in the form of property damage, personal injury, or wrongful death. To bring a lawsuit, the plaintiff must have suffered a loss of one or more of these forms.
4. There must be damages in the form of property damage, personal injury, or wrongful death. To bring a lawsuit, the plaintiff must have suffered a loss of one or more of these forms.

If any one of the four elements fails, the plaintiff has failed to prove its case and the defense prevails/wins. Naturally, defense actions focus on exposing weaknesses in one or more of these elements.

Liability must be based on proof that the manufacturer knew or should have known about the risk of harm based on, the scientific or technical, information reasonably available at the time the specific unit of the product left the control of the manufacturer. Sources of such information are described in more detail later in this chapter. Further, proof must show that if the manufacturer had responded to that knowledge, a different method or design would have resulted than what was produced.

PRODUCT LIABILITY PROCESS

In a typical situation, an individual is harmed (suffers damage) while using a product. If the harm is sufficiently severe, the individual may hire an attorney to file a complaint against the product manufacturer (and others in the production/distribution chain). The complaint names the injured party (the plaintiff), the manufacture(s), other defendant(s), and the alleged wrongs or torts, which the plaintiff contends were committed which resulted in his or her injury. The lawsuit works its way through the judicial system with the attorney(s) for the plaintiff and defendant discussing monetary solutions to settle the complaint. The intent of monetary compensation is to "make whole" the wrongly injured party; that is fairly compensate the plaintiff for the injury and related losses.

If the parties cannot agree on a settlement, the case enters discovery where testimony from the plaintiff, manufacturer, witnesses , and others is recorded. The discovery process can be arduous and invasive for the designer or manufacturer. Often engineering, medical and other experts are involved to help the attorneys analyze and evaluate the facts of the case and the merit of their client's position. Discovery will often bring to light more facts and evidence which shed light on what happened and why. Once the discovery testimony is produced, most of what is known or can be deduced about the accident is known. In theory, each side should have a better appreciation of the other's position and its own case. Many cases settle at this juncture.

If the parties still are unable to resolve their differences and reach a settlement, the case goes to trial. Trial is a forum where a judge or jury hears all the evidence each side produces and listens to each party's arguments as to why their case has merit and the other does not. Product liability trials are most often heard before a jury. Based on the information presented the jury or judge renders a decision for the parties as to a fair resolution.

There are many factors that influence the outcome of a trial, only some of which are the facts at issue. Personalities, appearances, presentations, timing, duration, and many other factors influence jury members. They are sometimes equally important, as the core facts, to the outcome of the case. Predicting the outcome of a trial is very difficult, especially with these confounding factors. For the foregoing reasons and others, many cases settle just before or early into the trial. The design of the U.S. product liability system is intentionally structured with these incentives to encourage mutually agreeable (or more often mutually disagreeable) settlements before trial.

RISK-UTILITY TEST

In design defect and other product liability cases a risk-utility balancing test is often the metric juries use to determine if products are reasonably safe. Under this test, a product is reasonably safe if its utility outweighs the risks associated with the design of the product; for example, the residual risk is acceptable. In a product liability lawsuit, juries conduct this test based on the testimony. Although intuitive, the risk-utility test presents some significant technical problems. The test itself requires an analysis to determine (a) the risk, (b) the utility, and, (c) whether these balance appropriately. Current test protocol suggests that a jury conduct the analysis itself based solely on the evidence surrounding the particular case in litigation. Although this test makes intuitive sense, it is very difficult to implement in a practical manner, both by juries and manufacturers with proactive intentions.

Jurors are often novices in conducting a risk-utility test. They have received no training in conducting such a test. Few, if any, have ever conducted such an analysis prior to a trial. As with any other skilled analysis, one would expect novices to make mistakes and achieve little success without practice or training.

The lack of instructions on how to conduct a risk-utility test also introduces variability to the result. There is no formal methodology, handbook, or objective benchmarks describing how to conduct the test. There is no rating or ranking system that a jury can use to evaluate a specific product. There is no measure they can use to compare the relative safety of the product in question to other products then existent (for example, how can one compare a mechanical press, a table saw, and a toaster?). Thus, with little specific information describing how to conduct the test, judges and juries are left to develop their own methodology for each case.

Jury members are not familiar with the terms used in conducting the risk-utility test. Few jurors have a common understanding of the definitions of the terms "risk" and "utility" because these terms are very difficult to define in a practical manner. Fewer still understand how to apply these definitions for this analysis. If different jurors or juries define these terms differently, chances are the manner in which they apply the test and the test results will vary greatly.

Juries are not alone in struggling with definitions. Technical committees spend many hours wrestling with the definitions of risk and other terms. Often different technological committees or communities have varying definitions, or understanding, of these and similar terms.

The risk-utility test can be very difficult to conduct in a repeatable fashion. Two juries applying the same test to the same case facts may not likely come to the same conclusion. There is very little, if any, objective data available for risk or utility measurements in the context of a product liability lawsuit. Given the variations in inputs (people, instructions, understanding, etc) one would not expect the results to be repeatable. Therefore, the test itself introduces variability to the outcome.

The limitations of the risk-utility test are not raised to necessarily suggest that the test be discarded in favor of another test. The objective is to examine the message the law sends to engineers, and how they can improve their designs with knowledge of the metric against which such designs will be judged. The limitations of the risk-utility test, particularly in the subjective definitions, lack of training and instruction, and application, make it a poor test. In engineering terms, this test is not reliable, repeatable, robust, or very useful. These limitations can lead to errors and unfair results (to the benefit or detriment of either party).

Given the existence of the risk-utility test, one might expect manufacturers or designers to apply a risk-utility test during the design process. However, manufacturers also have difficulty assessing utility. A risk-utility test is not typically discussed in current engineering curricula; therefore, engineers are generally unfamiliar with such a test. Engineers are not trained to think in terms of risk-utility.

SAFETY THROUGH DESIGN AND PRODUCT LIABILITY
RISK ASSESSMENT VS. RISK-UTILITY

Many safety techniques, tools, and methods have been developed within the safety community to implement hazard elimination and control. Which technique is best depends on the design, its stage of development, the level of complexity and sophistication, the availability of data, and personal preference. However, perhaps the closest relation to the risk-utility test is risk assessment.

A risk assessment is "the process of determining the elements of risk by identifying the severity of harm and the probability of occurrence of a hazardous event."[2] A risk assessment provides an evaluation of the risk derived from identified hazards, and prompts the engineer or safety practitioner conducting the analysis to reduce the risk to an acceptable level.

A risk assessment is a tool used by engineers to identify possible hazards and to prompt alternative design solutions to mitigate or control the risks. They offer the manufacturer the opportunity to identify hazards associated with its intended uses and anticipated misuses, and to take steps to eliminate or control them. For example, the analysis can identify the problems associated with using warnings, when a design approach is more appropriate. Risk assessments are a primary mechanism to implement safety through design early in the design process.

The outcome of a risk assessment is a documented analysis. In the past, product liability concerns reduced documentation for fear of creating a discoverable "smoking gun" document (which could be used against a manufacturer to prove the plaintiff's case). In practice, a documented risk assessment increases the likelihood that hazards will be identified and that risks will be reduced to an acceptable level thereby decreasing product liability exposures. There is far less likelihood that hazards or risks will be overlooked or "slip through the cracks." Documented analyses can provide evidence that a manufacturer made reasonable efforts to identify hazards and minimize risks associated with the hazards which can be used in defending a design in a product liability lawsuit.

Risk assessments are gaining acceptance in several industries (machine tool, automotive, robotics, airport ramp operations, and others). Current industry methods advise using a task-based approach to risk assessment where users, tasks and the hazards associated with the tasks are properly identified. The European Union (EU) explicitly requires risk assessments in accordance with the hazard elimination and control hierarchy (see section on international influences). Therefore, manufacturers of products sold in the EU are required to conduct a hazard analysis and risk assessment. In the United States, there is currently no such requirement.

With appropriate training or new computerized risk assessment tools, engineers can conduct risk assessments during design development. Risk assessments, to be most effective, should be conducted by a team consisting of as many affected individuals as reasonably possible including engineers, operators, maintenance personnel, and marketing. If product liability is a significant concern to the company, an attorney should be involved in the risk assessment team. An attorney can bring the legal perspective to bear to the project and may protect documents through the attorney-client privilege.

The omission of a risk assessment does not necessarily imply that the product fails to meet the state of the art. Although still rare, safety analyses are beginning to appear in plaintiff's complaints of negligent design (for example, "failed to complete an adequate hazard analysis and risk assessment"). Hence, although not legally required, the existence of hazards analyses or risk assessments conducted during the design process will likely bolster the liability defense provided it is well done (as with any other engineering analysis).

Risk assessment provides manufacturers a practical means to get nearer to the risk-utility test. It places the analysis portion of the risk-utility test largely in the control of the manufacturer. In turn, the risk assessment permits a jury to evaluate the manufacturer's risk assessment effort and its results rather than the jury attempting to conduct the analysis on its own.

FORCES PUSHING SAFETY THROUGH DESIGN IN PRODUCT LIABILITY

There are several key reasons for the emerging interest in the safety through design process including the issue of deep pockets, international influences, state of the art requirements, and costs. These factors have particular significance to product liability. The first three factors are discussed below in greater detail. The cost factor is analyzed separately.

DEEP POCKETS

Larger manufacturers face the legal challenge of being 'deep pocket' targets. Deep pocket refers to the propensity of larger companies to be sued rather than smaller companies simply because the larger company generally has more assets. This phenomenon is directly related to the greater wealth of the larger company, rather than related to negligence or fault. The deeper the pocket, the larger the target. As a result, a larger company needs to keep abreast of advances in the state of the art since it faces a greater likelihood of being targeted than a smaller company. With the advent of engineering and design outsourcing, it remains to be seen whether the liability for the services follows the outsource provider or manufacturer (the deeper pocket). Given the greater threat of a product liability suit, larger companies stand to achieve considerable benefits from safety through design efforts which minimize liability threats.

INTERNATIONAL INFLUENCES

One very recent set of international product safety regulations comes from the EU in the Safety and Health Directives.[3] As of 1997, most products sold in the EU are required to bear a "CE" mark. To obtain the mark, a "responsible person" (most often the manufacturer) must ensure that documentation concerning the safety of the product is available for inspection by enforcement authorities. This documentation, referred to as the "technical file," includes materials sufficient to demonstrate that the product satisfies the essential health and safety requirements, the appropriate conformity assessment procedure has been followed, an EU declaration of conformity has been issued, and the product is in fact safe.[4]

The EU requirement for the CE mark is pushing the state of the art in the United States and may prompt hazard analyses and risk assessments for domestic products too. For instance, a firm manufacturing products exported to EU member countries, and other products sold domestically, could face difficulty if the U.S. product development process is less rigorous than the export product process. In the long run, EU requirements may have a broad impact on all domestic manufacturers. As exporting manufacturers begin instituting hazard analyses and risk assessments in order to secure CE marks for products, the state of the art will likely advance beyond the confines of the EU to the general U.S. market. This may have the effect of inducing other manufacturers to rely on hazard analyses and risk assessments to keep up with the state of the art and reduce liability.

International influences may also impact the way strictly domestic manufacturers design and produce products, especially if there is a similar product being manufactured in the United States and exported to Europe. If a domestically producing manufacturer competes with a company exporting to the EU, the exporting firm may advance the state of the art differently than it would in strictly domestic competition.

The Asia/Pacific region is no longer immune to product liability exposure. Product liability laws are one of the fastest growing imports of legal principles into the region. Australia, People's Republic of China, Taiwan, and Japan have product liability statutes. Japan passed its product liability statute in 1995, modeled after the Restatement of the Law on Torts. Previously, a manufacturer was immune from suit in Japan unless the product was sold directly to the injured party. Product related personal injury litigation was virtually unheard of in Japan before the statute was enacted. Korea has a product liability statute pending. Countries in the Asia/Pacific region that do not have statutes do have tort based legal theories for product liability exposure. Manufacturers can expect that there will be less tolerance in any country if a product causes injury when it is designed with less than the state of the art design used with comparable products and processes sold elsewhere in the world.

STATE OF THE ART REQUIREMENT

Product liability and related costs of litigation are encouraging manufacturers to increase their efforts and keep pace with advancements in the safety through design process. Currently, in the United States, there is no legal requirement for a manufacturer or designer to conduct any particular analysis, including a hazard analysis or risk assessment, granting the designer the freedom to create the product or process design in any manner they choose. In many jurisdictions, current law requires that a manufacturer design products in accordance with the state of the art existent at the time of manufacture. Meeting the state of the art is an admissible defense in an increasing number of jurisdictions. If product development processes are at the leading edge of industry practice, defense counsel can argue that rather than being defective, the manufacturer's product and process are state of the art. However, to make this argument the process must be documented and traceable.

RECALLS

A product liability lawsuit typically, although not always, concerns one individual bringing a claim against one or more defendants. A product involved in several similar incidents may lead to it being recalled by the manufacturer either voluntarily or by government requirement. Recalls can be costly to implement because the manufacturer attempts to contact all purchasers and prompt them to return the purchased item for replacement, repair, or refund. This can be difficult in an industrial setting where the manufacturer has records of the purchasers and their locations. In the case of commodity or consumer, applications where such records do not exist, the effort required for a recall can be imposing. The time, energy and effort to execute a recall are resources taken away from more constructive efforts.

For logistical reasons alone, recalls can be very difficult to conduct effectively, and the implications of a recall to product liability claims can be significant. Beyond the costs, logistic and liability challenges, a recall also places a manufacturer at a competitive disadvantage. It presents an opportunity for competitors to seize market share, shelf space, etc. While one manufacturer implements a recall, its competitors have the opportunity to gain ground.

REMEDIES FOR PREVENTION

Product liability cases derive from an allegation that the plaintiff has encountered a hazard. In many cases the remedies are relatively easy to develop once a hazard has been identified, provided it is identified early in the design process. Design changes identified after a product is in production, or tooling is made, presents considerably greater financial and logistic challenges.

Implementing safety through design requires that remedies be developed for hazards following the order of design precedence (see Chapter 2):

- ➤ Design for minimum risk.
- ➤ Incorporate safety devices.
- ➤ Provide warning devices.

➤ Develop and institute operating procedures and training.

Examples of product liability cases, taken from the public domain, which illustrate the potential gains from safety through design follow.

CASE 1. PUNITIVE AWARD

In 1995, a man aged 22 was operating a meat cutter which was equipped with a slant blade (*Scoggins v Hobart Corp*)[5]. The machine allegedly began to self-feed, drawing plaintiff's right hand into the machine. The plaintiff's injuries consisted of partial amputation of his right index finger. Medical expenses totaled about $5,800 and lost wages totaled about $4,800.

The plaintiff brought a lawsuit against the machine manufacturer alleging that the slant blade design was defective and unreasonably dangerous. The plaintiff, through his expert, claimed that the blade design permitted the saw to move meat forward into the blade with sufficient velocity that operators may be unable to remove their hands before blade contact. Plaintiff made no claim that the manufacturer was or should have been aware of the alleged defect prior to sale of the machine. However, plaintiff claimed that the manufacturer was aware of the alleged defect and associated risk within months of the machine first being sold in 1982. Plaintiff further alleged that despite the knowledge of the risks, the manufacturer made no attempt to remedy the hazard and reduce the risk.

The case went to trial before a jury. The jury determined that the residual risk was not acceptable and that the manufacturer erred in its design decisions. The jury awarded $510,000 in compensatory damages and $10 million in punitive damages.

In this case the hazard involved a slant blade design which came in contact with the plaintiff. Potential remedies to this hazard could include an interlocked or alternate guard design that would prevent the operator from contacting the blade. Alternatively, an improved meat feeding mechanism that would better separate the meat input from the blade hazard might be developed.

CASE 2. DEFENSE VERDICT

Plaintiff managed a family-owned construction company that was working on a residential renovation project in Boston (*Chute v. Sears,*

Roebuck & Co)[6]. Two of his employees were using a Sears/Craftsman radial arm saw to trim approximately two inches from the end of ten-foot timbers for shoring up a wall. One employee supported an end of the timber while the other attempted to cut it.

Plaintiff, who was not wearing safety goggles, either walked behind or stood behind the saw while the cut was being made. An object was thrown from the saw table and struck him in the eye. It ruptured the choroid layer of his left eye, permanently scarring the eye tissue leading to a 70% loss of vision.

Plaintiff's expert contended that a rear guard on the saw would catch objects thrown by the blade off the back of the table. He demonstrated a prototype guard. The plaintiff also argued the table should have displayed warnings against standing behind the saw when in use and recommending use of a guard.

The defense contended the proposed guard would not prevent objects from being thrown, and would interfere with some uses of the saw. They also argued the plaintiff's employees used the saw improperly, saying the saw's instruction manual recommended use of a saw horse to brace oversize pieces, and use of a larger fence to hold larger pieces in place.

The jury rejected the plaintiff's argument that the saw should have been designed with a rear guard to block any objects that might be thrown off the saw table by the saw blade. The jury found that the plaintiff's negligence caused the accident. This case resulted in a defense verdict. In essence, the jury found that the hazard exposure behind the saw was acceptable without additional risk reduction remedies by the manufacturer for the particular accident.

Case 3. Plaintiff Verdict

A 29-year-old man was working on a baking assembly line *(Dajani v AMF Mach. Co.)[7]*. He was placing empty trays into a basket loader when a tray became stuck in the loader. He reached into the loader in an attempt to free the tray. The jam was in the vicinity of a chain and sprocket, which drove the machinery. His left hand "became caught" in the chain pinch point. He received crushing injuries and amputation of four fingers of his left hand. His medical expenses totaled about $225,000. He missed about 14

months of work during his recuperation. He was unable or unwilling to return to his former position. He became a taxi driver with earnings about $10/hour less than his prior employment.

The plaintiff sued the machine manufacturer alleging that there was a design defect. The plaintiff hired two engineering experts who opined that the machine was defective since it was equipped with a once-sided pinch point guard rather than a clam shell guard that would have fully enclosed the pinch point. The manufacturer asserted third-party claims against the plaintiff's employer alleging that it had either removed or modified the guard originally provided with the machine.

The case went to a jury trial, and it returned a verdict in favor of the plaintiff in the amount of $2.1 million. The jury divided responsibility for the incident, 8% against the employer (approximately $168,000), and 92% against the manufacturer ($1.9 million).

In this case an alternate guard enclosing the chain may have helped prevent the injury. In the case description, the employer modified the original guard in a manner presumably to enable a necessary task on the machine (such as cleaning or clearing a jam). Having operators perform tasks near exposed pinch points with the machine in operation is generally a risky proposition. A task-based risk assessment can be useful in identifying hazards such as occurred in this accident. Identifying the jam clearing task and analyzing the hazards associated with the task would likely have identified this potential problem. If identified early enough in the design process, means to prevent the jam or a method for clearing a jam safely may have been developed through alternate configurations, or using light screens or other devices.

ANALYZING COSTS

The earlier in the design process a hazard is identified, the easier, cheaper, and better it can be remedied. Hazards not identified early in the design process can lead to unnecessary injury incidents and product liability exposure. Overlooking hazards can have considerable detrimental effects, particularly financial. As illustrated by the awards in the cases cited, product liability can have a significant monetary impact on business even if the defendant manu-

Table 12–A. Costs from Cases.

Quantifiable Costs:	Case #1	Case #2	Case #3
Lost wages	$4,800	not available	Not available
Medical expenses	$5,800	not available	$225,000
Punitive portion	$10 million	not applicable	Not applicable
Total Award	$10.51 million	$0	$2.1 million

Table 12–B. Analysis of Costs.

Estimated Costs:	Case #1	Case #2	Case #3
Total Award	$10.51 million	$0	$2.1 million
Compensatory portion	$510,000	not applicable	$2.1 million
Estimated total costs (3 times award)	$1.53 million	not applicable	$6.3 million

facturer prevails. However, the jury award is only part of the cost as seen in examining cost issues in more detail.

Frequently the primary media attention paid to a product liability case is the dollar amount of the jury award. Although an easily identified value, the monetary jury award is only one portion of the costs of litigating a product liability claim. The publicly available information concerning economic cost to a manufacturer to defend a product liability lawsuit is limited. Part of the reason is that the costs of litigating a claim are spread over time, usually between an insurance company and the manufacturer, which makes tracing them very difficult.

AWARDS

A tabulation of costs associated with the three previous cases is reflected in Table 12-A. This analysis does not include less quantifiable but still significant costs of pain and suffering, lost work time, employee morale, public relations, shareholder value, and lost sales.

Table 12-A captures only the costs associated with the jury award. Total costs of a product liability case will include the costs borne by the plaintiff, the defendant insurance company, and the defendant manufacturer. Conversations with senior managers in the insurance industry suggest that the following cost equation is reasonably accurate.

Total cost of litigation = 3 x Judgment

One-third of the total cost of litigation is attributable to the defense costs (legal counsel, experts, medical treatments, and so on), one-third to the defendants' internal costs (lost time, productivity, responding to discovery requests), and one-third to the plaintiff and plaintiff's counsel. The equation does not include the punitive portion of the award, if any. This estimate is based on experience rather than explicit scientific data so variations for specific cases may be significant. This equation only works in cases that result in a plaintiff verdict. Using this equation, the total cost in each of the cases is shown in Table 12-B. The table shows that the costs of defending a product liability lawsuit are considerable.

The manufacturer bears the cost of supporting the defense (one-third of the total estimated costs). Insurance companies typically bear the costs of the award plus the costs of defending the lawsuit (amounting to two-thirds of the total estimated costs). These costs are reflected back to the manufacturer in workers' compensation insurance premiums.

Even where the defendant manufacturer's insurance company realizes most of the costs (two-thirds under this model), the manufacturer's portion is sizeable. Over time the manufacturer's insurance premiums will likely rise to match the insurance risk thus further increasing the operating costs.

Table 12-C. Additional Sales Attributable to Product Liability.

	Case 1	Case 2	Case 3
Manufacturer's estimated costs	$510,000	$50,000 (assumed)	$2.1 million
Hypothetical profit margin	10%	10%	10%
Required additional sales to cover manufacturer's costs	$5.1 million	$500,000	$21 million

SALES PERSPECTIVE

Table 12-C presents an analysis of the additional sales needed by the manufacturer to cover its portion of the expense associated with the three cited product liability cases.

Table 12-C demonstrates that the additional sales needed to cover the costs of product liability defense are very significant when evaluated from an additional sales basis. Even in the hypothetical situation of Case 2, where a manufacturer devotes $50,000 to supporting the legal defense (management time, document research and preparation, testimony, etc), additional sales required to cover these expenses for a company with a 10% profit margin is $500,000. Additional sales necessary in the other two cases are substantially greater.

WORKERS' COMPENSATION PERSPECTIVE

An analysis of workers' compensation costs yields additional insight to the product liability cost issue. A discussion with a major manufacturer of aircraft components indicated that the company had analyzed both the direct and indirect costs associated with workers' compensation claims. The analysis determined that for every dollar in direct costs associated with workers' compensation there were four dollars of indirect costs.

$$
\begin{aligned}
\text{Total workers'} & \\
\text{compensation costs} &= \text{direct costs} + \\
& \quad \text{indirect costs} \\
&= \$1 + \$4 \\
&= \$5 \text{ total cost}
\end{aligned}
$$

Efforts that reduce injuries and workers' compensation claims yield a return factor of five by eliminating both the direct and indirect costs. Although 4:1 indirect to direct costs ratio could be much higher or lower depending on the business, this ratio is commonly used.

Analyzing these costs in terms of additional sales needed makes the costs loom even larger. Assuming a 10% profit margin for the company, for every dollar spent on direct workers' compensation expenses the company would need additional $10 in sales. For every indirect dollar spent on workers' compensation expenses it would require additional sales of $40.

Additional sales required to cover workers' compensation costs
$$
\begin{aligned}
&= \text{total costs} / \text{profit margin} \\
&= \$5 / 10\% \\
&= \$50
\end{aligned}
$$

In terms of additional sales, there is a 50:1 ratio of sales to workers' compensation expense (assuming a 10% profit margin). In a situation where workers' compensation expenses are $10,000, the manufacturer would need additional sales of $500,000 to cover the direct and indirect costs:

$$
\begin{aligned}
[\$10,000 \text{ direct costs} + \$40,000 \text{ indirect cost}] / 10\% \\
= \$500,000
\end{aligned}
$$

Safety through design offers an opportunity to eliminate both the injury and the associated costs yielding marked cost efficiencies and productivity gains.

When examining the total costs, two conclusions can be drawn. First, the cost in terms of absolute dollars is very significant particularly when viewed from a profit margin and sales perspective. This is a fertile area for cost reductions. Second, relatively small investments made to improve a manufacturer's design and development processes can yield considerable returns and cost efficiencies if they lead to reductions in injury incidents.

INFORMATION FOR PRODUCT DESIGN DECISIONS

Effective product liability prevention and good design requires the use of current, state of the art information in product design decisions. Safety through design is no exception. Engineers must draw current information from a variety of sources beyond their personal experiences.

Current information is critical because it forms part of the legs on which a product design must stand in a product liability lawsuit. The decisions made during product design and development affect long-term liability. In a product liability lawsuit, those decisions will be carefully and deeply scrutinized, potentially many years after they have been made. For products with long service lives such as machine tools, the longevity of the decisions is critical as is the information used in making them.

Documentation plays a key role in product liability prevention because of the changes in the state of the art. Changes occur both in technology methods and capabilities, and in the assessment of acceptable risk. The risks that are deemed acceptable by persons in our society today may not be deemed so in the future.

RESOURCES FOR STATE-OF-THE-ART INFORMATION

Establishing the state of the art for a given point in time is a contentious issue between opposing sides in product liability litigation. Often plaintiffs attempt to apply current information or standards to equipment developed under an earlier state of the art. Such an approach fails to take into account the dynamic nature of information and technology. At the same time, defendant manufacturers attempt to recast the product design decisions under the state of the art existent at the time of manufacture. This latter approach is consistent with current law in many jurisdictions. This dynamic complicates the effort to determine the state of the art at a particular time. Consequently, litigants, experts, juries and the courts wrestle with determining the state of the art and how to establish the state of the art at the time of manufacture becomes one of the key issues.

Using state of the art information therefore becomes very important in conducting risk assessments and in making product design deci-

sions. The engineer must consider the external and internal information available to, or generated by, the manufacturer. Several different sources of information are available.

GOVERNMENT STANDARDS/REGULATIONS

One of the more obvious ways to determine the state of the art is to look to government standards/regulations in effect at the time of manufacture at the state, federal, and international levels. Noncompliance with a regulation is a violation of law and is one of the most overt measures of noncompliance with the state of the art. Examples of U.S. government standards include OSHA, NHTSA, and CPSC regulations.

INDUSTRY/NONGOVERNMENT STANDARDS

In the United States, industry standards are typically written by the consensus of knowledgeable members from a particular industry. The standards are written for specific kinds of products (printing presses, ladders, press brakes, etc.) rather than general classifications. Industry standards provide technical information, promote consistency, ensure a minimum level of safety, and provide an excellent information source for eliminating and controlling hazards. Most experts agree that consensus standards establish a minimum state of the art in an industry. Examples of U.S. industry standards organizations include ANSI (American National Standards Institute), ASME (American Society of Mechanical Engineers), NFPA (National Fire Protection Association), and ASTM (American Society for Testing and Materials).

RECOMMENDED PRACTICES

Recommended practices are less stringent forms of standards, and are typically written by industry participants in much the same way as standards. They do not have the rigorous consensus ratification process which standards must pass and therefore do not carry the strength of standards. Compliance with a recommended practice is entirely voluntary and discretionary. Departure from a recommended practice does not imply a shortcoming of a design, as would noncompliance with a standard. Recommended practices are explicitly written such that noncompliance is not a design omission of industry standards. Examples of recommended practices are SAE J2068-94[8] and SAE J1814-93[9].

TECHNICAL REPORTS

Technical reports are typically based on studies conducted by fewer individuals than with committees who write recommended practices. These reports can be written by standing consensus committees such as ANSI, or private companies, or industry partners. They are usually less comprehensive than recommended practices or standards in that they usually do not attempt to address the complete product or application. Technical reports often address a subset of information in greater detail than that which is contained in a standard or recommended practice. Information from a technical report often serves as a basis for procedures or specifications developed for standards or recommended practices.

"COLLATERAL" STANDARDS

Many products have no applicable government or industry standards. This is especially true for new products since standards tend to typically develop later in the product life cycle. Standards for products that are similar, but not strictly applicable to the subject product, can be a useful source of information to define the state of the art. Departure from these "collateral" standards carries little weight because they do not explicitly apply to a product design. Collateral standards comprise useful information to designers and represent an information source that they may or may not have been aware of during the development of the product. As an example, a collateral standard for a residential chair (which has no standards) would be the ANSI/BIFMA X5.1 (10) standard for office chairs. Compliance with objective measures included in collateral standards can be an important part of demonstrating compliance with the state of the art.

BENCHMARKING

Another means of determining the state of the art is to benchmark against the competition. Comparing and contrasting the designs of a competitor product existent at the time of manufacture to the subject design may help to determine whether a product was designed in accordance with the state of the art. In the same way that collateral standards can be used as an information source, similar product designs can also prove useful.

TECHNICAL LITERATURE

Technical literature is another useful resource in assessing the state of the art. Research, studies, and handbooks published in the technical literature offer insight into the state of the art, particularly when seeking to show the existence, or non-existence, of specific practice, knowledge, or information.

MANUALS, BROCHURES, AND GENERAL LITERATURE

Manuals, brochures, and general literature can also help to establish the state of the art. These documents are typically end-user oriented and represent the type of knowledge that an end user can be expected to have. Skilled trades or unions, the National Safety Council, and industry organizations publish this type of literature.

DATABASES

Publicly available databases of product history, accident statistics, product performance, and litigation history can establish a portion of the state of the art. The absence of information can often be as conclusive as the presence of data. With the advent of the Internet, accessing information has become considerably easier than previously possible, although information validity has become an increasing concern. Publicly available database examples include the following:

1. Westlaw, (www.westlaw.com) a large legal database
2. Lexis/Nexis, (http://web.lexis-nexis.com), a large publications database
3. National Electronic Injury Surveillance System (NEISS), database of hospital emergency room accidents and injuries, Consumer Product Safety Commission (CPSC)

COMPANY STANDARDS, PROCEDURES, OR INFORMATION

There are several different types of information within a company, which may help to define the state of the art and should be considered in making design decisions. Written internal company standards, company procedures for a product or product line and processes may exist in graphic or other forms.

Product specific tests and simulations, statistical data, product histories, and engineering analyses and evaluations can all be used to establish the state of the art for a particular product. Internal information is often retained experientially by employees, and employee turnover complicates the knowledge capture issue. Given the volume of information and the breadth of sources, staying abreast of the state of the art can be a difficult task. In many situations this task is well suited to a team approach.

SUMMARY

Safety through design is a means to reduce product liability exposure by decreasing the likelihood of an injury incident. It is a proactive, preventative approach, which reduces the costs of product liability, and decreases the time spent on defense. When instituted early in the design process, safety through design identifies hazards so that appropriate remedy actions can be taken to minimize risks.

A better understanding of the legal frame of product liability can be useful to design engineers and safety practitioners. Although risk-utility is the metric that will be used to evaluate product designs in litigation, a documented risk assessment affords the manufacturer the opportunity to prepare for product liability litigation. A task-based risk assessment conducted by a team is the initial step in implementing safety through design.

Reducing product liability exposures and costs directly impacts a company's bottom line, whether expressed in profits, earnings per share, or another metric. As illustrated through the three cases, the costs associated with defending a product liability lawsuit can be sizeable and fertile ground for cost reductions, especially when viewed from a sales perspective. Significant time and cost savings can be achieved by employing safety through design to prevent injury incidents. It is a method to prevent incidents and injuries and the product liability costs associated with them.

Designers need current information when making design decisions. Keeping abreast of the changing state of the art can be very difficult, particularly in the current information deluge. Engineers and manufacturers can draw on a variety of information sources to evaluate products and design processes with respect to the state of the art in their particular industry.

REFERENCES

1. Main BW, Ward AC: What do design engineers really know about safety? *Mechanical Engineering,* Aug 1992.

2. Technical Report No. 3, *Risk Assessment—A Guide to estimate, evaluate and reduce risks associated with machine tools,* ANSI B11 Machine Tool Safety Standards Committee, a report to be released late 1999, American National Standards Institute.

3. European Council Directive on General Product Safety 92/59/EEC. Product Standards: Machinery, Guidance notes on UK Regulations, May 1995.

4. HP Ekelenburg, et al: A Practical Guide to the Machinery Directive. Mechanical Engineering Publications Ltd, 1995.

5. *Scoggins v Hobart Corp,* Ala., Lowndes County Cir. Ct., No. CV-95-159, Aug 22, 1997 as reported in Product Law and Liability Reporter, p 25, vol. 17, Mar 1998.

6. *Chute v. Sears, Roebuck & Co.,* DC Mass, No. 94-11680-WAG as reported in Product Safety & Liability Reporter, BNA. 19 Sep 1997.

7. *Dajani v AMF Mach. Co.,* IL., Cook County Cir. Ct., No. 89L-14546, Oct 31, 1995 as reported in ATLA Product Law and Liability Reporter, p 50, vol 15. Apr 1996.

8. SAE J2068-94. Recommended Practice for Combination Turn Signal Hazard Warning Signal Flashers, Society of Automotive Engineers.

9. SAE J1814-93. Recommended Practice for Operator Controls, Off Road Machines, Society of Automotive Engineers.

10. ANSI/BIFMA X5.1 Tests for General Purpose Office Chairs, American National Standards Institute.

Part III

SAFETY THROUGH DESIGN IN INDUSTRY

Chapter 13

APPLICATION IN GENERAL INDUSTRY

by Paul S. Adams

INTRODUCTION

This chapter describes a process for integrating safety into design that is being implemented and used at a major manufacturing company. The basic process is not unique to this company, as the author is aware of other manufacturers using similar processes. One important characteristic of this process is its versatility; it can be applied in virtually any manufacturing or engineering organization.

Like many manufacturers that expend significant capital dollars, this company recognized years ago the need to review designs as a strategy for reducing incidents. In recent years, the organization realized that design review alone was somewhat inefficient from a cost perspective, and that such reviews were not delivering adequate incident prevention. In addition, engineers seemed to lack accountability for the safety of their designs, so design reviews were often skipped. These and other process deficiencies were identified through an internal study of the process by a team of safety and engineering representatives. The process described in this chapter resulted from the work of that team. It has produced safer designs and saved significant time and cost.

The team assigned to shoring up the Safety Through Design process made the following recommendations that were subsequently implemented:

- Safety needs to be addressed at the earliest possible point in a project, preferably at the scoping and specification phase;
- Safety-focused events are needed to give proper attention to hazard identification and elimination;

- Engineers need a model for understanding their role in preventing incidents; and
- Engineers need to be trained on the process for designing safe systems.

Management recognized the need to change the design culture to embrace a renewed emphasis on safety through design, and supported the initiatives outlined by the team. Later, it became apparent that process measures were needed to assess the performance of both company engineers, and of external engineering firms providing design services.

This chapter begins with a discussion of the theoretical basis for incident prevention. The Energy Control Model of Accident Phenomena provides an incident prevention model that engineers can understand and systematically apply. Next, the basic process for integrating safety into design is presented. This is followed by a discussion of process performance measures. Measurement helps drive the process and cultural change, but it tends to be problematic for many organizations. This section provides ideas and methods that can be tailored to fit the needs of most engineering organizations. The chapter ends with a brief discussion of organizational changes that this and many other companies face. These changes can pose significant challenges to achieving an effective safety through design process. Among these challenges are organizational restructuring, outsourcing of engineering services, significant acquisition and divestiture activity, and globalization. A case study at the end of the chapter illustrates a hypothetical application of the company's process for integrating safety into design.

Table 13–A. Energy Forms and Agents That Can Result in Injury and Illness.

Energy Form/ Agent	Condition Resulting in Injury/Illness	Examples of Resulting Injury/Illness
Biological	Agents such as bacteria, blood-borne pathogens and other micro-organisms invade the body	Legionnaire's Disease, respiratory illnesses, tuberculosis, hepatitis, tetanus
Chemical	Substance toxic to the human enters the body via skin contact, inhalation, ingestion, or injection through skin openings	Dermatitis, acid burns, black lung disease, silicosis, asbestosis, lead poisoning, genetic damage, numerous occupational illnesses
Electrical	Contact with electrically energized parts, electrical arcs, or explosions. Current passes through the body to ground or another conductor.	Heart failure, burns, secondary injuries such as falls
Mechanical	Force is exerted against human tissue	Falls, cuts, tears, muscle strains, fractures, cumulative trauma disorders
Physical/Noise	Sound pressure levels exceeding the ability of the body to recover	Hearing loss, burst eardrums, bends, hypoxia
Radiological	Exposure to ionizing or non-ionizing radiation	Welding flash burns, laser burns, radiation sickness, sun burn
Thermal	Exposure of body tissues to ambient or surface temperatures above or below their damage threshold	Frostbite, hypothermia, burns

ENERGY CONTROL MODEL OF ACCIDENT PHENOMENA

All injury incidents and incidents, as discussed in Chapter 2, involve the transfer of energy to the human body, or exposure to a harmful agent. Humans are capable of withstanding or absorbing energy levels or agent exposures up to an injury threshold. When transferred energy or agent exposure exceeds a threshold, then human tissues or systems become damaged or diseased. Table 13-A summarizes the basic forms of energy and agents and gives examples of occupational injuries and illnesses resulting from overexposure.

If incidents only occur when there is energy transfer or agent exposure, then a useful approach is to maintain control of energy and agents and prevent injurious transfers to the body. This concept was first proposed by William J. Haddon, Jr. in his paper, "The Prevention of Accidents" (1966).[1] An adaptation of Haddon's energy release theory is illustrated graphically by the Energy Control Model of Accident Phenomena in the Figure.

When a system or equipment is started, energy is added to allow the system to produce its intended output. Energy release is normally controlled, yielding expected and useful consequences. When the energy release is not controlled, one of the following events will occur:

➤ Control of the energy will be regained, with few or no negative consequences (for example, steering a car back onto the road, resulting in a "near-hit" or "near-miss" incident); or
➤ Release of the energy in an unexpected and uncontrolled manner.

Uncontrolled energy must be dissipated or transferred in accordance with the laws of physics. If the dissipation is adequately controlled, then damage to people, property, and the environment will be limited or avoided. When energy or agents are not adequately contained, unexpected damage and loss will occur.

A safe design is one that prevents all harmful forms of energy and agents from being transferred to a human or other asset in a manner that has the potential for causing damage and loss.

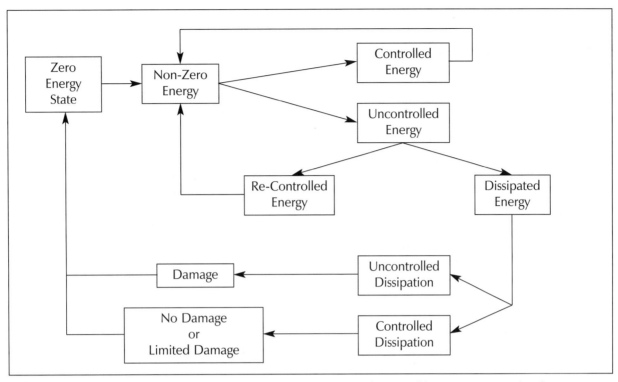

Figure 1. *Energy Control Model of Accident Phenomena* (Adapted from Haddon's *Energy Transfer Theory*, 1966.)

Safe design is accomplished by controlling energy and agents, both during use and dissipation. Fundamental strategies for preventing uncontrolled energy transfer or agent exposure are listed below in their general order of effectiveness.

1. *Avoid using a hazardous energy/agent form.* Examples: substitution of a toxic chemical with one that is non-toxic; use of non-flammable materials.

2. *Build in reliable control systems.* Examples: redundant systems used to maintain or regain control of energy in the event of primary control failure; artificial intelligence to override operator control in the event of operator error.

3. *Prevent the build-up of energy beyond system capacity for control.* Examples: pressure relief valves; shear pins; blow-out panels; use of non-metallic bearings to eliminate a high noise source; periodic cleaning to reduce colonies of bacteria.

4. *Isolate the energy source to prevent the human from coming in contact with the energy during release.* Examples: machine barrier guards; heat shields; total energy lock-out; noise enclosures; glove boxes for handling biological agents.

5. *Isolate the human to prevent contact with the energy during release.* Examples: control rooms; personal protective equipment, such as gloves, respirators, ear plugs.

6. *Control the rate or amount of energy dissipation to minimize damage.* Examples: air bags in automobiles; personal fall arrest systems; safety nets; sound mufflers.

The Energy Control Model works well for understanding acute trauma incidents, but a corollary is needed for cases of cumulative trauma and some occupational illnesses. Cumulative trauma disorders are associated with repeated exposures to mechanical energy. While a single exposure does not exceed the human's injury threshold, multiple exposures do result in tissue damage. Typically the body is able to recover from a single dose of such energy transfer, but does not fully recover from repeated transfers. In these cases, the energy in the system is typically controlled within design specifications, but the level of energy transferred to body tissues over time still exceeds the tissue damage threshold. That is, energy is controlled, but at inappropriate levels.

Designing ergonomically safe equipment is especially challenging for two reasons. First, injury thresholds vary widely among humans, and an individual's threshold can change dramatically with age, physical conditioning, and other physiological factors. To minimize injury risk, the production system needs to accommodate the most susceptible individuals in the workforce.

Second, the energy source is often the worker, rather than the process. Ergonomic injuries and illnesses occur when there is a mismatch between the task requirements and the ability of the human to meet those requirements. Safe designs enable workers to perform tasks and expend energy without damaging soft tissues, even with repeated exertions. Therefore, designing out risk requires an understanding of the types of movements and exertions most likely to result in soft tissue damage. Task characteristics or requirements associated with increase injury risk are known as ergonomic risk factors. Common risk factors are summarized below:

→ *Excessive exertion of force requirements* (results in tearing of tissues);

→ *Repeated or prolonged exertions* (causes soft tissues to "wear out" faster than the body can repair them);

→ *Awkward or static postures* (a joint is mechanically disadvantaged when working near the limits of its range of motion, and blood flow to working muscles and tendons is reduced when postures are sustained);

→ *Localized mechanical stress* (pressure exerted against soft tissue can damage that tissue and reduce blood flow);

→ *Vibration* (damages nerve endings and small blood vessels; low frequency whole body vibration can accelerate vertebral disk degeneration); and

→ *Extreme temperatures* (cold temperatures alter blood flow and increase the damaging effects of other risk factors).

A similar model to that used for ergonomic hazards can be applied to harmful agent exposures, such as carcinogens. Low level, single dose exposures may not be problematic, but continuous or repeated exposures can be fatal. Illness thresholds vary widely among workers, as does susceptibility within individuals over time. In the case of toxic agents, the designer needs to be concerned about mode of entry/exposure and other dose factors, and prevent unhealthy or risky exposures, which is best done by applying the strategies discussed above.

INTEGRATING SAFETY INTO DESIGN

The task force charged with improving the safety through design process identified three principles that needed to be followed if safety is to be successfully incorporated into a design process.

1. Safety needs to be considered continuously throughout all phases of design.
2. Safety needs to receive focused attention at strategic points in the design process.
3. Engineers and designers need to be held accountable for meeting their safety responsibilities.

The first principle appeared to be obvious, but as in many organizations, safety was often addressed as an after-thought or as a necessary add-on to a project. This resulted in a patchwork approach that often yielded high costs and inefficient protection. This approach was illustrated in later training sessions using automobile design, where an engineer designs and builds a prototype automobile. He then attempts to meet safety requirements, but soon discovers that adding fire walls, steel door rails, structural roof supports, and air bags at this stage is expensive and impractical.

One consequence of the "add safety on later" approach is that safety gets viewed as adding substantial cost, and rarely as saving money. Considering safety continuously through all phases of design clearly required a change in the design culture. An important message to communicate was the concept of *total* safety related costs over the full life of the project.

Unfortunately, merely stating Principle 1 rarely changes the way engineers design systems. Principle 2 implies that process discipline and direction must be instilled. This was achieved by requiring three safety focused events in the design process.

1. Preparation of safety fitness-for-use (FFU) criteria.
2. Completion of an Engineering Design Safety Review.
3. Completion of a walk-down of installed equipment and processes prior to start-up.

Controlling energy is an underlying principle intended to guide discussion during each of these events. The following discussion outlines these events, as described in the company's training materials.[2]

SAFETY FITNESS-FOR-USE CRITERIA

Fitness-for-use criteria (FFUs) are the starting point for engineering project design. They define project goals in terms of scope, cost, and process or product performance. They also provide a means for measuring project success. FFUs are typically developed by customer plants and business leaders, with mutual agreement between customer and the engineering service provider. Project FFUs are not considered to be complete unless specific safety FFUs are included. Safety FFUs typically address inherent hazards due to high levels or unusual forms of energy, regulatory, and standards compliance, ergonomic considerations such as manual material handling requirements, hazardous materials control, noise levels, and impact on peripheral processes outside the immediate project scope. Safety FFUs are developed by a team that includes the customer's safety practitioner. As with all FFUs, safety objectives should be measurable, mandatory, and realistic. In addition, safety FFUs address both normal operations and non-routine or upset conditions.

DESIGN SAFETY REVIEWS

The time between FFU development and design completion is typically filled with detailed information gathering, project specification, concept development and finally design. Throughout these activities, the design professional consults safety practitioners, the customer's production and maintenance staffs, and other experts who can help ensure the final design meets all FFUs. This process culminates in the completion of a final design safety review.

The *engineering design safety review* is a formal check to ensure that safety has been appropriately considered and integrated into a design. This review, or set of reviews, occurs when design drawings and specifications are sufficiently complete to allow all parties involved to understand the project and to visualize potential hazards. Normally, formal design safety reviews are conducted just prior to the release of drawings and specifications for bid. Review meetings are held at either the customer plant to facilitate involvement by production and maintenance personnel, or at the offices of the engineering service provider.

Engineering design safety reviews have several objectives:

- ➤ Identify and correct hazards to prevent injury and illness;
- ➤ Assure compliance with applicable regulations and standards;
- ➤ Prevent property loss due to incidents, fires, spills, and avoidable downtime;
- ➤ Resolve any outstanding safety related issues;
- ➤ Contain project cost by reducing redesign and rework; and
- ➤ Facilitate project planning, including installation and debugging.

Design safety reviews are conducted by a team composed of project design engineer(s), production and maintenance representatives from the customer plant, safety practitioner(s), and disinterested engineers. Disinterested engineers are critical for success, since they do not have a vested interest in or detailed familiarity with the project, and can bring an outsider's objective perspective. Multiple engineering disciplines may be involved, depending on the size and complexity of the project. Specifically, the number and expertise of participants depends on the following:

- ➤ *Project size and scope*—Larger projects often have more stakeholders, justifying review by more participants;
- ➤ *Level of human interaction*—The amount of human exposure is perhaps the single most important consideration, as it largely determines injury risk;
- ➤ *Amount of inherent energy*—Systems with highly toxic chemicals or high amperages warrant close scrutiny, perhaps including systems safety analyses such as Failure Modes and Effects Analysis;
- ➤ *Accidental loss potential*—Financial loss in the event of an energy or agent release may be more expensive for the organization than the cost of the system itself. Financial risk considerations include physical property damage, business interruption, and collateral damage;
- ➤ *Project complexity*—Systems using multiple forms of energy typically involve engineers from multiple disciplines and all are involved in the review process.
- ➤ *Experience with similar systems*—Initial installations understandably receive more scrutiny than subsequent ones that copy the design; and

➤ *Interest level of the customer*—Occasionally, factors such as an involvement team sponsorship, or a project undertaken to address a union demand, warrant increased participation by plant management and other interested parties.

The standard approach for conducting a formal design safety review is to methodically work through a checklist. The company maintains a set of checklists designed specifically for this purpose. The set includes a General Design Safety Checklist that addresses ergonomics and generic issues common to most projects, as well as specific discipline checklists (electrical, chemical, mechanical, site & physical) that address specific concerns relevant to those types of engineers. For each system element, reviewers address the various forms of energy present and the steps taken to control unwanted release.

A typical design safety review meeting proceeds as follows:

1. Project manager distributes drawings and copies of the checklists.
2. Review team chooses a facilitator, often a disinterested engineer.
3. Project engineer/manager describes the project and its scope, and answers general questions about major areas of concern.
4. Project engineer/manager keeps notes.
5. Facilitator leads a methodical review using a generic checklist, with team members asking detailed questions to ensure thorough consideration of hazards and their control. Checklist items and sections that are not applicable are so noted.
6. Additional discipline checklists are reviewed as appropriate.
7. A marked up copy of the checklists is retained with project documents.

Specific deliverables from a design safety review include the following:

➤ Set of marked-up drawings and specifications.
➤ List of identified hazards and consensus plans for their elimination or control.
➤ List of design modifications requiring attention prior to release for bid.
➤ List of specific items to be checked during installation and the final walk-down. (There are often items identified as potentially problematic that can not be adequately assessed at the time of the review due to lack of detailed knowledge.)
➤ Assignments for resolving specific details or making design corrections.

Following the review, it is the responsibility of the project engineer/manager to follow up and ensure that all issues raised during the design safety review are resolved and appropriate revisions completed.

Formal design safety reviews may seem tedious; however, they are critical for the delivery of inherently safe designs. The participants are all stakeholders and share responsibility for the safety of the final design. Most experienced engineers approach design reviews as an important team problem-solving event. A spirit of cooperation, and even fun, is maintained by restricting criticism to constructive debate on specific design features. Although the focus is always on safety, review teams frequently identify additional opportunities to reduce costs and improve productivity. Constructibility and maintainability issues often surface, and these alone can pay huge dividends for the comparatively short time invested reviewing a project. These sessions also provide some of the best possible training for both novice and experienced engineers, as collective knowledge and experience are openly shared.

FINAL SAFETY WALK-DOWNS

The *final safety walk-down* is a safety-focused team event that occurs near the completion of a project. It is most efficiently performed when construction is virtually complete but prior to the project being turned over to production. The walk-down provides a final opportunity to identify and correct hazards as part of the engineering project. (Once the project has been turned over to the customer, it is the responsibility of the facility to correct any unresolved safety issues.) To save time and minimize costs, as many hazards as possible are identified and addressed prior to the walk-down, through informal inspections of equipment and installations by the project manager, construction manager, plant engineers, plant safety practitioners, and maintenance personnel.

Safety walk-downs address both routine and non-routine procedures and operations. Proper functioning of process monitoring and control systems is verified, and protective systems such as machine guarding are checked to assure regulatory compliance. Walk-downs also provide a final opportunity to assess the adequacy of lockout/tagout procedures and other energy control measures. As a bonus, they provide a unique opportunity for training production and maintenance personnel on safety features and procedures.

Walk-down teams may be led by safety practitioners, construction managers, or project engineers. A good team is multidisciplinary and includes plant engineers, safety practitioners, and plant production and maintenance representatives. An ergonomist or other specialist may also participate, as appropriate. Walk-downs are typically organized geographically; for example, the group follows the natural flow of material through the process or equipment. Team leaders document outstanding issues, and the resulting punch list is reviewed upon completion of the event. Outstanding issues from the design safety review are also reviewed to assure that they have been properly addressed. Plans are then developed for correcting the remaining hazards or deficiencies.

PROCESS MEASURES

Regardless of whether a design process uses safety-focused events or some other model, it is important to assess process use and effectiveness. Ultimately, time is the true test of a safety through design process; i.e., whether or not incidents and injuries occur on a system due to design errors. However, even this measure is dependent upon thorough incident investigation and the ability to correctly identify root causes. In small plants where the safety coordinator wears multiple hats, it is unrealistic to expect incident investigators to distinguish among design, installation, maintenance, or operator errors. Further, injury reports usually surface well after project completion, so their value in assessing a designer's performance is severely limited.

Given these realities, the reader may be wondering why they should even bother with process measurement. The objectives of process measurement are to drive the process, to assess engineering performance, and to validate process value. The company whose process is described in this chapter is currently redesigning its measurement tools following a reorganization. However, the basic concepts and measurement tools presented below can be applied to almost any engineering organization.

DRIVING THE SAFETY THROUGH DESIGN PROCESS

A credible process measurement system can be very effective in driving performance. The adage, "That which gets measured, gets done" applies to design processes as well as any other management system. The goal is to develop process measures that minimize bureaucracy and administrative work, while enabling managers and safety auditors to hold project engineers accountable. It is also much easier for engineering executives to push the process when they see clear evidence of its value.

Process measures, in general, are developed by a stakeholders team. Such development takes advantage of collective wisdom and fosters process ownership. It also facilitates alignment with other project measures, such as schedule and cost objectives. Process measurement tools can be electronic, such as a manager's spreadsheet for tracking project status, or paper, using a simple sign-off form. Clearly, assessment tools need to be tailored to fit the organizational culture and existing management systems. Buy-in at all levels is also critical for success.

The following *principles* help guide the development of process measures.

➤ The design leader/engineer is responsible for assuring that safety FFUs have been written by the customer; i.e., treat safety FFUs like any other specification and reject as incomplete projects without them.

➤ Responsibility and accountability for completing safety design reviews are a joint responsibility. It is in the best interest of the design manager, construction manager, and customer to assure that these are conducted in a meaningful way. Joint sign-off following a review reduces finger pointing later.

➤ Walk-downs are often the last opportunity for the customer to make modifications and have the cost charged to the project, and they provide the project/construction manager the opportunity to close out a project with mutual agreement.

- Closing the books on a project may be contingent upon acceptance by the customer.
- Direct, open communication occurs when the leader for each phase of a project is responsible for verifying completion of preceding work, and when leaders have the right (and responsibility) to reject incomplete work without reprisal.

A project log is one example of a simple measurement tool; it can effectively show whether a safety through design process is being implemented. Logs that include safety activities enable managers and safety practitioners to quickly determine if safety FFUs were received, what design reviews were held, and whether walk-downs included plant maintenance personnel. Sign-off or right-to-reject accountability also drives action. Sponsors are more apt to include safety FFUs if they realize engineers will reject projects without them as having insufficient specification. Similarly, safety design reviews are more likely to occur when the engineers know their projects are being audited to verify completion of design reviews.

Including the plant safety practitioner in the project measurement process also has some distinct advantages. This individual is usually the 'customer' safety representative, and it is the customer, not the project engineer, who decides when and if a project has been successfully delivered. Joint accountability provides a strong incentive for the design and construction engineers to work closely with safety personnel throughout installation to avoid missing delivery dates. It also requires the plant safety practitioner to be an active partner and participant in the project and precludes subsequent finger pointing for safety deficiencies.

ASSESSING ENGINEERING PERFORMANCE

Engineering managers are primarily interested in assessing design performance at two levels. First, they need to know how individual engineers and designers are performing so that they can provide fair performance appraisals. Process measures enable safety to be incorporated into the performance appraisal process for design professionals, and safety should be an important part of their performance evaluation, just as it is for production leaders. Second, managers often benchmark with other engineering organizations, and design performance needs to be assessed for comparison purposes.

Three types of measures are suggested to managers for assessing how well a design professional is performing with respect to safety. First, a manager can check the project logs to see whether design reviews and other safety activities have been completed. These can be supplemented with review and walk-down notes to assess the quality of these events, as well as the quality of the preparatory work. Second, the number of safety modifications performed after start-up is a very clear indicator of how thoroughly safety was considered in design. (Some modern management information systems may enable an analyst to tie costs of post-installation safety modifications back to the project.) Finally, subjective feedback can be gathered directly from production and maintenance workers and leaders. Users can be asked to rate the safety of the system after it has stabilized. This feedback is useful in targeting certain aspects of design, such as maintainability, ergonomic performance, and ease of use. The results also help identify training needs for engineers and designers.

In addition to assessing performance for subordinates and peers, engineering leaders and safety professionals frequently need to respond to the following questions:

- ➤ Are we delivering safer designs?
- ➤ How do we compare with our competitors?
- ➤ What aspects of the design safety process most need improvement?

Finding the answers to these questions requires benchmarking the overall process against history and with similar engineering organizations. Table 13-B lists representative questions that can be used by engineering managers for benchmarking.

VALIDATING PROCESS VALUE

Although the company and its engineering managers have not attempted to quantify the value of its safety through design process, the writer suggests two approaches for readers interested in demonstrating the value of their process. First, link incident investigation data with capital project records, including both near-miss and accidental loss experience. If this can be accomplished, then

Table 13-B. Sample Questions for Benchmarking.

➤ What percentage of design engineers view safety as a post-design consideration?

➤ What project cost overruns were attributed to correcting safety hazards? How many dollars per year?

➤ How many engineers have design safety goals in their performance objectives?

➤ What rewards exist for designers who produce safe designs?

➤ What processes are in place for providing feedback to design engineers on field modifications to their designs for safety reasons?

➤ How many hours of training do engineers receive annually on safety related aspects of design?

➤ How have the average number of safety punch list items changed over time?

➤ What percentage of projects were delayed or missed the scheduled start-up date due to work required to correct safety hazards?

➤ When designing systems for foreign operations, what standards and guidelines are followed when local standards are weak or non-existent?

➤ What safety requirements are included in contracts for engineering services? Generic safety specifications? Training and proficiency requirements?

➤ How are external engineering service providers held accountable for safety design deficiencies; i.e., who absorbs the costs?

an incident profile can be developed for each major capital project. Projects with significant deficiencies in design or installation will often be the site of multiple incidents within the first year or two, assuming a high level of worker interaction with the process. Incident experience on start-up operations should improve following implementation of an effective safety through design process. Unfortunately, loss experience data is retrospective, but nonetheless it provides a bottom line measure.

Second, study the first year or two of maintenance records on capital equipment. Incidents, near-misses, and hazard recognition all prompt work orders for correcting design and installation deficiencies. Counting safety work orders provides a good indicator of process performance. In addition, it may be possible to quantify part of the process value by comparing modification costs before and after process implementation. Similarly, start-up and debug time can be compared, as a good design process reduces the required number of field changes.

CHALLENGES TO PROCESS IMPLEMENTATION AND MAINTENANCE
CULTURE CHANGE
Implementing an effective safety through design process, as discussed in Chapter 3, often requires changing the culture within an engineering organization. At the company discussed in this chapter, the amount of change required and subsequent resistance varied widely among the engineering groups. It was recognized that if an organization had customarily addressed safety as an "add-on," then it could take several years to achieve full integration of safety in the design process. Tools such as upgraded checklists were needed, training had to be conducted and later refreshed, process measures had to be developed and implemented, and a few managers needed to be convinced of the value of the process.

It was anticipated that achieving a breakthrough performance in design safety would not be met with the same enthusiasm and recognition as a breakthrough in production or quality performance. This may be a reflection of the organization's safety culture, but it may also result from difficulty in quantifying the value of incidents that don't occur.

PERCEIVED REDUCTION IN DESIGN PRODUCTIVITY
Another hurdle was the perception among engineers and their managers that safety training and reviews increase design time. Engineering managers have to pay for time spent in training and reviews, and there often appears to be no immediate payback. Administrative time is also required to coordinate these activities and to handle the associated documentation.

Resistance to process measures was expected if they were perceived as bureaucratic or time consuming. To reduce this resistance, engineering representatives were not involved in measure development. The adopted tools were simple project safety logs that documented receipt of FFUs, participation in design reviews, and completion of walk-downs. More sophisticated tools may be introduced later as the process matures.

Finally, it was challenging getting some engineers to perceive safety as part of the solution and not as a burdensome distraction. Those engineers tended to approach design as a problem solving exercise with one clear objective: production.

OUTSOURCING OF ENGINEERING DESIGN SERVICES

Like many modern manufacturing firms, the company decided to out-source much of its design work to external engineering firms, thereby reducing "fixed" costs. A reduced engineering staff was maintained to oversee design, and to manage projects, with the detailed design work contracted out. Several core groups of engineers were retained to design process elements that were sensitive, proprietary, or highly complex.

Outsourcing can frustrate efforts to achieve safety through design in several ways. Lack of access and experience place an outsider at a disadvantage when designing production equipment. Off-site engineers do not have quick and easy access to either the production facility or its employees. Without this access, operational subtleties get overlooked that can directly affect the adequacy of a design. This results in retrofitting and a negative reception by floor workers. Both production and maintenance workers often have their own FFUs that can only be understood by direct communication. In addition, company employees tend to be better informed about previous incidents, including their causes and corrective actions. External engineers are generally not privy to these experiences and repeat design errors, unaware that modifications were made to similar systems to address a design deficiency.

Management structures of outside engineering service providers can also challenge the safe design process. Engineering firms have relatively little incentive to provide extensive safety training for their professionals, since training time is generally not billable. Inadequate training is often most evident in design deficiencies related to ergonomics; most engineering schools do not include ergonomic fundamentals in their required design curricula. Unfortunately, the customer assumes some liability if he tries to provide safety "training." As a result, it can be difficult for the safety practitioner or engineering project manager to receive a high level of safety performance in design.

Improving safety in externally developed designs is exacerbated by customer inability to measure performance and provide feedback in a timely manner; i.e., in time to affect the provider's design process. By the time safety problems surface, the customer often has little recourse as the engineering contractor has been paid and is now working on a new project. In addition, the customer is often powerless to affect the performance appraisals of individual design professionals, once project installation is complete. Project managers may choose to ignore the problem and avoid a confrontation, rather than risk tainting an otherwise positive business relationship. This inaction is itself a reflection of the safety culture.

Raise the safety banner too high for an outside engineering firm, and the immediate response is likely to be increased cost. Liability is a major concern of design companies. Close scrutiny of designs for safety deficiencies can have a chilling effect, not unlike the patient who informs the doctor prior to surgery that they will sue if the procedure is unsuccessful. The external firm may increase their charges to cover time for carefully reviewing all standards, even when the designer's experience would not require such reviews. In addition, guards tend to be over-built and redundant systems added, even though the application does not warrant such add-ons. Such additions can result in equipment with poor maintainability and operating reliability. Sometimes the safety process gets unfairly blamed for the negative operating performance.

Finally, the move toward outsourcing has typically resulted in external design of material handling, packaging, and other non-proprietary systems. These same types of processes often have the largest amount of human interface in the production process, and incident risk is largely a function of human exposure.

Outsourcing tends to place design responsibility for some of the systems most likely to cause incidents or injury, in the hands of an external service provider. This is especially evident when trying to build systems that are both ergonomically sound and maintainable, two traditionally weak aspects of design for many design firms. Interestingly, design lawsuits are not prevalent in general industry for either of these important deficiencies.

GLOBALIZATION

Another recent trend has been the rapid globalization of trade. Like many other companies, this manufacturer has opened and acquired operations outside the United States, requiring it to learn and adapt to unfamiliar cultures. Globalization places new demands on engineering organizations, requiring adherence to unfamiliar standards and engineering practices. Although globalization itself does not threaten the existence of a safety through design process, it does complicate the picture.

The proliferation of international design standards requires engineers to learn and work with unfamiliar design parameters. In addition, some countries have adopted stringent codes of practice, such as those required for CE certification, and standard design procedures. These practices mandate the exercise of due diligence and a process for considering safety in design. This can be a positive move from the perspective of the safety professional, but it also adds complexity to efforts in North America to implement a design process. The appropriate strategy is to design a basic process for integrating safety that is flexible enough to be used around the globe. The process described above seems to work well in this regard.

Numerous other differences also affect the entire engineering process. Training and process measures sometimes have to be adapted to account for differences in language, business culture, and divergent levels of education. Developing countries are especially challenging, as risk-taking behavior tends to be more prevalent. In some third world countries, maintenance tools are unavailable, as are reliable sources of power. Even body dimensions deviate substantially from North Americans. Careful design work plays an even bigger role in preventing incidents in developing nations, since the local workforce often lacks the necessary resources and skill to modify equipment. It can also be extremely difficult to train workers to avoid hazards due to cultural norms. The increased reliance on design safety has a positive side, however, it helps drive the overall safety through design process. In a few instances, it has also been counterproductive, as the risk taking norms of another culture have rubbed off on designers.

ORGANIZATIONAL CHANGE

Today's business world is filled with rapid change, including personnel realignments, reorganizations, downsizing, outsourcing, and acquisitions. A particular concern with such personnel changes is the loss of experience and associated understanding of why designs were modified. When leaders and players change frequently, it becomes more difficult for an organization to establish stable management processes. Safety through design is a management process that requires some stability to implement. Champions and drivers are needed to lead a change in the design culture, and it is difficult to convince engineers to follow a new process when their leadership is in a state of flux. Those engineering organizations that have been successful in implementing a safety through design process have benefited from champions whose positions were viewed as stable, and who had the power to push the process.

CASE STUDY. INSTALLATION OF A ROOFING LINE

Note: This case study is hypothetical and draws on multiple experiences for the purpose of illustration. Any similarity between this discussion and a particular project is unintentional and coincidental.

BACKGROUND

Most single family homes in North America have roofs made of asphalt shingles laid over a wood deck. The most common shingle, called a "three-tab," is 36 inches long and 12 inches wide. A basic shingle consists of a fiberglass or cellulose mat, a coating of asphalt based sealant, a layer of granules on the exposed surface, and a layer of sand "back-dust" on the underneath side. Shingles are sold in bundles weighing between

68 and 94 lbs, with three bundles providing enough shingles to cover 100 square feet of roof area, or 1 "square."

Roofing plants tend to be relatively small, operating with less than 20 people per shift per production line. Transportation costs restrict how far the product can be economically shipped, hence the small plant size. Most shingle lines are highly automated, with much of the equipment made by a single vendor who specializes in equipment for roofing manufacturers.

The process for manufacturing shingles begins with a large continuous roll of mat that is placed in an unwind stand. Mat rolls are typically the width of three to five shingles, or 3 to 5 feet across, and 0.5 mile or more in length. Mat is pulled off the unwind stand by a set of pinch rolls. It passes through a vertical accumulator or dry looper, then through a dip tank filled with hot asphalt based sealant. The coated strip passes through an applicator section where granules and back-dust are applied to the top and bottom, respectively. The roofing strip then winds up and down through a vertical "cooling section" which cools the material, along a second accumulator or finished looper, and on to the shingle machine. The shingle machine uses a rotary cutter to notch and cut shingles to length. Finished shingles are then automatically separated and stacked by an automatic catching and stacking machine. Bundles of shingles are dropped by the auto-stacker onto a conveyor that transports them to a wrapping system. The automatic wrapper applies either a paper or plastic wrapper around each bundle, and the completed bundles move to a palletizer where they are automatically stacked for shipment. Line speeds are approximately 400 feet per minute.

In this case study, engineering support is provided by one plant engineer, and corporate staff representatives. Major project work is managed almost entirely by corporate staff, relying heavily on external engineering firms for the detailed design effort. This arrangement is typical among the roofing manufacturers with multiple plants.

PROJECT DESCRIPTION

ABC Roofing had a plant with an existing three-wide line that it wanted to expand. A new four-wide line was to be installed adjacent to the existing line, and because business was good, the ABC did not want to shut down the three-

wide line during construction. The project included expansion of the existing building, installing a new granule handling system capable of supporting both lines, expansion of the asphalt melting and distribution system to service both lines, and installation of an entirely new production line.

Because the scope of the project was very large, a corporate project manager divided the design work among the following teams:
- Plant and Utilities;
- Mat Handling and Preparation;
- Coating, including asphalt and granule support and application systems;
- Cooling and Cutting; and
- Stacking and Packaging.

Engineers from ABC's corporate office led the Coating and Cooling and Cutting teams. The Plant and Utilities team was led by a large construction contractor, who had been awarded an Engineer/Procure/Construct (EPC) contract. The remaining two teams were led and staffed by an engineering contractor, with limited technical support provided by ABC, and the equipment supplier.

Installation was managed by an ABC construction manager, with the actual work performed by subcontractors. The plant was responsible for FFU development, production coordination, and local support.

FITNESS FOR USE CRITERIA

The plant engineer and members of the plant management team developed FFUs to specify requirements for production capacity and quality. The engineer also set up a meeting to develop safety FFUs, and included the production leader, the maintenance leader, the plant safety leader (safety along with other responsibilities), and a member of ABC's Corporate Health and Safety staff. The goal was to highlight requirements that would be unusual or beyond the expectations of contractors unfamiliar with the manufacturing process. The following is a sample of the output from that meeting.
- Noise levels in mat and coater areas are not to exceed 82 dBA.
- Elevated motors and drives shall be mounted such that they can be lifted by a forklift for servicing, or provisions shall be made for removing them without the use of portable cranes.

- Local disconnects shall be installed adjacent to each piece of electrical equipment to facilitate lockout.
- Steps and hand-holds shall be provided to assist workers during mat thread-up.
- Conveyors through the packaging area shall be at 36 inches to facilitate manual jam clearing and bundle removal/replacement.
- Guarding shall be in accordance with ABC internal guarding specifications, which meet or exceed OSHA requirements.
- A positive locking mechanism shall be provided for the dry looper carriage (to enable employees to block the carriage in the raised position without having to worry about it falling in event of a sudden loss of air pressure).
- The shutter on an in-line radiation gage (used to measure thickness of coated mat) must fail safe in the closed position, and also be interlocked, to prevent inadvertent exposure to maintenance personnel in event of power loss.
- The control system for the asphalt melt system shall alarm in the event that temperatures exceed specifications, or if fluid levels fall below a specified point.
- Lighting levels at the coater and shingle machine will exceed 30 foot-candles. Light levels at the wrapper shall exceed 70 foot-candles.
- Emergency stops for the line shall be installed in accordance with the ABC Roofing Emergency Stop Control Standard.
- A fume hood shall be installed over the coater and ventilation provided such that operator exposure levels do not exceed 10% of the OSHA limits.
- Waste water shall be handled such that bacteria growth does not pose a health threat.
- Service outlets in areas that could become wet (including all outlets in the coater area) shall have ground fault circuit interrupters.
- Asphalt charging station shall be equipped with splash guarding, as well as eyewash/shower stations.
- Conveyor corners and exposed equipment mounts will be protected from forklift contact by cement filled posts.
- Piping systems for asphalt, natural gas, water, and air would be color coded in accordance with ABC's corporate standard.

Following the design FFU meeting, the plant engineer met with the construction manager, the plant safety leader, and the corporate safety professional to discuss constructibility FFUs. A few of these FFUs are as follows:

- Electrical tie-ins will be performed during a weekend with the assistance of plant electricians.
- No loads will be hoisted over the existing 3-wide line during operation.
- Construction access routes will be established and maintained such that there must be no interference with production forklift traffic.
- Due to space constraints, the looping towers and coater must be installed prior to receiving the cutter and wrapper. This will prevent blockage of exits by staged equipment.

DESIGN REVIEWS

Individual designers and engineers occasionally met with ABC safety practitioners and the plant engineer throughout the design phase. Several modifications were made to improve the safety and maintainability of the system. After completing about 90% of its design work, each team called a meeting to conduct a formal design safety review. A total of seven design reviews were held, including separate reviews of the electrical control systems and the asphalt system. Some of the items from these reviews follow.

- Access platforms needed for servicing drives on top of the dry and finished loopers.
- Locations of emergency stop buttons discussed and agreed upon.
- Sloping the floor under the finished looper and installing a gutter would greatly facilitate cleanup.
- The location of a blower fan would be moved to outside of the building. (This would dramatically reduce ambient noise levels.)
- Strategically locating a control panel to protect it from forklift traffic would also enable one operator to control equipment for both lines, thereby saving $100,000 per year in operating costs.
- Design of the shingle cutter platform must be changed to provide better access when changing cutters.
- Handholds are needed at the automatic stacker to allow the operator to support his torso weight when clearing jams.

➤ Addition of the new roof changes the flow of water into roof gutters; one is now undersized.

➤ Additional service outlets needed to support maintenance equipment at the palletizer.

- A positive means of blocking the valve gates on large granule bins needed to provide lockout and prevent a potential engulfment hazard.

- Guarding scheme for automatic stacker does not allow adequate access for jam clearing. Use of independently mounted light curtains would provide much better access *and* cost $1,000 less.

- Incompatible power source requirements (resulted from a lack of coordination between the machine vendor, ABC, and the design engineering firm).

WALK-DOWNS

Periodic inspections of the construction site were conducted informally throughout the construction and installation phase by the plant engineer, plant safety leader, plant manager, and a corporate safety & health professional. These visits resulted in numerous field modifications, such as the relocation of conduit to improve access, and switching the locations of buttons on a control panel to reduce the likelihood of operator error.

Two weeks prior to start-up, a team was assembled to conduct a thorough safety walk-down. The team was comprised of each team's design leader, the plant safety practitioner, representatives from the engineering contractor firms, two professionals from the corporate safety and health staff, two maintenance craftsmen, two production representatives, and the plant operations manager. Due to the size of the worksite and the complexity of the system, the team was split into two subteams each assigned to cover half of the line and adjacent systems.

The intent of the walk-down was to identify installation errors that could pose a hazard, and to follow-up on completion of the items identified in the design reviews. The following items were selected from the resulting punch lists:

➤ A load beam for servicing an elevated drive was never installed (despite identification in the design review).

➤ Orientation of the asphalt pump blocks a fire extinguisher.

➤ Emergency stop cable on conveyor section leading to wrapper does not work.

➤ Warning label missing from radiation gauge.

➤ Flow rate on eyewash station next to asphalt charging station is inadequate.

➤ Guard missing from chain and sprocket on coater.

➤ Exit sign above new pedestrian doorway damaged.

➤ Piping on mezzanine at top of coater presents a "head knocker."

➤ Toeboards missing from one granule system service platform.

➤ Additional steps and handholds needed to facilitate thread-up.

➤ Posture (long reach) and force required to remove guard from mat pull roll too stressful. (Decision made to hinge and counterbalance it.)

➤ Pipe out fittings on palletizer so guards do not need to be removed during lubrication.

➤ Insulation needed on asphalt distribution line to prevent burns.

➤ Lower the "disconnect" for the palletizer so short workers can reach it without stepping on a guard.

PERFORMANCE ASSESSMENT

Each design team maintained a simple log sheet. It contained the date on which the leader received the team=s copy of the FFUs, the date and signatures of design review participants, documentation of significant modifications, and signatures of walk-down participants. Completed logs were turned in to the project manager following the walk-downs and kept with the archived project documents.

Six months after start-up, the engineering director needed to prepare performance appraisals for two of the engineers assigned to the project. The project log sheets were pulled and it was noted that one of the engineers had failed to attend a design review, even though this individual played a critical role in the design. The engineering director then contacted the plant and asked the operations manager, safety leader, and maintenance leader to fill out a simple subjective survey. From this survey, it was learned that the plant was delighted with the performance of line, but that maintainability continued to be a problem on the granule system. Several safety related, work orders had been written for that system, including requests for additional lighting and truck grounding straps at the loading station, and rework of a service platform. The engineer responsible for the granule loading station design was the same individual who had failed to attend the Coating team's design safety review. In the annual performance assessment, the manager highlighted these deficiencies, and made safety one of this individual's top three improvement objectives for the following year.

SUMMARY

All incidents involve the transfer of energy or exposure to a hazardous agent, so a straightforward incident prevention strategy is to design for complete energy control. If this is not feasible, then strategies need to be implemented to minimize damage and exposure in the event of an unexpected release.

This chapter presents one proven method for integrating safety into design. It uses safety focused events during the project scoping, design and construction phases. All relevant forms of energy/agents are systematically considered during each of these events in order to adequately plan for complete hazard control.

Process measures help drive the safe design process. They are also necessary for assessing both individual and process performance, and for demonstrating the value of the process.

A big challenge for the safety professional and engineering manager is changing the design culture; for example, from one where safety is viewed as a costly add-on, to a culture where safety is fully integrated and is seen as a strategic advantage. This is made even more challenging by today's environment of outsourcing, globalization, and rapidly changing organizational structures.

Manufacturing companies seeking operational excellence must implement a safety through design process to prevent injuries, avoid process upsets, and minimize loss. Hazard avoidance through design is usually more effective, and in the long run cheaper, than continuously training and disciplining employees. This fundamental principle rings true across all of general industry.

REFERENCES

1. Haddon WJ Jr: The prevention of accidents. *Preventive Medicine.* Boston: Little, Brown, 1966.

2. Owens Corning: Integrating Safety into Design. (Revised unpublished internal training manual.) Toledo, 1998.

Chapter 14

APPLICATION IN THE AUTOMOTIVE INDUSTRY

by Michael J. Douglas

OBJECTIVE

The first portion of this chapter covers the history of safety through design of manufacturing equipment and systems at two of the major automotive manufacturers, Daimler-Chrysler and General Motors. The remainder of the chapter focuses on the **safety by design** process within General Motors. (Note that the term "safety by design" is a General Motors' term. In order to avoid confusion, hereafter the term "safety through design" will be substituted for General Motors' terminology.) While the process described is specific to General Motors, it is expected that the strategy and execution would work within any structure or organization.

INTRODUCTION

Safety through design has been an objective of the major automotive manufacturers for the past two decades. They all have recognized that one of the major keys to an effective safety and health process requires the application of health and safety guidelines, principles and requirements.

Each manufacturer may use different terminology or has a different process into which they have incorporated safety through design, but the goal is the same. The outcome of that goal is manufacturing equipment and systems that are designed to reduce the risk of injury and illness before the first production part is made.

From a historical perspective this section will present an overview of Daimler-Chrysler's process and General Motor's safety through design process.

DAIMLER-CHRYSLER'S SAFETY THROUGH DESIGN PROCESS

Midway through the 1980s, the now Daimler-Chrysler began a vast retooling and facility modernization program. Simultaneous to Daimler-Chrysler's activities the robotic industry under the auspices of the Robotic Industry Association began the development and ultimate issuance of a standard entitled ANSI/RIA 15.06 - 1986 for Industrial Robots and Robot Systems - Safety Requirements.

Using this robot safety standard as a minimum, and their own detailed understanding of their robotic production process, Daimler-Chrysler developed a series of "Mandatory Technical Instructions (MTIs)." These internal standards incorporate best practice safety requirements specific to Daimler-Chrysler applications. The MTIs were written in a user-friendly manner that was meaningful to all users regardless of the process application.

The Daimler-Chrysler Technical Group, wrote supporting tool design standards. These standards allowed for a uniform implementation of the MTIs into the up-front process development. In addition, personnel were assigned from the Process Engineering, Control and Mechanical Design, Tool Follow-up and Launch activities to accomplish their design-in engineering goals. Their task and shared goal was, and continues to be, to provide a high level of safety in all Daimler-Chrysler facilities and manufacturing systems.

GENERAL MOTORS' SAFETY THROUGH DESIGN PROCESS

Designing-in safety into a manufacturing system in General Motors has been an entity since the late

1970s. The concept of reducing the potential for injuries by engineering the hazards out of new manufacturing equipment was certainly not new. However, in the past many safety systems were in place, but required extensive activity by the user that made it more difficult for them to perform the task. This, based on human nature, could have resulted in bypassing of safety systems which, in turn, would have resulted in an increased level of hazardous exposure. An example of where this can occur in the design phase is in the location of lockout devices. If a process requires that the equipment is locked out before performing a specific task, and the lockout device is not placed in a convenient location, based on human nature, it may not be used. This is especially prevalent if the task only takes a few moments to perform and it takes the same or more time to perform the lockout requirements.

Another past issue, dealt with older safety systems that were designed to keep people out of the operation during the automatic cycle. Little safety effort was directed at the service personnel who maintained the equipment. A case in point is, in the past, many gate and guard interlocks, throughout industry, were included in the emergency stop circuits. Therefore, if the gate interlock was part of the emergency stop circuit a maintenance person could not operate the equipment in the manual or teach mode, with the gate open, unless they bypassed the safety interlock. This made it difficult to perform the task and could send a message that it was acceptable to bypass safety devices. Often this bypass device was not removed upon completion of the job, and could lead to an exposure of the next person or operator. By understanding what tasks the maintenance personnel had to perform it became apparent the safety interlocks needed to only stop and prevent reinitiation of the automatic operation. This allows the maintenance person to operate the equipment in a manual mode, without the need to bypass any safety devices.

Within General Motors there was no common centrally coordinated effort in the engineering or safety communities to support a safety through design process. Individual plant locations developed their own requirements and processes to try and accomplish these goals. Some were very successful while others were less effective. One of the main reasons for success was the support received from their plant management, UAW and the local engineering community.

The main theme of the 1986 General Motors annual Joint Health & Safety Conference was safety through design. The conference was attended by all: General Motors plant managers, personnel directors, union presidents, shop chairpersons, and the management and union health and safety teams. The conference energized the attendees on the whys, the hows, and the benefits of a safety through design process. As a revitalized joint UAW-GM cooperative effort, there was more synergy around the involvement of the local joint health and safety committees in the design process, with support being provided by the UAW/GM Center for Health & Safety.

Unfortunately, one of the key stakeholders, the engineering community, was not at the conference. As a result, safety devices were frequently added to the equipment after it was built. This resulted in the joint health and safety committees spending their time and efforts trying to make a piece of equipment safe, either at the build shops or after it arrived in the plant. The problem with this philosophy was the equipment was either suboptimized, or it was harder for the operator and maintenance employees to perform the required tasks, in a safe fashion. This led to potential situations where safety devices could have been compromised or simply removed for the sake of obtaining production quotas (throughput) and to perform the required tasks.

Throughout the remainder of the 1980s and 1990s, contract language concerning involvement of the UAW/GM health and safety process at the equipment build and design phases became part of the national agreements. New health and safety programs and requirements continued to be developed and massive training programs were conducted to help reduce injuries and illnesses in our plants. Once again, however, a significant partner in the process, the engineering community, was not involved and they continued to have little or no understanding of safety through design or its potential benefits.

In the early and mid 1990s, as competition in the automobile industry became more fierce and the need for lean and more flexible equipment grew, engineers were forced to closely examine and seize every opportunity to increase equipment throughput, reliability and to simultaneously reduce cost. During this same period of time Health and Safety within General Motors underwent a significant change, which captured the dedicated attention and recommitment of the Presidents Council. Immediately following this recommitment to the safety of all General Motors employees, the Presidents Council rededicated the entire corporation to a safety mission that included two safety absolutes; "Safety is the overriding priority" and "All accidents can be prevented".

The safety support by the Presidents Council continued with very visible support for a new design-in safety process to include moving the entire corporation to undergo a cultural change about the way General Motors handled the safety of our people. Through this process the safety through design process was born which is lead by a corporate engineering function also known as Engineering for Health and Safety. As the safety through design process grew it partnered with the UAW and linked into each division, launching a rapid development of a design specification, and a process that included, safety design reviews, risk assessments and validations. Now a common goal is shared in General Motors with a global perspective to design-in safety into all of our new manufacturing equipment and systems.

GENERAL MOTORS' ENGINEERING FOR HEALTH AND SAFETY

The Engineering for Health & Safety (EHS) activity provides leadership and framework in the development of common internal standards and processes. Content experts from the electrical controls, mechanical, process, manufacturing, safety, and UAW-GM Center for Health & Safety communities are leveraged to provide resources and input into the continuous improvement of the Design for Health and Safety Specifications (DHS) and safety through design processes.

As the EHS team matured, the first significant outcome was the development of North America Common Design for Health and Safety Specification (DHS). This area was chosen as the starting point due to a myriad of new product programs, which contemplated massive capital expenditures. The group began the specification development by gathering all the pertinent health and safety standards from all sources within General Motors and outside such as the OSHA regulations and ANSI standards. DHS contains health and safety principles, processes, guidelines and requirements for the design and redesign of manufacturing equipment and systems at General Motors. DHS applies but is not limited to robots, CNC machines, transfer machines, conveyor units and systems, spray booths, ovens, and all related process systems.

While developing the specifications, data gathered to support the need for specific requirements make the specifications more readily accepted by the entire engineering community and easier to cost justify if it involves an additional expense to a project. One incident that occurred during the development of the safety standard dramatically highlighted why the use of data is so important. It involved a newly installed robot cell that was using scarce sheet metal pilot parts. The tradesperson needed to remove the pilot part from the robot's end effector. He was concerned that if it dropped damage to the part would occur. To prevent potential damage, he asked another tradesperson to hold the part while he opened the gripper using the robot teach pendant. Through a set of unfortunate circumstances, the robot ended up being put back into the automatic cycle. When the tradesperson reactivated the robot, instead of opening the gripper it resumed its interrupted cycle causing the part to rotate 90 degrees and continue on its path to the next operation. The tradesperson holding the sheet metal part received a deep laceration from mid-chest extending across and down his left arm.

At the time of the incident the procedure in place to prevent this type of incident was, the robot servo power should have been locked out and the part should have been removed manually. While there were many root causes identified that led to this incident, one of the major causes was that the control design de-energized the robot gripper when the robot servo disconnect was locked out. This prevented the tradespeople from being able to perform the operation of releasing the part from the gripper without a great deal of effort. It forced them to choose between a lockout requirement, and then manual activation of valves, or to simply enter the open gripper command on the robot "teach" pendant. They incorrectly decided to leave the power on and entered the "open gripper" command. This exposed them to the hazard of robot motion. As a result of this near tragic incident, robot servo disconnects were rewired to only de-energize servo power and not robot end of arm tooling. This, of course, was added to DHS. This incident in part gave rise to the development of the task-based risk assessment process.

Task-based risk assessment became the methodology that identified the tasks, hazards and paired them together which could then give rise to hazard control measures for incorporation into the GM equipment and DHS. User groups, consisting of skilled trades personnel and engineering from over twenty different plant operations, were brought in to review DHS at various stages of its development and to help identify tasks performed on the equipment and hazards they were exposed to. As a result of these efforts and others a comprehensive "Design for Health and Safety Specification" was completed in March 1998.

The importance of developing an internal common specification cannot be overstated. A perfect example of where DHS has had a major financial benefit is the development of common fencing for robot and automatic stations. Before the advent of DHS, each plant had the responsibility of deciding what type of safety fencing to build or purchase. This led to a proliferation of types, structures, attachments, and strengths. By engineering a common fence that provided all the strength and structural requirements for compliance to OHSA regulations and ANSI standards, the corporation was able to trim the cost of a fence for a typical four (4) robot cell from approximately $10,000 to $3,000 and provide the same level of safety. Multiplying $7,000 by the number of cells in a typical new body shop the savings quickly accrued to the six-figure range. In addition, with the flexibility of the fence design, installation costs dropped almost in half.

Using DHS will result in substantial cost savings and reduce the incidences of injuries and illnesses by eliminating the variables in manufacturing equipment and safety systems that can, in themselves, cause injury. One of the other major advantages of DHS is when a problem does occur it is easier to implement corrective action on common systems than on uncommon systems. In addition, common components

reduce inventory and maintenance costs. The list of benefits from DHS goes on and on.

Another important component, both in the DHS development and the safety through design process, is the inclusion of union personnel knowledgeable with the equipment and systems the specification is meant to address. Their involvement is critical to ensure DHS includes appropriate and workable safeguarding devices and technology. It also helps reduce the "not invented here" syndrome, which can create difficulties in the acceptance and use. While it is not possible to include everyone in the organization, most people will accept something if they feel a representative cross section of their peers were involved in the development.

As mentioned previously, concurrent with the development of DHS and based on the lessons learned from its development, an effort was undertaken to develop the common task based risk assessment process for use within all of General Motors. The task based risk assessment (TaBRA) that was developed has proven to be a valuable tool in identifying hazards associated with specific tasks and recommending solutions to eliminate or control exposure hazards in General Motors. It is termed "task based" to differentiate the process from other traditional risk assessments which primarily focus on hazards alone. It has also helped identify inefficiencies in our new and existing equipment that caused not only potential exposure to hazards but reduced the operational effectiveness, throughput and maintainability of the equipment.

In brief, the TaBRA is conducted using a cross section of participants including operators, skilled trades and engineers who actually work on the equipment being assessed. A brainstorming technique is used to first identify all tasks performed on the equipment and then all the hazards to which personnel are exposed during the performance of each task. Each resultant task/hazard combination is evaluated and a recommended solution is identified based on the level of risk.

Through the leadership of the Engineering for Health and Safety department and UAW/GM Center for Health and Safety, with a full understanding that "Safety is the Overriding Priority", the direction has been set to use a safety through design process in conjunction with DHS that

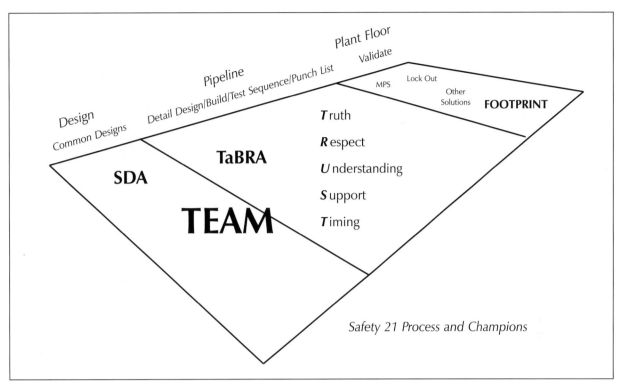

Figure 14-1. Consider your favorite team sport.

begins at the inception of a new manufacturing design and closes with validating the process on the plant floor. The following sports diagram is an analogy that can assist in introducing the contents of DHS (Figure 14-1).

Team: The members of the team represent the people for whom this specification was written. They are engineers, operators, skilled trades, suppliers and all supporting departments and functions within your organization.

Field/Arena: The team members play in the industrial setting over the Manufacturing Life Cycle (Sections 1 & 2) of equipment and systems and work within the requirements and guidelines contained in this specification.

Referee: The safety through design process (a.k.a.: Safety 21 Process) is the administrator of DHS as outlined in Section 2 of the document. This process describes the boundaries or the governing principles for machinery and equipment safety.

Strategy/Play Book: The team members will contribute by fulfilling their roles by designing, implementing and validating safety systems as outlined in Sections 4 through 12 of the document.

Coach: The Safety 21 Champions serve as the coaches of your favorite sport. These individuals

will interact and take action where behavior and/or conditions warrant their involvement and support.

DHS is a jointly developed specification between the UAW and GM that contains health and safety principles, processes, guidelines, and requirements for the design and redesign of manufacturing equipment and systems throughout its manufacturing life cycle. DHS is organized into three segments as follows:

1) fundamental principles
2) human interface applications
3) specific hardware applications

GENERAL MOTORS' SAFETY THROUGH DESIGN PROCESS (A.K.A.: SAFETY 21 PROCESS)

DEFINITION AND PURPOSE

General Motors' Safety 21 (Safety for the 21st Century) process ensures a common approach for designing-in "best practice" safety systems into new manufacturing equipment designs and retrofit s of existing equipment and systems. General Motor's safety through design process is known internally as the Safety 21 process. Increased involvement in the design-in safety

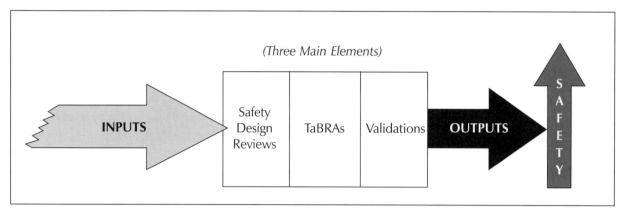

Figure 14-2. Safety 21 Process.

activity up-front in the manufacturing life cycle of new equipment will improve the safety systems in a cost-effective manner and reduce the need for costly, time consuming retrofits.

SAFETY 21 PROCESS

Figure 14-2 displays a macro view of the Safety 21 Process. The three main elements that comprise the process are Safety Design Reviews (SDRs), Task based Risk Assessments (TaBRAs), and Validation. The process incorporates all efforts involved in Design-In Safety that many people are familiar with such as: Failure Mode Effects Analysis, Safety Run-offs, and Safety Sign-off Tag Procedures.

Each main activity has three phases: preparation, action, and closure. For both the preparation and closure phases, deliverables must be achieved. Inputs for the Safety 21 process are the new manufacturing equipment designs that are to be built and installed to support the many new product programs within General Motors. By progressing through the Safety 21 process, outputs are new manufacturing equipment designs that will:

1) Be safer to operate
2) Be safer to maintain
3) Incorporate the latest common, "best practices" safety features
4) Reduce injuries and illnesses
5) Increase manufacturing throughput

The Safety 21 Process synchronizes safety and engineering deliverables to the Fast Vehicle Development Process, the 4 Phase Product Development Process, or any other type of manufacturing tracking system. However, the best approach to understand each activity of the Safety 21 process, is to view the manufacturing life cycle of new equipment (from inception to production release) through the three major manufacturing stages; New Design, Pipeline, and Plant Floor. New Design begins at conception through selection for the supplier. The Pipeline starts at the selection of the supplier through the delivery of the equipment to the plant. The Plant Floor begins when the equipment arrives at its end destination through decommissioning.

New Design is the stage manufacturing engineering determines the level of design content and requirements for the Tool Specification Bid Package or Statement of Requirements. Prior to the supplier quoting, the first Safety Design Review, SDR1, needs to be conducted. After the supplier bids are received, an extension of this review may occur if an alternative design approach (sometimes referred to as "free expression") is considered.

The Pipeline stage begins after the chosen supplier is identified to finalize the design of the new manufacturing equipment. Prior to building and integrating the new equipment, two important activities must take place: 1) a second Safety Design Review, SDR2, is completed on the detailed tool drawings, and 2) a Task Based Risk Assessment, TaBRA. After the supplier builds and integrates the new equipment, a third Safety Design Review, SDR3, takes place and is the official safety buy-off before the equipment is dismantled and sent to the appropriate GM facility.

In the Plant Floor stage, three major activities take place, which are: Install & Debug the manufacturing equipment/system, validation, and release to production. Depending upon the

GM location, each activity can overlap each other to support the new program production launch schedule. As the new manufacturing equipment is being installed and debugged, at the appropriate time, validation begins. As each piece of new manufacturing equipment has "passed" validation, it is incrementally released to the production organization.

SDA Tool

The Safety Design Analysis (SDA) tool is a deliverable that must be completed prior to conducting any Safety Design Review. The SDA tool can be completed in paper form or by using a computer database. The same tool is used at each of the three Safety Design Reviews but the level of completion increases as the new equipment proceeds from concept to production. The tool is much more than a checklist, because it requires the engineer(s) to document the safety system in detail and identify variances to common, "best practice" designs. Normally, the manufacturing and electrical control engineers work together to complete the SDA tool.

The SDA tool is formatted to accomplish a few important objectives for any new manufacturing equipment. First, it lists and cross-references the design-in safety principles and requirements per the NA Common Design for Health and Safety Specification (DHS) that must be considered. Second, it provides from the lessons learned database (from previous SDAs & TaBRAs), common, "best practice" safety designs for each principle and requirement. Third, it documents all variances to common, "best practice" safety designs that will be the basis for the respective Safety Design Review. Fourth and final, it thoroughly documents the safety efforts by each engineering discipline.

Safety Design Review 1 – Pre-Award (SDR 1)

This formal gate review occurs after the SDA tool is completed on a new manufacturing equipment design and before the purchasing organization requests a vendor quote. An extension of this review may occur after the quotes are reviewed if an alternative design approach (sometimes referred to as "free expression") is considered. In this instance, the SDA tool is revisited and used to analyze the alternative design approach.

Safety Design Review 2 – Detailed Design (SDR 2)

This formal gate review occurs after the design supplier is selected and the SDA tool is completed during the detailed tool design phase.

Task-Based Risk Assessment (TaBRA)

A "New Equipment" Task-Based Risk Assessment (TaBRA) is a joint activity conducted on a new manufacturing equipment design that has proceeded through Safety Design Reviews 1 through 2 and is near the end of the engineering design phase. This TaBRA must be conducted prior to the Supplier Builds Equipment phase to minimize changes after build.

One main objective of conducting this TaBRA is to allow plant personnel who will eventually operate and maintain the "new equipment" an opportunity to provide valuable input into the safety systems of the new manufacturing design. To generate the synergy needed for the TaBRA a team consisting of engineers (e.g., controls, process, and manufacturing), plant hourly personnel (production and maintenance) along with the Local Joint Health and Safety are assembled at the supplier's location and are facilitated through the assessment by the Safety 21 Champion. A TaBRA will always be successful because of the involvement of talented and experienced people who operate, maintain, design, and build the systems. The team members will uncover the deep underlying realities and document recommended actions that will enhance the safety and productivity of the entire system.

A TaBRA is a systematic method for evaluating all tasks and their associated hazards and capturing recommended solutions to protect personnel from potential injury. The TaBRA consists of five elements as shown in Figure 14-3.

During this phase, the supplier builds the new manufacturing equipment from the finalized process and tool drawings. These drawings will have incorporated all the appropriate design-in safety features per the results of the previous Safety Design Reviews and the "New Equipment" TaBRA.

Safety Design Review 3 - (SDR 3)

This formal gate review normally occurs during equipment run-off prior to dismantling the man-

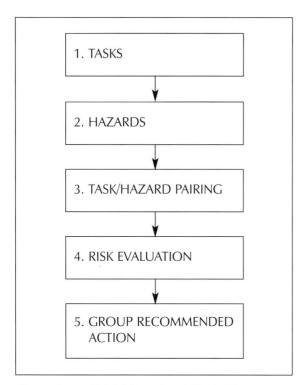

Figure 14-3. TaBRA Functional Block Diagram.

ufacturing equipment and shipping it to its intended destination. The SDA tool completed from SDR 3 is used as a basis for verifying content of the various design-in safety features.

Install and Debug

This activity refers to efforts by local skilled trades and engineering, and contracted installers after the manufacturing equipment has arrived from the supplier.

Validation

The validation process is conducted in order to verify that the key safety recommendations as documented in the TaBRA are met. The validation shall be successfully completed before the equipment is released to the production organization.

The validation process consists of two stages and shall begin after the equipment is installed in the plant and the safety system is debugged. Stage 1 Validations are to be performed by an approved third party. Local plant personnel will perform stage 2 Validations.

Production

The term "production" refers to the daily operation of equipment to build product. Generally, new equipment arriving at its destination will remain at that location for the remainder of its manufacturing life cycle. The term "equipment removal" refers to removing equipment from production for retrofit purposes (which could renew its manufacturing life cycle) or scrapping after it has exhausted its useful life.

DHS & LESSON LEARNED DATABASE (FROM SDAS AND TABRAS)

The application of common, best safety practices for new manufacturing equipment designs are essential to the Safety 21 Process. DHS and the Lessons Learned Database (from SDAs and TaBRAs) are the instruments to access throughout any stage of the Safety 21 Process to accomplish this objective. These two resources are periodically updated to reflect the latest common "best practice" design-in safety methods identified throughout General Motors.

GATE REVIEWS FOR THE SAFETY 21 PROCESS

Each gate review has deliverables in three categories: **preparation, action,** and **closure**. All deliverables discussed at each gate focus on timing, performance and quality as described below.

1. **Timing** - Gate reviews must be fast and flexible for synchronizing the Safety 21 process to any existing product or vehicle development process.

2. **Performance** - Deliverables are the focus during all Gate Reviews.

3. **Quality** - Reliability and consistency of the gate deliverables are reviewed based on the Safety 21 Process. The SDA is the mechanism to activity track and improve the quality of the overall Safety 21 Process.

APPLIED PRACTICES

Design-in safety through the safety through design process is best illustrated using real world examples and illustrations. The following examples are based on the GMNA Car Group.

The first step in applying both DHS and the safety through design process outlined in earlier sections of this chapter is to update engineers on any changes DHS since their last project. Through the use of actual examples they will be informed how the changes will affect their new equipment design. To properly conduct this type of update, the Safety 21 Champion must be cognizant of the engineer's current knowledge level and the previous programs they have worked on. The update can then be tailored to the specific audience.

For engineers new to the corporation or unfamiliar with the concepts of health and safety, an eight-hour introductory course is a company requirement. This course includes the philosophy behind the General Motors safety through design process, understanding the issues associated with the maintainability of equipment, and a review of DHS. The course is interspersed with practical application exercises drawn from actual cases. With this course as a prerequisite, a training effort is developed targeting the safety requirements specific for that program. Here again, actual layouts and designs for that system are used as practical exercises so that the participants can learn and apply the concepts directly to their work tasks.

At the New Design stage of the new product program, it is required that the preliminary designs and processes be the basis of SDR1 to guarantee the inclusion of all applicable safety requirements. This is a macro level review. It does not look at details rather it is focused on verifying that the appropriate safety concepts are included. For example, the review would verify that system controls include the cost for control reliable circuitry and safety devices. The type of device and placement comes later in the Pipeline stage. It was at this review level in the China program that the need for a substantial amount of additional safeguarding was uncovered. This was also the time where it was found that safety control circuitry for a future U.S. program, as was discussed earlier, did not include the need for control reliable implementation. This is the stage of the manufacture of new product programs that the Safety 21 Champions need to be first involved. As can be seen by just these two examples, their inclusion is crucial to the program's success.

During the Pipeline stage, a joint management and union team is selected and appointed to follow the design, build and installation phases of the equipment. This team is from the plant location that will be receiving the product program. The team normally consists of the Safety 21 Champions and various engineering and union representatives. It is the primary function of the team to work with design houses, manu-

facturing engineers, control engineers and plant production and maintenance representatives to achieve all of the program requirements.

It is at the SDR2 that the equipment is reviewed cell by cell and as a total system. It is important that all equipment be shown on these layouts. Physical items such as safe electrical working clearance, maintenance access, walkways, aisle widths, ANSI/RIA 15.06 robot clearance, location of all energy sources and a variety of other issues are defined and incorporated into the design. It is a lot less expensive to move equipment on paper than once it is built and installed on the floor. Decisions on the types and locations of safeguarding devices for operator and maintenance personnel are also determined. The team is also responsible for the completion of the task-based risk assessment process. This identifies the tasks and hazards associated with the design. The team compiles any task-based risk assessments performed on similar existing equipment. In addition, they research any incident and/or injury data and for existing hazard control measures. This information is reviewed in the aggregate with the design group to identify opportunities for safety, maintainability, and equipment reliability improvements that meet or exceed the overall program requirements.

Perhaps the best way to illustrate the application of the SDR2 and TaBRA is to take a sample robot cell and review some of the issues involved. Figure 14-4 is an illustration of a typical four-robot cell with an operator subassembly shared envelope workstation on an automated monorail system (AMS). The process sequence is as follows:

➤ When a station clear signal is given to the waiting AMS carrier, it travels into the tool station, drops down into position and is clamped;

➤ Robot R1 picks up a completed subassembly from the subassembly tool station and places it into the main tool tray;

➤ The part is then automatically clamped;

➤ Robots R2, R3 and R4 complete their spot welding sequences and then return to their home positions;

➤ The completed assembly is then unclamped and the AMS carrier raises to the "up" position and moves to the next station;

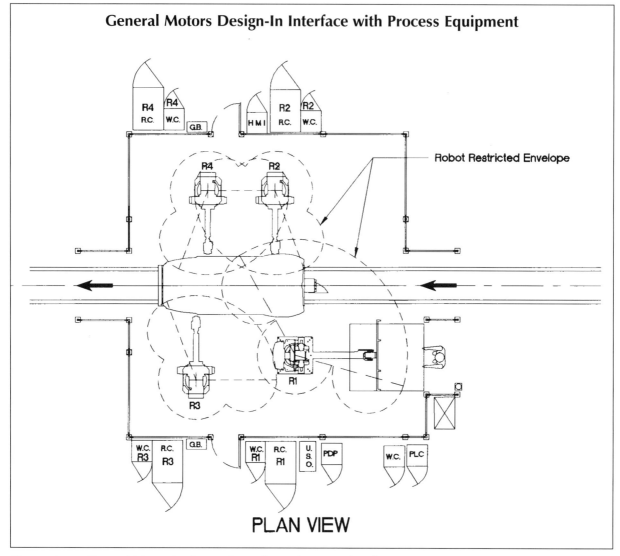

Figure 14-4. General Motors' safety and guarding robotic work cell.

➤ While this is taking place, robot R1 goes to a mid position between the main tool tray and the subassembly tool to wait for the operator to load the subassembly parts and press cycle start;

➤ Once the operator has loaded the subassembly parts, they initiate a "cycle start" signal;

➤ Robot R1 comes into the subassembly tool and performs its spot welding sequence;

➤ When R1 completes its sequence, it sends a sequence complete signal; and

➤ The cycle repeats once all indicators signal "station clear."

Through the use of SDR2 and TaBRA, the appropriate safeguards can be applied. In the example process, emphasis will be placed to utilize DHS and applicable standards (e.g.:

ANSI/RIA 15.06-Robot Safety Standard) and some suggested solutions to reduce the exposure to the identified hazards. The reader should be aware that the suggested solutions listed here are only examples and other methods of safeguarding that reduce the exposures to the hazards may be used based on user preference. Figure 14-5 shows the suggested safeguarding devices installed within our example process.

The standard referenced is the current ANSI/RIA 15.06-Robot Safety Standard.

➤ Clearance requirements requires 18-inch clearance from the restricted envelope to any obstructions not supporting the robot function (not including the point of operation) where teaching occurs inside of the cell at speeds greater than 250 mm/second.

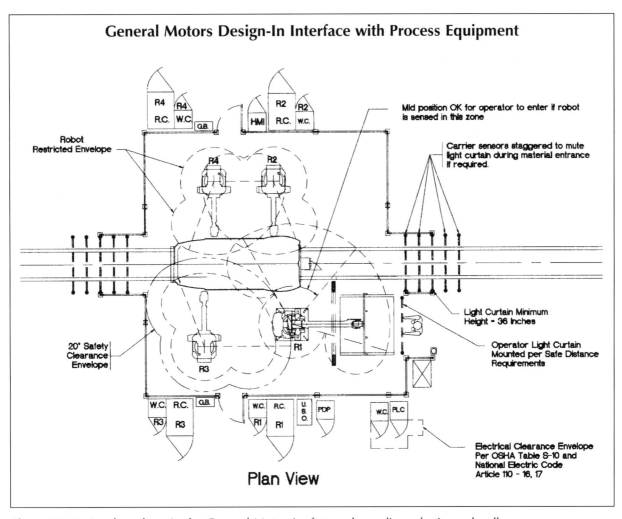

General Motors Design-In Interface with Process Equipment

Robot Restricted Envelope

Mid position OK for operator to enter if robot is sensed in this zone

Carrier sensors staggered to mute light curtain during material entrance if required.

Light Curtain Minimum Height = 36 Inches

20° Safety Clearance Envelope

Operator Light Curtain Mounted per Safe Distance Requirements

Electrical Clearance Envelope Per OSHA Table S-10 and National Electric Code Article 110 - 16, 17

Plan View

Figure 14-5. Another phase in the General Motors' safety and guarding robotic work cell.

Teaching is an activity performed using a pendant control device (teach pendant) to move the robot from point to point which creates its program path. After creating the program path, the teach pendant is used to replay the program path in sections or in its entirety. If teach speeds are 250 mm/second or less, the 18 inches is predicated on the operating envelope. For the sample robot cell, teach speeds are greater than 250 mm/second. Therefore, in this sample robot cell, clearance to the fences must be 18 inches. The key to reducing the required floor space, which is at a premium, is to restrict the robot envelope as close to the operating envelope as possible. This can be accomplished through a variety of means such as hard stops, light curtains, cam switches, and other control reliable devices.

→ The operator cannot share at the same time the same space as a robot. This requires a robot and operator location sensing system that will stop all hazardous motion if an unsafe situation does occur. A potential solution is to provide a control reliable switching circuit to sense that robot R1 is somewhere between its mid way position and the main tool tray. An operator light curtain, placed at a safe distance from any point of operation hazards outside the robot's restricted envelope, will sense the intrusion of a person into the shared space. If the robot enters the shared space while an operator's presence is sensed, or the operator enters while the robot is present, the operation goes into an emergency stop condition. Note: if you can stand between the light curtain and the tool, additional protection to continually sense presence must be installed.

➤ Prevent entry into the cell from the operator station. In most cases, the tool itself should prevent entry. If this is not the case, additional hard guarding needs to be provided.

➤ Prevent entry into the cell at the AMS entrance and exit. Light curtains or hard guarding needs to be placed at the entrance and exit. If there is the potential of someone walking into the safeguarded area with the carrier during the light curtain muted condition, safety mats, or some other horizontally mounted sensing device, needs to be added.

➤ Guarding of pinch points during clamping and closing of the spot welding gun on the robot. Placement of the operator light curtain, per the safe distance requirements of OSHA and the manufacturer, will provide this protection.

➤ Entry for maintenance tasks. These need to be identified through a TaBRA and safeguards installed to provide protection from the task/hazard combinations, or controlled through mandated safeguarding. Examples would include enabling devices for additional personnel inside the cell when drive power is "on" lockout per OSHA 1910.147, or other appropriate safeguards. It is important for the reader to understand they should not rely on just administrative controls such as lockout. In most cases, to troubleshoot equipment, power needs to be energized. It is up to the employer to provide safeguarding in these circumstances.

During SDR2, the SDA tool mentioned in the previous section is used as a guideline and template to verify common and consistent application of safety requirements.

As the reader is aware, no matter how inclusive a standard is, there are always items or issues that are either not covered or are unique to an individual set of circumstances. These are not problems, but should be viewed as opportunities for improvement. Issues that arise, that are not already included in DHS or existing specifications need to be captured by the SDA tool, resolved through a TaBRA, and update the lessons learned database.

The importance of involvement of the Safety 21 Champions at SDR1, SDR2, and TaBRA cannot be overstated. Once the preliminary designs are completed, this becomes the package that the equipment builder quotes on and builds the equipment to. Any changes to the design from this point forward are increasingly expensive. This is also an area where a builder can (and in some cases expects to) achieve a higher profit margin. In the past, before the safety through design process, most safety issues were raised and resolved at the build phase before shipment to the plant. This often resulted in "safety" being viewed as an inhibitor to the process, being labeled as the "ones" causing cost overruns, delaying equipment delivery and causing program start up delays. In addition, this has often led to equipment coming into the plant that did not comply with safety standards. This once again resulted in further costs and delays to achieve compliance to the safety requirements. Success at SDR1, SDR2, and TaBRA requires the support of engineering and manufacturing leadership.

The next step involves the actual equipment build phase and integration of the equipment components into a system. From a managerial health and safety perspective, the only issues that should have to be dealt with are the functional and installation requirements of the safeguarding devices. Most issues involve such things as the placement of the safety devices at the safe distance from the hazard, or redesigning a guard that does not adequately protect the hazard. This could result in some minor rearrangements or adjustments, but not be the cause of any major program delay or cost element. The team, at this point, becomes more of a resource to the machine builder and manufacturing engineer.

The team should visit the build location at the start of the build process to ensure the machine builder has an understanding of the safety requirements and to reinforce that the machine builder will be held accountable for implementation. One or two additional visits during the build process, proceeding the final buy-off, will help prevent any major problems from arising at the SDR3. The team, at this point, should begin to work on preparations for equipment installation at the plant location. This often involves reviewing existing equipment that needs to be relocated or rebuilt to accommodate the new program. The review is to ensure compliance with applicable standards.

Another key component of the safety through design process is to ensure a safe and efficient start-up of the new product program. This component is facilitated through the SDR3 (a.k.a.: safety buyoff). At this review the same SDA tool is used to verify that all the design requirements are incorporated and are functional. The machine builder and the General Motor's manufacturing engineer complete the SDA tool. The team uses the completed SDA tool as an audit document. The use of the SDA tool is once again crucial to insuring the inclusion of all the various safety requirements. No matter how good or competent the team may be, without the SDA tool as a guide-post, items will be missed or overlooked. As humans, we respond and are attentive to those issues we have the most interest in and knowledge of. The SDA tool helps eliminate this bias.

Once the equipment has received its final buyoff, through SDR3, it is disassembled and shipped to the receiving plant location. It is then unloaded, reassembled and placed in its final location. Before the equipment is energized for debugging purposes, it needs to be inspected to verify its proper location. Occasionally, items not previously noted on the design layout are discovered, such as a building or support column for other equipment. These in turn can cause clearance problems requiring further rearrangements. It also is an opportunity to verify that all safeguarding devices have been reassembled and installed so that all hazards are protected. Once again, the earlier in the process that problems are found the earlier they can be rectified.

Once the skilled trades have debugged the equipment and before turning the equipment over to production, validation stages 1 and 2 take place. The TaBRA results and SDA tool are used to verify that all safety systems and components are installed and functioning as intended.

Lessons learned at the design, build, and installation phases provide input into DHS and the technical memory database.

SUMMARY

Each corporation is at a different stage of understanding the need for and the incorporation of a safety through design process in manufacturing. Hopefully, readers have understood the main themes and seen that a safety through design process is not only possible to implement within their organization, but is absolutely critical to the success of safety efforts and the competitiveness of an organization's bottom line. To some it may seem that it would be a lot of work to develop, implement, and integrate a process within their organization. Some would argue that if they have an experienced safety staff there is no need for a formal process. The problem with this argument is people change, companies change, and it is extremely difficult to outline your process when it is not formalized. The day an OSHA inspector, or a lawyer during a lawsuit, asks the tough questions on what was done to the equipment to ensure its safety, it is too late to decide that a formal process does indeed make sense.

Chapter 15

APPLICATION IN AIRCRAFT MANUFACTURING

by John M. Thaler

INTRODUCTION

An insight into the safety-related challenges that employers face in the building of aircraft and air-craft components is provided in this chapter. The integration of safety into the manufacturing design and implementation phases of new products and the modification of existing processes, when feasible, have resulted in improved injury and illness rates, productivity gains and heightened quality. Those words are music to the ears of manufacturing managers, who for many years have considered safety as an extra, nice to have, but not necessarily a tool to improve the bottom line.

It is the intent to show how one aircraft manu-facturing company is proving these prophetic statements through the partnership of design and manufacturing engineering, safety, manufacturing, facilities/maintenance and other support organiza-tions. Over the years aircraft manufacturers have made great strides in designing safeguards into the products and manufacturing processes. However injury rates continue to be less than acceptable because of inherent risks built into the past designs. When it comes to safety in the aircraft industry, designing for safety has become synony-mous with designing for ergonomics.

Aircraft companies have spent many years taking care of the workplace conditions that were causing injuries. Machine guarding, improved housekeeping and other safety and health related initiatives have reduced injuries and illnesses from processes that were causing these incidents. That does not mean that other sources of injury are not present in the workplace, only that they no longer make up the majority of injuries. Most air-craft manufacturers would agree that ergonomic related incidents make up as much as 40% to 60% of their OSHA recordable entries and perhaps as much as 50% of their workers' compensation costs. Injuries resulting from awkward posture or position, repetitive manual material handling, the application of force, such as from torqueing oper-ations, the continued use of hand tools and those illnesses normally associated with repetitive trau-ma would be included in the definition of ergonomic related.

WHOSE JOB IS THIS ANYWAY?

In previous years it has not been a traditional role of an engineer to consider the safety and health of the workers in the design and manufacturing of aircraft components. Customer requirements such as cost, schedule and quality have been the lead-ing drivers in design considerations. The success of any company's safety program relies on the people responsible for providing direction and guidance to senior management to find ways to integrate safety into the core business processes. That means getting into the front end of the plan-ning stages for new products. Engineers need to adopt ergonomic principles in their designs.

They need to be aware that a human being is at the end of the design cycle and that the deci-sions made on the drawing board will ultimately impact the person who has to physically make the final product of those designs. Figure 15-1 identi-fies the leading activities that result in injury and illness.

With this in mind, it is essential that a trend analysis be developed that pinpoints the root cause of a company's injuries and illnesses and that a strategic plan be formulated as to how to

185

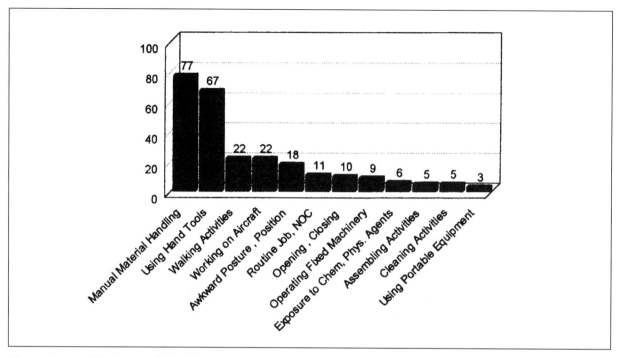

Figure 15–1. OSHA recordables by activity in an aircraft manufacturing company.

combat these drivers. Aircraft manufacturers find that a large percent of their incidents stem from the difficult positions and postures that the workforce must contort themselves into in order to get the job done.

Companies that change the product line often or modify existing products may be able to continually incorporate good ergonomic principles into their designs. However, this is a rare opportunity for an aircraft company. New products are long in the design stage and even longer on the manufacturing floor.

Once the product designs are completed, the employees will live with that design for a long time and, as the product approaches the end of its life cycle, it will be even harder to justify changes in the design. Other injury causes include the misapplication of hand tools, inadequate work instructions and less than adequate fixtures for the placement and removal of parts and equipment. All of these activities should be of concern to the manufacturing engineer or organization responsible for developing the work practices and policies. The following considerations should be applied by the manufacturing engineer when producing a new fixture or work instruction.

➤ Avoid repetition by building dynamics into the job. Consider multiple tasks for the oper-

ator to allow stressed muscle groups to recover between tasks.

➤ The forces necessary to assemble products need to be reduced through the use of holding fixtures, mechanical assists and other devices.

➤ Impacts to soft tissue must be avoided.

➤ Provide space for material to be placed a maximum 16 to 18 inches in front of the operator.

➤ Provide tiltable storage bins or shallow bins so those employees do not have to reach behind or bend over to retrieve parts. Materials should be placed at heights between the waist and shoulders of the operators.

➤ Keep controls within the neutral position so that the operator does not have to use excessive reach where the arm or forearm is elevated in a forward reach position for extended periods or when repetitive adjustments are required.

➤ Gages, visual displays, and other control devices should be placed such that employees do not need to constantly bend their necks to read the controls.

The study of ergonomics has shown that jobs requiring the following repetitive tasks will likely result in muscle fatigue, reduced productivity, and result in injury to the hands, wrists, elbows, shoulders, and backs:

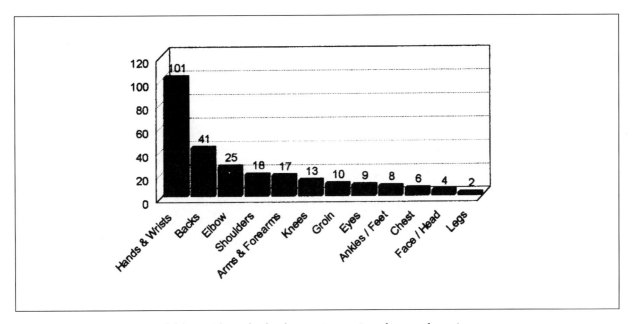

Figure 15–2. OSHA recordable incidents by body part in an aircraft manufacturing company.

→ Bending over;

→ Twisting or turning the upper torso;

→ Raising arms over the head;

→ Twisting or flexing of the hands, wrists;

→ Repetition;

→ Exposure to vibration; and

→ Forceful exertion.

Other considerations include the size and weight of the object to be carried or grasped, the frequency of the task, the operator's position (sitting or standing) and the workstation design.

Let's take a look at the top drivers (Figure 15-2) to determine what design activities might be helpful in reducing the occurrence of cumulative trauma.

HANDS AND WRISTS

Some of the common occupational injuries to the hands and wrists that are associated with cumulative trauma include carpal tunnel syndrome, tendonitis, and DeQuervain's disease. Symptoms such as numbness, tingling and burning sensation of the fingers, pain, loss of grip strength, swelling and tenderness of the hand, wrist, and forearm are common.

Cumulative trauma to the hands and wrists may be caused by the repetitive motion associated with flexing and extending the wrists (back and forth) or deviating the wrists from side to side while grasping, turning or applying other forces.

In electronic shops for instance, the use of manual crimpers, cutters, fasteners screwdrivers, and other small hand tools have resulted in cumulative trauma. The automation of many of these tasks and the use of counterbalanced and adjustable equipment and workstations has alleviated much of the problem.

Other actions such as applying direct pressure on the palms or other delicate parts of the hands from small hand tools with sharp edges, exposure to vibration from pneumatic tools and exposure to low temperatures such as the discharge air from pneumatic tools can result in cumulative trauma disorders.

Considerations should be given by the engineering designer to modify tasks in order to reduce the frequency, reorient the tool (bend the tool, not the hand) or the work, by way of a rotatable jig or other device to reduce the need to bend the wrists into awkward positions. Tasks should be designed to keep the wrists in a neutral position. Use a holding fixture to reduce the force needed to complete the task, raise or lower the work station or redesign the product to eliminate or minimize undesirable tasks. Tool grips should be small enough to fit in the palm of the hand and sharp edges need to be padded to reduce the pressure on the palm of the hand. Cylindrical grips should be approximately 1.5ö in diameter to account for the diverse workforce. In addition, replacing the trigger with a dead man switch that requires the use of all four fingers or the whole palm to activate the tool may reduce trigger forces.

BACKS

Chronic low back pain continues to be a leading cause of workers' compensation costs. Repetitive loading or unloading, twisting, or bending while lifting, and using awkward body postures due to the shape or placement of the object to be lifted, or the layout of the work area can result in back injuries. Design engineers must give consideration to the following:

- ➤ Frequency of lift;
- ➤ Weight and shape of packaging;
- ➤ Distance materials are carried; and
- ➤ Height of material at loading and unloading stations.

Materials should be held close to the body while being carried. Carrying distances should be kept short, weights minimized and load/unload stations maintained at about knuckle height. Any of these problems can be minimized by the following:

- ➤ Hoists;
- ➤ Carts;
- ➤ Scissors lifts;
- ➤ Rollers;
- ➤ Counterbalancing equipment;
- ➤ Jib cranes; and
- ➤ Tiltable containers and other material handling devices.

ELBOWS/SHOULDERS

Cumulative trauma to the elbows and shoulders can result in injuries such as tenosynovitis, arthritis, bursitis, and rotator cuff tendonitis. These injuries are the result of repetitive flexion and extension of the shoulders (arms straight out in front and straight back) and side to side motions as well as elbow flexion (bent at 90 degrees) and extension (straight down). They normally occur when employees are required to reach behind for parts while seated or while reaching above eye level to adjust controls or activate equipment.

Changing the workplace orientation can minimize these stresses. In order to reduce extension of the arms and elbows, change the position of the controls, such as hand controls at waist level rather than at eye level. Provide clamps or fixtures to allow work to be rotated or secured in place. Provide arm and wrists support for sedentary operations and remove sharp edges from worktables and raise or lower the height of the workstation as needed. Workstation designs should allow the operator to work in a neutral position requiring the work to be completed between the waist and eye level if possible.

WHERE DO WE BEGIN?

DEVELOPING A POLICY ON THE ASPECTS OF SAFETY THROUGH DESIGN

The first step in any successful program is the development of a strategy that includes the creation of a policy or procedure. This document must clearly identify the purpose and scope, who is responsible for what and when. The following is a sample policy that identifies the roles and responsibilities of key personnel within an organization.

LINE MANAGEMENT

Responsible for insuring that the infrastructure has been established to carry out this policy and that responsibility has been clearly assigned. The policy is carried out by communicating support of safety through design guidelines to all employees and by periodically reviewing the progress of this program with responsible personnel.

DESIGN AND MANUFACTURING ENGINEERING

Responsible for actively participating in safety through design training programs and initiating and utilizing safety design practices applicable to their assigned area of responsibility consulting with medical and safety practitioners as needed to insure compliance with these guidelines. Assure through self-audits and by evaluating corrective action that personnel involved in the design, procurement, installation and repair of tools, equipment, workstations, machinery and other processes consider and incorporate good safety through design principles into new and existing operations.

SAFETY PRACTITIONERS

Identify and evaluate manufacturing processes that have been responsible for creating injury or illness or have the potential risk of creating injury/illness in the workplace. Coordinate, in concert with engineering personnel, applicable training programs for management, safety through design team members and affected employees. Develop a system to monitor employee injury trends and employee complaints related to tasks resulting in workplace injury.

MEDICAL PERSONNEL OR COMPANY/ CONTRACT PHYSICIANS

Identify at-risk operations based on employees who have sustained injuries or who exhibit early signs/symptoms of disorders attributed to cumulative trauma. Develop protocols for personal protective equipment that may be useful in the early treatment of, or prevention of work-related injuries or illness. Also, assist in the evaluations of workplace processes and work environments. In concert with the line organization, assist in the placement of employees returning to work with medical restrictions as a result of their injury or illness.

LINE SUPERVISION

Responsible for communicating support for this procedure by participating in training programs, by advising employees of this procedure, and by alerting their management, medical and safety practitioners of work place hazards that are identified in their respective areas.

EMPLOYEES

Responsible for supporting this policy by actively participating in training and communication programs and team projects established to identify evaluate and control workplace health and safety hazards.

BUILDING AN INFRASTRUCTURE

This policy must insure that an infrastructure is put in place to carry out the intent of the policy. In other words don't put the cart before the horse. The last thing an employer wants is to create a general awareness of poor workplace conditions without the ability to solve the problems. This will only result in a frustrated workforce and a lack of enthusiasm to bring these conditions to the attention of management in the future. Better the employer establish a core group of individuals that are trained to assess the workplace conditions, that can develop sound and reasonable

solutions and are capable of implementing corrective action.

This team should consist of an inter-disciplinary group of employees from the manufacturing floor, manufacturing engineering, tooling, facility maintenance, industrial engineering, safety, and medical and human resources. This core team should be assigned the task of prioritizing projects, coordinating the assessment activities and assisting in the implementation of any corrective action.

In order to establish an effective team it is imperative that a means be provided to financially support the projects identified. Once this team has been established don't cut them off at the knees by leaving them defenseless to make the needed changes. If you are going to make them responsible for the work give them the authority and, when necessary, the dollars, to affect change. Research has shown that for every dollar spent on safety there is a four-dollar return on the investment.

TRAINING

This team will become the backbone of your program and they should receive the highest level of training. Once the team has been established you can begin to develop the awareness level in the workforce. The training required for the remaining workforce need not be extensive but provide them with enough detail so that they can assist in the identification of the workplace hazards.

DATA COLLECTION

Without data, you are just another person with an opinion and senior managers are likely to say that what gets measured, gets managed. In order to conduct a thorough analysis of the data you have to look in all the right places. OSHA records and workers compensation data would probably come to mind first. Medical reports and first aid records, employee complaints, safety inspections, safety audits, and internal safety related documents as well as external sources such as insurance reports and OSHA citations are very useful in finding out where the problems lie. Other sources including productivity data from the engineering organization, quality records showing defects, rework and scrap rates should be added to this list.

CAPTURE THE TALENT

The employees know more about designing for safety than you may think. Just ask them what hurts and why. You'll not only find out where the problems are but the employee is just as likely to tell you how to fix it. After all, the employees have been living with and thinking about his or her work environment for a long time.

They are eager to improve their work areas and with some awareness level training and empowerment, your workforce will be able to identify those processes that have caused or are likely to cause injury or illness. Given the opportunity, many of these same employees will make great team members. In addition, your workforce is highly creative and given some direction; they can also help produce your awareness campaign. In the writer's company, empowered teams conduct job safety analyses, develop posters and safety campaigns, assist in the assessment of machine guards and participate in the identification and control of ergonomic hazards.

HOW MUCH WILL THIS COST?

For any newly instituted program to be successful you need to have some quick wins. When starting out take on some small projects that don't take a lot of design time and can be completed quickly and with little cost. The satisfaction that the team will receive for these successes and the reinforcement your employees will gain by their participation will keep your program energized. The following case study describes one such quick win that took a team less than three weeks to complete.

CASE STUDY

A bench-work ergonomics team was assessing a job where employees were polishing the entire surface of a part using a hand-polishing tool. Several employees complained of sore wrists and there had been a diagnosis of carpal tunnel syndrome. A quick review of the manufacturing work instruction indicated that only small sections of the part actually needed to be polished. Upon further investigation it was determined that over the years employees had decided the part looked better completely polished rather than follow the work instruction. Employees were reinstructed on which area of the part needed to be polished. Subsequently employees were no

longer experiencing pain and the job was performed in less than half the time. This team determined that reviewing the operation sheet was important in several other processes as well and eventually took pictures of the parts and inscribed arrows depicting those areas that needed to be polished. The only cost associated with this project was the time spent by the team investigating the process.

Approaches vary between companies on how they justify the expenditure of capital and expense dollars related to their businesses. The costs for safety related improvements should be similar. Some companies will bear the costs associated with safety-related improvements based on the moral need, "because it's the right thing to do." Others may look for a return on investment, a payback. Companies may require that payback on capital projects not exceed one to three years. Calculation of a simple cost/benefit analysis that you can use to justify the costs of your improvements will be discussed later.

The first rule of thumb is, that whenever possible, design in safety at the front end of the operation to avoid the more costly retrofitting that may be necessary to improve an unsafe process after the fact. Make sure that you include sufficient language in your policy requiring the consideration of safety through design at the time of development or purchase. If you uncover a piece of equipment or process that is already in service and causing or is likely to cause injury or illness, it is important to make the case for corrective action. Start by using the data that was discussed earlier in the chapter. Find out what the present operating costs are associated with the equipment. What are the current production rates for this job?

Once you collect all of the pertinent data, you're ready to calculate a simple cost justification model (Figure 15-3). The recurring expenses and savings listed may vary. Check with your finance or accounting department.

PROVE IT

Taking an interdisciplinary approach to designing for safety has been discussed. The following examples demonstrate the power of this approach.

EXAMPLE 1. AIRCRAFT DOOR CELL

Prior to the redesigning of this process, aircraft doors were assembled and trimmed in a

Recurring Expenses / Savings

CATEGORY	$ COST	$ SAVINGS
Labor Costs		
Hourly		
Supervision		
Other Salaries		
Safety Related Costs		
Workers' Comp		
Medical		
Indemnity		
Equipment		
PPE		
Other		
Cost of Quality		
Rework		
Scrap		
Tools		
Supplies		
Utilities		
Environmental Costs		
Waste Disposal		
Storage and Handling		
Training		
Other		
Total Costs / Savings		
Annual Costs / Savings		

Figure 15–3. Cost-Benefit Worksheet.

cramped, congested area. Housekeeping was poor and there had been several back sprains and other abrasion/contusion type injuries associated with this process that had been documented in the past. Tracking of the scrap and rework had determined that the work process needed to be improved. The process was also determined to be time consuming and manual material handling intensive.

The manufacturing engineer responsible for the area had been trained in basic ergonomic concepts and had undergone more specialized training in "Design for Ergonomics." After discussing the manufacturing process with the employees and after collecting injury-related data from the safety department, the engineer decided to establish a baseline before beginning the redesign of the work area. The engineer identified the production rate, quality indicators, injury rates and workers compensation costs. In addition, it was recognized that the work required employees to leave the area several times to work on parts of the door that resulted in delays and redundant material handling efforts. Employees also needed to sort through boxes for small parts and excessive reaching was required during benchwork activities.

The employees were required to hold the concave doors with one hand while drilling with the other. Not only did this result in lower back and shoulder/arm injuries but resulted in improperly drilled holes which needed to be reworked. Also, the employees manually lifted the 30 to 40 pound doors to shake out any chips left inside the doors after drilling.

The engineer believed that a manipulator with a universal holding device capable of being adjusted for the height and position of the work would reduce injuries as well as improve the production rates and cost of quality metrics. He designed the door cell around the manipulator. The benchtops were cut in half to reduce reaching and parts carousels were added to the tables to reduce the sorting required to find the fasteners and other small component parts. A surplus downdraft table was found and brought into the area to reduce the travel distances. The downdrafts were fitted with silencers to reduce ambient noise levels.

As with most safety through design projects, quality and productivity improvements were impressive. Under the old manufacturing process, the tracking of employee production hours and quality control was less than adequate. The cell-manufacturing concept established accountability and allowed for the correction of poor work habits through the retraining of the operators. Over the next two years the department realized a 63% reduction in OSHA recordable injuries and significant reductions in workers' compensation costs. In addition, a saving of 310 feet of travel distance per aircraft door was obtained taking some 10 miles out of the distance employees had to travel annually. The ability to work in an area that was redesigned and that considered the safety of employees resulted in a 33% reduction in production time per door. This equated to approximately a $200,000 annual savings for one door model alone! Similar savings were being realized for other aircraft models as well.

EXAMPLE 2. EXHAUST EXTENDER ASSEMBLY

Employees in a sheet metal fabrication department asked for the assistance of the local ergonomics team to improve an assembly operation. Three soft tissue injuries had occurred in the department that were directly attributed to the awkward posture and positions in which assemblers had to place themselves in order to drill and rivet the exhaust extenders. Each extender was secured to a permanent holding fixture during assembly which was not capable of being adjusted and they had to reach, kneel, stretch and bend over to position themselves in order to drill and rivet. Approximately 20 to 40 parts per month were needed for assembly. Rework and scrap was significant according to the manufacturing engineer due to miss-drilled holes and improperly installed rivets.

With the support of the senior manufacturing manager for the department, the ergonomic team decided to redesign the process. The manufacturing engineer determined that a manipulator could be used to hold the exhaust extender in place for assembly.

The manipulator was capable of being fully adjusted, allowing employees to work in a neutral position while riveting and drilling. An adjustable stool was also provided for the operator. The employees advised that muscle fatigue was eliminated and no further injuries were observed on this job. In addition, the team reported that set up time for each extender was immediately reduced and the scrap from the assembly process was virtually eliminated. According to the manufacturing engineer the assembly time was reduced by two hours per part. This resulted in labor savings alone of $2000 to $4000 dollars per month based on anticipated deliveries.

SUMMARY

In the past, industry tended to rely on safety practitioners to identify unsafe work practices and to develop corrective action. This resulted in less than acceptable improvements as the costs for retrofitting existing work processes was extensive and difficult to justify. In addition, the safety practitioner was seen as an interloper, questioning the designs and ownership of another engineer.

The future is now, and companies who have embraced safety through design are seeing their injury rates reduced, their productivity improved and the quality of their products enhanced. Doesn't it make sense then to train those most capable of affecting manufacturing changes and to take advantage of the expertise that resides in-house?

As an engineer, take up the banner in the protection of your company's most valuable asset, the highly skilled employee. The results will astound you. Once involved, you will see the value of designing safety into the front end of the process and the leading business indicators (cost, quality and schedule) will also improve.

In this global market economy we cannot afford to stand by and let our companies become less than competitive because of our inability to share our knowledge and assist our companies in meeting their bottom line.

Chapter 16

APPLICATION IN THE CHEMICAL INDUSTRY

by Dennis C. Hendershot

OBJECTIVES

This chapter will discuss tools and techniques for safety through design in the chemical process industry (CPI). The emphasis is on early consideration of safety, with the greatest potential for designing safety into a chemical plant or process occurring when the basic process chemistry and technology is determined. The selection of an "inherently safer" chemistry, avoiding the use of toxic, flammable, or unstable materials, energetic reactions, and extreme conditions, eliminates the need to design safety systems to manage these hazards when designing the chemical plant. However, it is not possible to eliminate all hazards from all chemical processes. The chemical process designer must understand and manage the risks associated with the remaining hazards. A hierarchy of risk management strategies will be discussed, as well as tools the chemical process designer can use to incorporate appropriate risk management and safety features into the plant design.

One of the by-products of the spectacular growth of the chemical industry since World War II has been an increase in the potential magnitude of occupational and environmental incidents from industrial operations. This can be attributed partly to the growth in total production of chemicals, as well as to an increased number of commercially manufactured chemicals. Another major contributor to the increased hazard is the increasing size of chemical plants. Globalization and competitive pressures have forced companies to take advantage of economies of scale by building very large, world-scale plants. The larger inventories of material and energy in these plants mean that, although the industry maintains an excellent safety record, there is an increased potential for serious incidents. Maintaining and further improving the chemical industry's safety record requires consideration of safety at all phases of the life cycle of a chemical process, from initial conception of the process chemistry, through process development, design, operation, shutdown, and decommissioning.

INTRODUCTION

UNIQUE CHARACTERISTICS OF THE CHEMICAL PROCESS INDUSTRIES

The chemical process industries (CPI) must deal with all of the hazards and safety concerns associated with industry in general—trips and falls, noise, ergonomics, and rotating and other moving equipment. In addition, the unique operations of the CPI give rise to other types of hazards. The CPI transforms matter from one form into another, either through physical operations such as distillation, crystallization and filtration, grinding and milling, or by chemical reactions. These operations may involve toxic, flammable, and reactive raw materials and intermediate compounds; processing may require elevated temperature or pressure; and large amounts of energy may be required for, or liberated by, the physical and chemical processes. Often, the characteristics or properties of a material that make it hazardous are the same as those that make it useful. For example, vinyl monomers such as styrene are used to make useful polymers for a wide range of applications such as paints, adhesives, binders, plastics, and water treatment resins. These monomers are useful for these applications because their controlled reaction (polymerization) allows us to create a huge variety of useful products. However, the same polymerization reaction liberates large amounts of energy, and it can be extremely dangerous if it occurs in an uncontrolled or unplanned fashion.

The term *process safety* refers to the understanding and management of those unique hazards associated with the physical and chemical processes practiced by the CPI. Process safety concerns include fires and explosions, unexpected chemical reactions, uncontrolled chemical reactions, and the acute and chronic toxicity hazards of materials. This discussion will focus on those safety issues unique to the CPI—on design for process safety.

LIFE CYCLE OF A CHEMICAL PROCESS

A chemical manufacturing process has a life cycle beginning with an initial product or process conception, most likely in a research laboratory, and continuing through process design, construction, plant operation, and finally to shutdown and dismantlement. Center for Chemical Process Safety (CCPS)[1] has divided this life cycle into eight phases as shown in the left column of Figure 16-1. The phases in the life cycle usually overlap and blend together, and the categorization of the phases could be done in other ways by combining or further subdividing those listed, but in general the life cycle will follow this pattern. For example, Bollinger et al[2] have simplified the categorization into the five phases shown in the right column of Figure 16-1.

OPPORTUNITIES FOR SAFETY IN DESIGN

When we talk about safety in design in the CPI, we are usually concerned with the early phases in the life cycle of the chemical process— research and development, conceptual design, and detailed engineering. However, it is never too late. A chemical process and plant evolves and changes through its operational lifetime. Process and equipment improvements, equipment replacement, and plant expansions offer opportunities for design engineers to improve safety through improved design of new or modified equipment in the plant. There are even opportunities in "designing" the decommissioning and demolition of a plant that is no longer needed— opportunities to improve the safety of the demolition process, and to ensure that there are no long term risks to safety, health, or the environment after the plant has been demolished.

However, the greatest opportunities to design a safe chemical process occur in the earliest stages of research and development—when the basic chemistry is selected. The research chemist should try to identify a chemical synthesis route, which avoids the use of flammable or toxic materials, unstable materials, high temperatures and pressures, highly corrosive materials, and highly energetic reactions.

With our present knowledge of chemistry, it is not possible to eliminate all hazards from the chemical synthesis route for many useful products. Indeed, it may never be possible to do this for many materials. The properties that make the material useful and valuable may also make it hazardous. For example, a noncombustible replacement for gasoline would not be very useful. Once a process chemistry has been selected, there are many options available to the chemical engineer for implementation of that chemistry on a commercial scale. Chemical reactions can be done in many different types of reactor. There are many different types of equipment for various physical operations such as distillation, filtration, separation, and extraction. Each type of equipment has a different set of hazards associated with it, and the engineer must consider safety aspects along with the other design requirements such as capital investment, operating cost, and product quality in selecting equipment.

Design safety opportunities continue through detailed design of the process equipment and layout, as the engineer works at a finer level of resolution on the plant design. Details matter in a chemical plant design—a poorly located $1/_2$ inch drain valve in a pipe containing a highly toxic material could cause a serious injury or fatality. This is why attention to safety has the greatest benefit early in the life cycle. If the chemist could have eliminated the need to use the highly toxic material, the design engineers would not have to be concerned about protecting people from exposure to the material in each of the hundreds of valves, pumps, flanges, instrument connections, and other potential leak points in the plant.

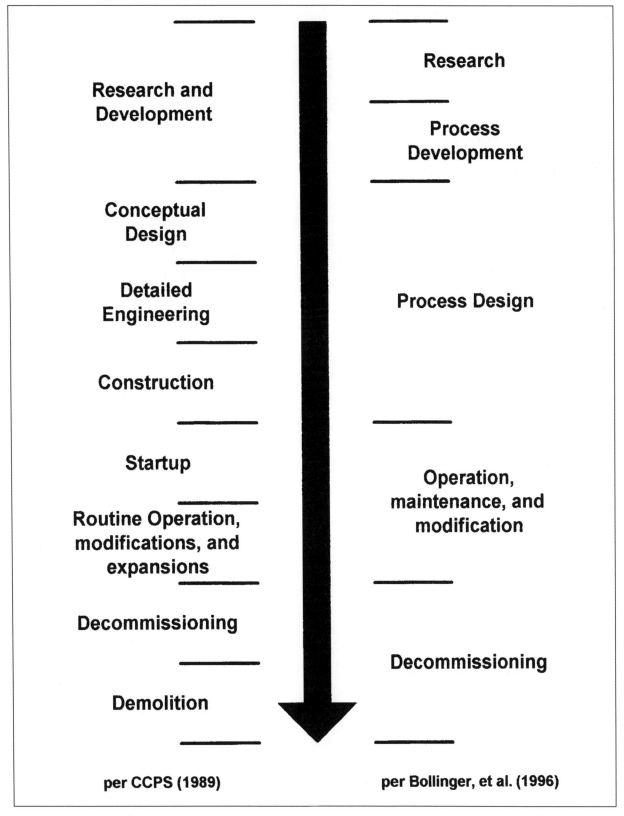

Figure 16–1. Typical phases in the life cycle of a chemical process and plant.

REVIEW OF BASIC CONCEPTS

DEFINITIONS

In Chapter 1, the following definitions were given:

- *Safety*—that state for which the risks are judged to be tolerable.
- *Hazard*—the potential for harm.
- *Risk*—a measure of the probability of a hazard-related incident occurring, and of the severity of the harm or damage that could result. In the CPI, risk is often described in terms of a "risk triad" consisting of
  - *Incident*—an accident scenario, consisting of a specific set of events that results in a hazard impacting upon the subject of concern (people, the environment, or property).
  - *Likelihood*—a measure of the probability or frequency of the incident.
  - *Consequence*—a measure of the harm or damage resulting from the interaction of the hazard and the subject of concern.

An *incident* is a specific sequence of events resulting in harm or damage to the subject of concern from a hazard. Crowl and Louvar[3] describe a generalized three-step process for most incidents:

- *Initiation*—the event that starts the incident.
- *Propagation*—an event or sequence of events that maintain or expand the incident.
- *Termination*—events that stop the incident, or diminish it in size.

The objective of safety in design in the CPI is to eliminate or minimize initiation and propagation events, and to interrupt incident sequences with termination events.

EXAMPLES—CHEMICAL PROCESS INDUSTRY HAZARDS

A *hazard* is intrinsic to a material, or its conditions of storage or use. In the CPI, it is defined as a physical or chemical characteristic that has the potential to cause harm to people, the environment, or property (CCPS).[1] Some examples include the following:

- Chlorine is toxic by inhalation;
- 98% nitric acid is highly corrosive to the skin, emits toxic nitrogen oxide vapors, and is highly reactive with many organic materials;
- Gasoline is flammable;
- Styrene monomer can self-react (polymerize), releasing large amounts of heat;
- Compressed air in a cylinder at 600 psig contains a large amount of potential energy; and
- Heat transfer oil at 250° C can cause severe burns.

These hazards cannot be changed—they are intrinsic to the material or its conditions of use. All we can do to eliminate the hazard is change the material or the conditions of use. Indeed, that should be our first question in approaching safety in design—is the hazardous material or condition really necessary to accomplish our design objective?

CHEMICAL PROCESS SAFETY THROUGH DESIGN

DESIGN STRATEGIES FOR SAFETY

Strategies for the design of safe chemical processes and plants fall into the following four categories (CCPS)(4)(5); (Bollinger et al)[2]:

- *Inherent.* Eliminate the hazard by using materials and conditions that are non-hazardous.
- *Passive.* Minimize or control the hazard by using process and equipment design features that reduce either the frequency or consequence of incidents without the active functioning of any device
- *Active.* Control or mitigate incidents using controls, safety interlocks, or emergency shutdown systems to detect hazardous conditions and take appropriate action so that the plant is placed in a safe condition.
- *Procedural.* Use operating procedures, administrative checks, emergency response, and other management systems to prevent incidents, or to detect incidents in time for operators to place the plant in a safe condition.

CCPS[5] provides an extensive set of checklists of hazards and incident scenarios for ten common types of chemical process equipment, along with descriptions of inherent, passive, active, and procedural strategies for managing these hazards.

These categories are not rigidly defined, and a particular design may exhibit characteristics of more than one category. The application of these safety strategies to the handling of a combustible organic solid (for example, a plastic) is shown in Table 16-A. Safety strategies in the inherent and

Table 16–A. Example of Design Safety Strategies Applied to Handling of a Combustible Organic Material.

Safety Strategy	Description	Comments
Inherent	Handling a combustible organic solid, such as a plastic, as large granules or pellets incapable of supporting a dust explosion.	The combustible material is in a form which cannot support a dust explosion.
Passive	Handling the same combustible organic solid as a powder which can explode if dispersed in air and subjected to an ignition source, in equipment which is strong enough to withstand the maximum pressure generated by a dust explosion.	An explosion can occur, but it will be contained within the process equipment, eliminating the potential for injury or property damage outside the process equipment. However, the explosion could occur, generating pressure and a fireball inside the equipment—the hazard does exist. If there is a flaw in the equipment resulting in its premature failure at a pressure below the design pressure, injuries or property damage could occur.
Active	Handling the same combustible organic solid as a powder which can explode if dispersed in air and subjected to an ignition source, in low strength equipment which cannot withstand a dust explosion, using explosion venting or explosion suppression systems to prevent failure of the equipment.	An explosion can occur, and it will either be vented to a safe place, or controlled by the suppression system. However, the explosion vents could fail to open, the suppression system could fail to detect the explosion or inject the fire suppressant, or somebody could be working in the "safe place" when the explosion occurs.
Procedural	Handling the same combustible organic solid as a powder which can explode if dispersed in air and subjected to an ignition source, in low strength equipment which cannot withstand a dust explosion, and instructing the operator to manually inert the equipment with nitrogen and periodically check the oxygen concentration in the equipment using a portable meter.	The operator could forget to follow the procedure and inert the equipment, he could connect to a compressed air supply instead of nitrogen. If there is an ignition source present, there can be an explosion, and the process equipment will fail because it is not protected in any other way.

passive categories are generally considered to be more robust and reliable. They depend on the physical and chemical properties of the system, rather than on the successful operation of instruments, safety devices, and procedures. Inherent and passive strategies are often confused, but are in fact different. A truly inherent solution to a safety concern will completely eliminate the hazard, or reduce the potential magnitude of an incident associated with the hazard sufficiently that it presents no danger. On the other hand, passive strategies do not eliminate the hazard, but prevent injury and damage by eliminating or reducing the exposure of people or property to the hazardous condition, without the active functioning of any device.

Marshall[6] categorizes safety and risk management strategies as strategic and tactical. Strategic approaches include measures that have "wide significance, and that represent a 'once and for all' policy decision." Tactical approaches include measures "which are added on at a late state or those which entail frequent repetition." Safety through design can include both strategic and tactical risk management approaches.

Inherent and passive approaches tend to fall into the *strategic* category. The greatest potential for realizing an inherently safer process design is early in development. At this time, the designer still has considerable freedom in technology selection. For a chemical process, perhaps the greatest opportunities lie in the selection of the chemical synthesis route, including the raw materials, solvents, chemical intermediates, reaction steps, and other physical and chemical operations.

Active controls and procedural approaches tend to be *tactical*. Active and procedural safety features can also be identified and incorporated during design. In fact, they should be incorporated into the process design—we should anticipate potential incidents during design and provide the appropriate protective systems, procedures, and devices, rather than discovering the need for these layers of protection later on as a result of incidents and near misses. It is clearly much easier and cheaper to install a high level alarm on a storage tank to prevent overflow of a hazardous material when the tank is being built than it is to retrofit a high level alarm to a tank that is already filled with the hazardous material.

However, it is important to remember that it is never too late to consider inherently safer design options. In an existing plant, there will be different kinds of opportunities for modifications to improve inherent safety, but these opportunities can result in significant improvements. It may not be feasible to change the basic process chemistry and technology, but it may be possible to reduce inventory, simplify the plant, or otherwise make the plant more "user friendly." Significant improvements in the inherent safety of plants that have operated for many years have been reported (Wade)[7]; (Carrithers et al)[8]; (Gowland).[9]

LAYERS OF PROTECTION

A traditional approach to managing the risk associated with a chemical process is by providing layers of protection between the hazardous agent and the people, environment, or property that is potentially impacted. This approach is illustrated in Figure 16-2.[10] The protective layers may include one or more of the following:

- Process design;
- Basic controls, alarms, and operator control;
- Critical alarms, operator control, and manual intervention;
- Automatic actions—emergency shutdown systems and safety interlock systems;
- Physical protection equipment such as pressure relief devices;
- Physical mitigation systems such as spill containment dikes;

- Emergency response systems—for example, fire fighting; and
- Community emergency response—for example, notification and evacuation.

The layers of protection are intended to reduce risk by reducing either the likelihood of potential incidents resulting in an impact on people, the environment, or property, or by reducing the magnitude of the impact should an incident occur. The risk can be reduced to very low levels by providing a sufficient number of layers of protection, and by making each layer highly reliable (Figure 16-3). However, the basic process hazards remain, and there is always the potential—perhaps very small, but never zero—that all layers will fail simultaneously and the hazardous incident will occur. Furthermore, the layers of protection require significant expenditure of resources, both to design and build them initially, and to maintain their reliability throughout the life of the plant. Failure to adequately maintain the layers of protection may result in a significant increase in the process risk (Figure 16-4).

INHERENTLY SAFER DESIGN

Kletz[11] defined an inherently safer design as one that "avoids hazards instead of controlling them." Inherently safer design strategies for chemical processes and equipment have been categorized as follows:

- *Minimize.* Use smaller quantities of hazardous substances (sometime referred to as "intensify").
- *Substitute.* Replace a material with a less hazardous substance.
- *Moderate.* Use less hazardous conditions, a less hazardous form of a substance, or facilities that minimize the impact of the release of hazardous material or energy (sometimes referred to as "attenuate").
- *Simplify.* Design processes and facilities that eliminate unnecessary complexity, and that are tolerant of operating errors.

A number of excellent books on inherently safer chemical processes provide many specific examples of the implementation of these strategies, including Kletz, [12,13] CCPS,[4] and Bollinger et al.[2] A few examples will be briefly discussed here.

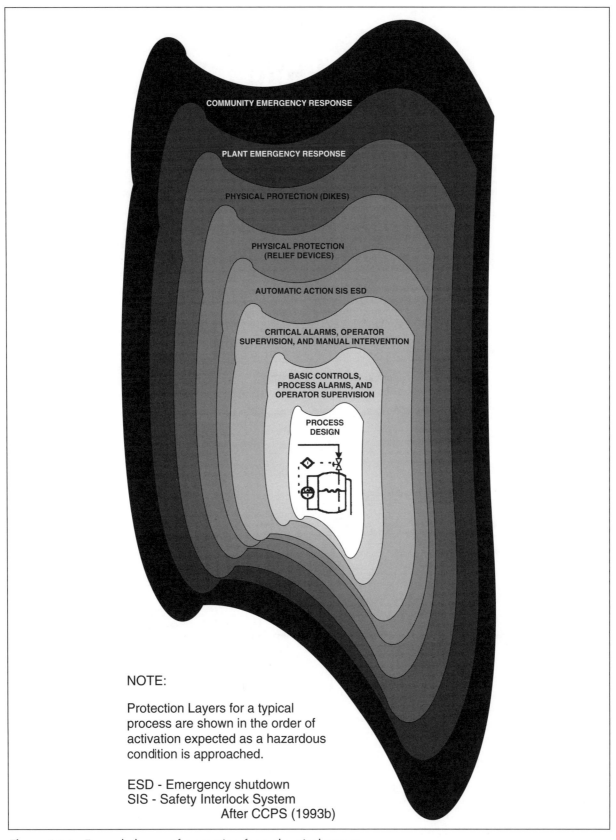

Figure 16-2. Example layers of protection for a chemical process.

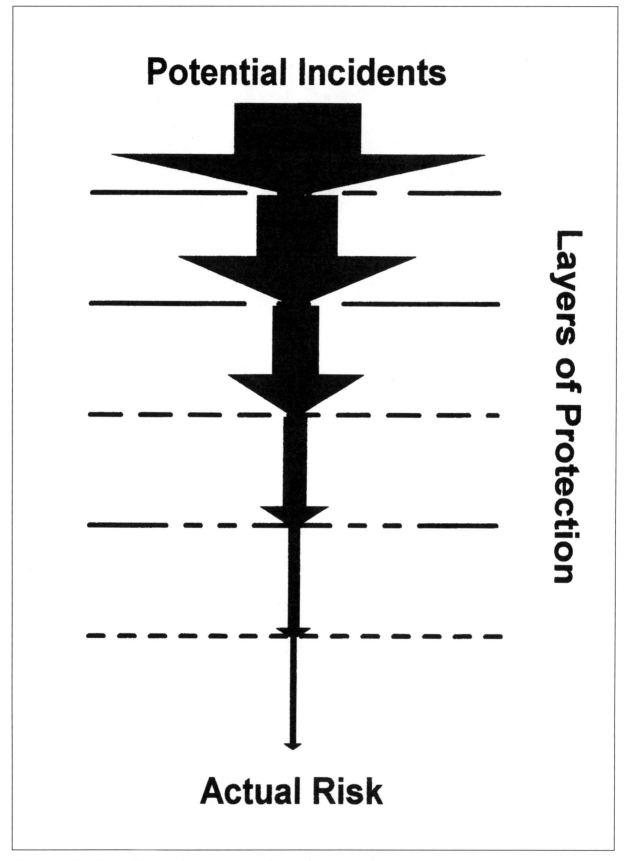

Figure 16–3. Effect of layers of protection on chemical process risk.

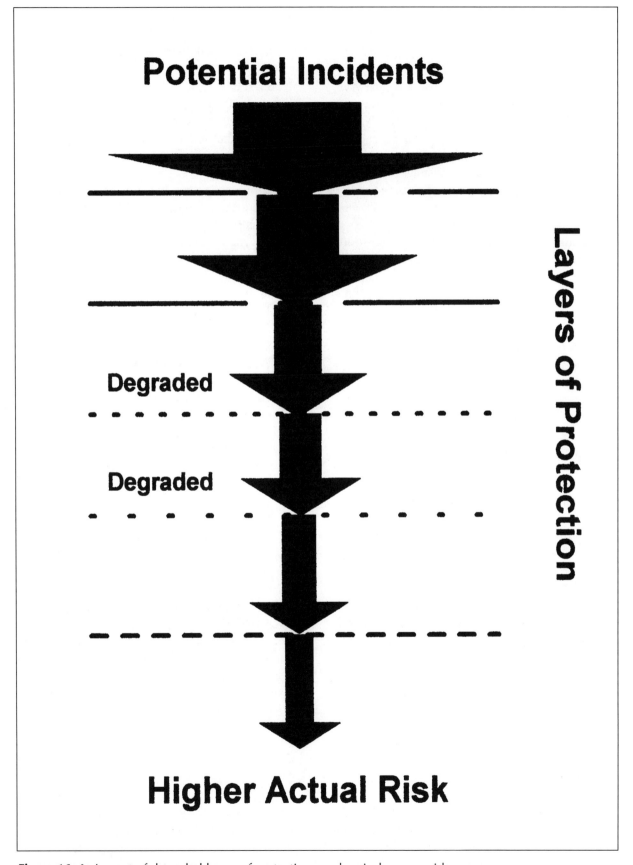

Figure 16–4. Impact of degraded layers of protection on chemical process risk.

MINIMIZE

Risk is a function of both the frequency or likelihood of an incident, and of the consequence of the incident should it occur. If the plant design can minimize the quantity of hazardous material and/or energy, it also minimizes the magnitude of the consequence contribution to risk. Ideally, the quantity of hazardous materials or energy would be reduced to a point where it would not be capable of causing any injury or damage even if it were all released in an incident. Some specific ways to reduce the size of equipment in a chemical process include the following:

➤ Continuous reactors (stirred tanks, loop reactors, tubular reactors) in place of batch reactors;

➤ Reduced inventory of raw materials and in-process intermediates; and

➤ High-efficiency heat exchangers.

Some examples of the implementation of inherently safer processes using the minimization strategy include the following:

➤ A continuous process to manufacture phosgene "on demand" was developed and eliminated the need to store large quantities of liquid phosgene. When the batch process consumers require phosgene, the small continuous manufacturing unit is started up, and it quickly reaches steady state and supplies the required quantity (Osterwalder).[14]

➤ Intermediate storage of large quantities of hazardous material is often included in the design of chemical plants to increase flexibility, and also to make up for poor reliability of various sub-units in the plant. This inventory allows sections of the plant to continue to run, either filling up downstream intermediate storage while downstream processing units are off line, or being fed from upstream intermediate storage while upstream units are shut down. Often this intermediate storage is not really needed, but instead allows the manufacturing unit to tolerate unreliability in its components. If the individual components could be made reliable, the intermediate storage could be reduced or eliminated. For example, Wade[7] describes system improvements that eliminated storage of hundreds of thousands of pounds of hydrogen cyanide and chlorine from a large manufacturing plant.

➤ A 50-liter loop polymerization reactor has a capacity equal to that of a 5000-liter batch reactor (Wilkinson and Geddes).[15]

SUBSTITUTE

Substitute means to replace a hazardous material or process operation with a different material or operation that reduces the hazard. For example, process designers should search for process alternatives that use

➤ different synthesis chemistry to manufacture the desired project, using less hazardous raw materials or process intermediates;

➤ alternate chemistry with less energetic reactions;

➤ alternate chemistry that operates at lower temperature or pressure; and

➤ less toxic or flammable solvents.

Some specific examples of substitution include the following:

➤ Acrylic esters were formerly manufactured using the Reppe process, using acetylene, carbon monoxide, and a nickel carbonyl catalyst. The newer propylene oxidation process uses significantly less hazardous materials (Hochheiser).[16]

➤ Water-based paints and coatings are inherently safer than solvent-based products, both in the manufacturing process, and also for the product consumer.

➤ Many industrial cleaning and de-greasing operations have replaced flammable or toxic organic solvents with water based systems (Davis et al).[17]

MODERATE

The hazard of a chemical process is significantly impacted by the conditions under which process materials are handled. Hazards can be reduced by inventing processes that operate at lower pressure or lower temperature. Hazardous material storage risks can be reduced by dilution with a less hazardous material, or by refrigeration of hazardous gases such as chlorine and ammonia. Changing the form of a material, for example, increasing the particle size of a combustible powder, can also significantly reduce hazards. Some specific examples include the following:

➤ Aqueous ammonia was substituted for anhydrous ammonia in a manufacturing process, greatly reducing the potential consequences of a leak (Carrithers et al).[8]

→ Improvements in the manufacturing process for ammonia has reduced operating pressures from 600 bar in the 1930s to 100-150 bar for modern plants (Kharbanda and Stallworthy).[18]

SIMPLIFY

A simpler plant is generally a safer plant. Incidents are more likely to occur in a complex design that operating personnel have difficulty understanding. Furthermore, designs should be tolerant of mistakes, with wide safe operating limits for critical operating parameters and allowing operators to safely recover from a mistake. The chemical process designer should try to develop fundamentally simpler technology with fewer reactions and processing operations, eliminate unnecessary equipment, remove unused or abandoned equipment, and consider human factors.

Some examples of simplification include the following:

→ Design vessels to withstand the maximum pressure that can be generated, rather than providing complex emergency relief systems, including devices such as scrubbers, catch tanks, or flares to contain the relief system effluent.

→ Develop "one pot" processes in which hazardous materials are generated and consumed "in-situ" in a single vessel, rather than being transported through a number of vessels, pipes, pumps, and other equipment.

→ Consider gravity flow systems for hazardous liquids, eliminating pumps that require maintenance and represent potential leak sources.

DESIGN CONFLICTS AND TRADE-OFFS

Engineering design is the art of compromise. Design objectives are often in conflict, and may be mutually exclusive. The designer must choose which of the alternative solutions has the best overall balance of characteristics with respect to all of the design objectives. Safety is one of many potentially conflicting objectives of a chemical process design—other important considerations include environmental impact, long term health impacts on the plant workers and the surrounding community, product quality and ability to meet market requirements, capital investment, and operating costs. Each of these broad categories may also include a number of separate considerations that may also impose conflicting requirements. For example, safety considerations may include fire, explosion, and concern about acute toxicity.

In general, chemical processes have a number of different hazards. Ideally, we would like to identify safer process alternatives that simultaneously reduce or eliminate all of the potential hazards. Unfortunately, in the real world this seldom, if ever, occurs. A process alternative that is safer with respect to one hazard may increase other hazards. For example, one process solvent may be non-flammable and toxic. An alternative solvent is flammable and non-toxic. Which is safer? There is no general answer. The designer must identify and consider all of the hazards and apply appropriate decision making tools to identify the best overall solution.

Understanding safety-offs can be difficult, but not nearly so difficult as understanding trade-offs among less closely related design criteria. For example, how do you compare a process that reduces waste generation and potential environmental contamination, but uses a very toxic chemical intermediate, to an alternative process that uses less hazardous materials but generates more waste? There is no "correct" answer to this question—ultimately it is a matter of values. Decision analysis tools are appropriate for consideration of these questions (CCPS).[19]

Measurement of safety characteristics is a key element in good decision making. A number of risk or safety indices have been developed to measure specific safety characteristics of processes, including the Dow Fire and Explosion Index[20], the Dow Chemical Exposure Index[21], and the INSET Inherent Safety, Health, and Environmental indices (Mansfield et al)[22]; (Turney et al)[23]. Gowland[9] reviews the use of the Dow Fire and Explosion Index as a tool for improving the inherent safety of a hydrogen cyanide facility. Edwards and Lawrence[24], Edwards et al[25], and Hendershot[26] also discuss tools for measuring safety characteristics of chemical processes. Additional research into developing tools for measuring safety characteristics of chemical processes and plants is needed. The existing tools, for the most part, focus on specific aspects of safety—for example, fires, explosions, or acute toxicity—and there is no single set of measures that covers all areas of concern, including environmental and health concerns, in a consistent fashion.

TOOLS FOR SAFETY THROUGH DESIGN

PROCESS HAZARD ANALYSIS TOOLS

There are a number of process hazard analysis (PHA) techniques that apply to safety in the design of chemical plants. Most of these techniques are well documented in the literature, and cannot be described adequately in the space available in this book. Greenberg and Cramer[27], CCPS[1], Wells[28], Lees[29], and Skelton[30] provide excellent reviews of PHA techniques useful for incorporating process safety into the design of chemical processing plants. Table 16-B lists the tools most commonly used in the CPI, along with a brief characterization of each tool. Table 16-C provides guidance on which tools are most commonly used at various stages in the life cycle of a chemical process.

Many of the process hazard analysis methods in Tables 16-B and 16-C incorporate the use of hazard and risk assessment tools described in Chapter 2. The hazard/risk matrix is commonly used in chemical process hazard analyses, and is a part of many of the common PHA techniques (CCPS)[1]. Some of the PHA techniques, particularly the logic model techniques such as fault tree analysis, are well suited for detailed quantification and can be used to develop a fully quantitative risk analysis (QRA). In the CPI, QRA is most often applied for understanding the risk of high consequence, low frequency (likelihood) events, for example, large releases of flammable or toxic material that could cause injury in the community surrounding a chemical plant. CCPS[31] describes the application of quantitative risk analysis methods in the CPI, and CCPS (19) discusses the use of QRA in making process risk management decisions.

Regardless of the PHA technique used, preparation and collection of background information is essential to a good, effective, and efficient process safety review. Table 16-D summarizes some of the information that is required for a process safety design review. Early

in the process life cycle, much of this information will not be available in extensive detail. However, whatever information is available should be considered and evaluated, even at the earliest stages of process conception and design. As the project moves through the life cycle to detailed design, construction, and operation, the quantity and quality of the available information will increase, allowing a more detailed and thorough design safety review.

Most of the PHA techniques used to evaluate the safety of a chemical process design are team or group activities. This is important because a chemical process is very complex, and many different kinds of knowledge and expertise are required to fully understand all of the hazards and potential incident scenarios. The design engineer should adopt the approach of Woodrow Wilson, who once stated, "I use not only all the brains I have, but all I can borrow." Table 16-E lists some of the disciplines and areas of expertise that should be considered for participating in a process design safety review.

Two process hazard analysis tools are particularly valuable for application very early in the design of a chemical process—the interaction matrix and the process chemistry guideword hazard analysis. These tools are not as well described in existing literature, and they will be reviewed more extensively in the following sections.

INTERACTION MATRIX

The interaction matrix, as shown in Figure 16-5, is a useful tool for understanding possible reactions, both intended and unintended, among the various materials used in a chemical process. This can be a very useful tool, particularly early in the development of a new chemical process. To create an interaction matrix, list all of the materials, materials of construction, likely contaminants, potential sources of energy, process utilities (such as steam, water, nitrogen, compressed air, ethylene glycol coolant and heat transfer oil), and other relevant parameters along each axis of the matrix. It is a good idea to also include "people" on one of the axes, to prompt questions about toxicity and other adverse impacts of materials on people. Then, ask what happens for each interaction where the matrix columns and rows intersect. The matrix should

Table 16–B. Process Hazard Analysis Tools Commonly Used in the Chemical Process Industries.

Category	Process hazard analysis tool	Description and comments
Brainstorming techniques	Interaction matrix	A matrix format prompts questions about chemical interaction hazards; restricted to this specific type of hazard.
	Safety review	Relatively unstructured brainstorming techniques to identify hazards and potential accident scenarios.
	Preliminary hazard analysis	
	What if	
	Process chemistry guideword hazard analysis	A structured analysis procedure focuses brainstorming activities, including use of a specific set of guidewords or knowledge and checklists of known equipment failure modes.
	Hazard and Operability Study (HAZOP)	
	Failure Mode and Effect Analysis (FMEA)	
Checklist techniques	Checklist	Predefined checklists based on previous experience compare a design to specific standards or good practice. When combined with "What if" analysis, the checklists are used to prompt brainstorming activities.
	What if/Checklist	*Note:* Some particularly valuable checklists for chemical processing operations can be found in CCPS (1992, 1998).
Risk ranking techniques	Relative ranking	A general category which includes a large number of quantitative and semi-quantitative techniques which use checklists or equations based on material properties, quantities, and handling conditions to numerically rank risk. Examples include the Dow Fire and Explosion Index and the Dow Chemical Exposure Index (Dow, 1994a, 1994b).
Logic model techniques	Fault tree analysis	Logic models which identify specific causes combinations of events which lead to a potential accident scenario. These techniques require a lot of detailed design information and usually focus on analyzing a few specific accident scenarios in detail. These techniques can be quantified, and are important tools in quantitative risk analysis.
	Event tree analysis	
	Cause consequence analysis	
	Human reliability analysis	

go beyond a simple yes–no answers. It will be much more valuable for future reference if detailed information on the nature of the interaction can be provided in a set of attached notes. Often an interaction matrix will generate more questions than answers—the result of the interaction may not be known. In this case, it may be appropriate to recommend a literature search or laboratory experiments.

There is extensive published literature on chemical reactivity and interactions that can be useful in constructing an interaction matrix. *Bretherick's Handbook of Reactive Chemical Hazards*[32] lists thousands of reported reactions

and chemical incompatibilities, and includes literature citations for more information. This is probably the best single source for chemical compatibility information. The United States Coast Guard maintains a database and compatibility chart of chemical combinations known or believed to be dangerously reactive if accidentally mixed. This information is updated periodically and is available in the *CHRIS Manual* (Chemical Hazards Response Information System)[33]. The United States National Oceanic and Atmospheric Administration (NOAA) has developed a Chemical Reactivity Worksheet, which provides information about reactions

Table 16–C. Process Hazard Analysis (PHA) Techniques Through the Life Cycle of a Chemical Process.

(based on CCPS, 1992, with additions)

Chemical Process Life Cycle Stage / Process Hazard Analysis Technique	Interaction matrix	Process chemistry guide word hazard analysis	Safety review	Checklist	Relative ranking	Preliminary hazard analysis	What if	What if/checklist	Failure Mode and Effect Analysis (FMEA)	Hazard and Operability Analysis (HAZOP)	Fault tree analysis	Event tree analysis	Cause consequence analysis	Human reliability analysis
Research and development	●	●	○	○	●	●	●	○	○	○	○	○	○	○
Conceptual design	●	●	○	●	●	●	●	●	○	○	○	○	○	○
Detailed engineering	○	○	○	●	○	●	●	●	●	●	●	●	●	●
Construction	○	○	●	●	○	○	●	●	○	○	○	○	○	●
Startup	○	○	●	●	○	○	●	●	○	○	○	○	○	●
Routine operation, modifications, and expansions	●	●	●	●	●	●	●	●	●	●	●	●	●	●
Decommissioning	○	○	●	●	○	○	●	●	○	○	○	○	○	○
Demolition	○	○	●	●	○	○	●	●	○	○	○	○	○	○

● PHA technique commonly used   ○ PHA technique rarely used or not appropriate

among various combinations of chemicals (Farr et al)[34]. This worksheet has been implemented as a personal computer program which can be downloaded from the NOAA Internet web site.

PROCESS CHEMISTRY GUIDEWORD HAZARD ANALYSIS

The Process Chemistry Guideword Hazard Review (PCGHA) is derived from the Hazard and Operability (HAZOP) study methodology. HAZOP was developed for the study of a detailed plant design, or an existing facility. For this reason, a HAZOP requires a lot of detailed information about the plant design and operation. Much of this information will not exist early in process development, and the HAZOP methodology is not applicable. However, the thought process of a HAZOP study, and the general methodology, can be applied at any stage in process development. HAZOP assumes that a process is safe if operated as designed (the designer must, of course, confirm that this is

indeed true), and that safety incidents occur as a result of a deviation from the intended operation. A study team applies a series of guide words to the stated design intention for the plant as an aid in identifying potential deviations. It then identifies potential causes, consequences, safeguards, and required actions for each deviation identified.

This concept can also be applied to a chemical reaction, and it has been called a Process Chemistry Guideword Hazard Review to differentiate it from the more detailed HAZOP review, which requires much more plant design information. The PCGHA need not be a team activity. A chemist or engineer who is knowledgeable in the chemistry can apply the methodology alone, but the quality of the review will be enhanced if he reviews the results with colleagues and other experts to broaden knowledge and experience base.

The methodology of a PCGHA can be shown using a generalized chemical reaction:

Table 16-D. Information Requirements For a Process Safety Design Review.

Process chemistry
- Raw materials, solvents, catalysts, intermediates, products
- By-products and impurities
- Desired reactions
- Side reactions and undesired alternate reactions
- Thermochemistry and kinetics

Plant and Process
- Process flow diagrams, piping and instrumentation diagrams, material and energy balances, material inventories and storage conditions
- Equipment design basis
- Plot plans and building layouts
- Safety systems, including alarms, interlocks, shutdown systems and fire protection systems

Site Data
- Population data, both on site and off site
- Environmental impact areas
- Surrounding geography
- Weather, hydrology, and geological data

Operating philosophy
- Operating instructions and procedures, training
- Emergency response plans
- Previous safety studies on similar facilities
- Incident reports from similar facilities
- Maintenance philosophy
- Control philosophy (manual, degree of automation)

Material properties
- Physical properties
- Flammability
- Toxicity (acute and chronic)
- Thermal stability
- Environmental impacts
- Corrosion

Regulatory
- Codes and standards (company and outside organizations)
- National, state, and local regulations
- Permit limits and restrictions

Table 16-E. Potential Participants in a Process Design Safety Review.

- Corrosion specialist
- Other engineering disciplines (mechanical, electrical, civil)
- Environmental specialist
- Plant/business management
- Equipment manufacturer
- Process chemist
- Industrial hygienist
- Process control engineer

- Instrument engineer
- Process engineer
- Maintenance engineer
- Project engineer
- Medical/toxicology expert
- Raw material supplier experts
- Operating personnel (operators, mechanics, instrument technicians)
- Research process engineer

$$A + B \xrightarrow[\substack{\text{Catalyst} = C \\ \text{Solvent} = S}]{\substack{\text{Temperature} = T \\ \text{Pressure} = P}} Y + Z$$

To do the PCGHA, apply the seven basic HAZOP guide words (CCPS)[1] to the chemical reaction:

- No
- Less
- Reverse
- Other
- More
- Part Of
- As Well As

In a HAZOP study, the analysis team looks for specific causes and consequences for each deviation identified by the application of the guide words to the stated intention for the plant. However, in a PCGHA, we are more interested in the conse-quences of deviations from intended operation than the causes and specific incident scenarios, which may be impossible to fully identify for a process and plant that are early in development. Therefore, the chemist or engineer can simply assume that the deviation identified by the application of the guide word to the chemical reaction does occur for some reason, and investigate the consequences. Table 16-F gives some examples of how the guide words might be applied to the example generalized chemical reaction. If the consequences are known, the designer should determine if they represent a hazard that must be understood and managed as a part of the process development, and document this information for future action or reference. In many

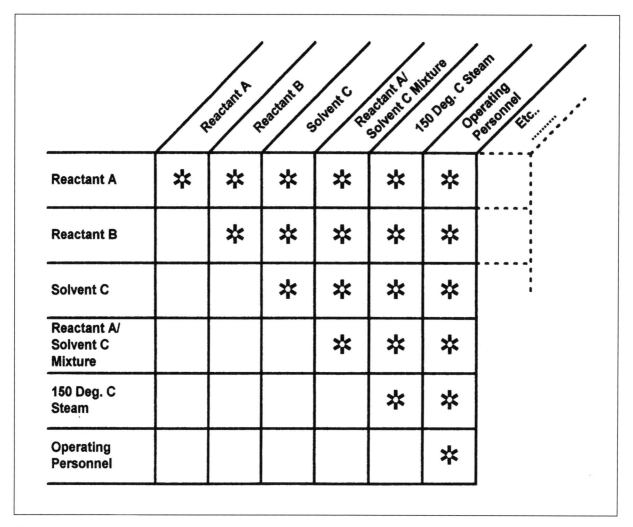

Figure 16-5. An example interaction matrix.

cases, early in process development, the consequences may not be known, and additional research or experiments may be needed.

The results of the PCGHA can be documented in a tabular form, with columns listing the guide words, deviations, consequences, and actions. An example is shown in Table 16-G.

CHALLENGES AND FUTURE TRENDS

SYNERGISM WITH OTHER IMPORTANT INITIATIVES

The design of a chemical process and plant is, like the design of any other engineering artifact, a multidisciplinary activity. The designers must consider a large number of different customers, each of which has different needs and desires. The requirement for a safe plant is one of those customer demands, but there are others that must also be considered—environmental friendliness, employee and surrounding population health, product quality, capital investment, operating costs, plant operability, plant reliability, product quality, and others. An effective design must consider all of these requirements—it does no good to design a very safe plant if nobody can afford to operate it or the product quality is unacceptable in the market. It is most effective to consider as many of the various customer requirements for a process and plant together so that the designer can choose design options that most effectively meet the combined requirements of all customers.

SAFETY IN DESIGN AND "GREEN" PROCESSES

A number of efforts to combine design safety initiatives with other areas of concern have been

Table 16-F. Process Chemistry Guideword Hazard Analysis Guidewords, and Examples of their Application to the Example Generalized Chemical Reaction.

Guide Word	Examples of possible deviations for consideration
NO	No reactant A; No reactant B; No solvent S; No catalyst C; No reaction; etc.
MORE	More reactant A; More reactant B; More Solvent S; More catalyst C, More (higher) temperature; More (higher) pressure; More reaction time; More reaction rate; More (faster) rate of addition of material; etc.
LESS	Less reactant A; Less reactant B; Less solvent S; Less catalyst C; Less (lower) temperature; Less (lower) pressure; Less reaction time; Less reaction rate; Less (slower) rate of addition of material; etc.
PART OF	Part of A dissolved in S; Part of B dissolved in S; Partial reaction; etc.
REVERSE	Reverse order of addition of materials; Reverse reaction
AS WELL AS	Anticipated contaminants in supplied materials (reactants A and B, solvent S, catalyst C) As Well As intended materials; Common industrial contaminants (air; water; rust or iron; oil; lubricants; greases; glycol, brine, or other heat transfer fluids) As Well As intended materials
OTHER	Other (wrong) materials charged (particularly materials with a similar name which might be present in the facility where the process will ultimately be run—for example, acetic anhydride instead of acetic acid); Other possible reactions; Other form of materials (for example, solid materials as a powder instead of a granule or pellet)

Table 16-G. Examples of Deviations and Consequences.

Guide Word	Deviation	Consequence	Comments/Actions
NO	Catalyst C left out	No reaction; if catalyst C is added after reactants A and B are present a rapid and violent reaction can occur.	Develop kinetic and thermodynamic data on this reaction.
MORE	Higher Temperature – greater than 70 C	Other side reactions have been observed in similar systems at temperatures above 70 C, and may also occur with this chemistry.	Investigate the behavior of the reaction at elevated temperature.
AS WELL AS	Rust as well as normal materials	The effect of contamination with iron or rust is unknown.	Determine the effect of iron or rust contamination.

reported. The INSIDE (INherent SHE In DEsign) Project is a European government/industry project sponsored by the Commission of the European Community to encourage and promote inherently safer chemical processes and plants. The INSIDE Project expands the inherent safety concept to include inherent approaches to Safety, Health, and Environmental (SHE) aspects of chemical processes. The project has developed a set of tools, the INSET Toolkit, to identify inherently safer design options throughout the life of a process, and to evaluate the options. Table 16-H summarizes these tools, which are described in detail by the INSIDE Project[35].

In the United States, the Center for Waste Reduction Technologies (CWRT) and the Center for Chemical Process Safety (CCPS), directorates of the American Institute of Chemical Engineers, are planning a project on Inherent Safety and Pollution Prevention. The focus of the project will be on how best to develop new products and processes, which minimize both safety

Table 16–H. INSET Inherent SHE Toolkit (INSIDE Project, 1997).

INSET Inherent SHE Tools

A Detailed Constraints and Objectives Analysis

B Process Option Generation

C Preliminary Chemistry Route Options Record

D Preliminary Chemistry Route Rapid ISHE Evaluation Method

E Preliminary Chemistry Route Detailed ISHE Evaluation Method

F Chemistry Route Block Diagram Record

G Chemical Hazards Classification Method

H Record of Foreseeable Hazards

I ISHE Performance Indices

J Multi-Attribute ISHE Comparative Evaluation

K Rapid ISHE Screening Method

L Chemical Reaction Reactivity - Stability Evaluation

M Process SHE Analysis - Process Hazards Analysis, Ranking Method

N Equipment Inventory Functional Analysis Method

O Equipment Simplification Guide

P Hazards Range Assessment for Gaseous Releases

Q Sting and Plant Layout Assessment

R Designing for Operation

and environmental problems from the beginning. CWRT is also working on a project on Total Cost Assessment, which focuses on methods for measuring the total life cycle costs of a process, including safety and environmental costs.

OVERALL INHERENT SAFETY MEASUREMENT

Some initial work on the development of an overall inherent safety index has been done at Loughborough University in the United Kingdom (Edwards and Lawrence)[24]; (Edwards et al)[25]. A number of factors related to inherent safety are evaluated, including inventory, flammability, explosiveness, toxicity, temperature, pressure, and process yield. A single number overall index characterizing the inherent safety of the overall process is generated. The relative contributions of the various components of the index to the total value may also be useful in understanding the process charac-

teristics. This index is considered a prototype by the developers, and more work will be needed. Table 16-I summarizes the application of this proposed inherent safety index to a number of alternative routes for the manufacture of methyl methacrylate.

SAFETY AND RELIABILITY IN DESIGN

In recent years, the CPI has started to adopt many of the reliability-centered maintenance and design methodologies that were originally developed in the aerospace industry. The CPI has found that these methodologies have much in common with process hazard analysis tools, often using the same methods, such as failure modes and effects analysis. Some companies are experimenting with combining these reviews into a single safety and reliability review. They believe that the combined reviews are more efficient than separate reviews, and also that they produce better quality results because the combined review includes a wider spectrum of personnel. Process personnel are present who might not participate in the reliability/maintenance study, and maintenance and reliability personnel are present who might not participate in a design safety study. Hazard and Operability Studies, in particular, appear to be good candidates for combining safety and maintenance/reliability reviews (Chastain and Jensen)[36]; (King et al)[37]: (Alley et al)[38]; (Hendershot et al)[39].

SUMMARY

Safety considerations are an inseparable part of the development of a chemical process and the design and operation of a chemical plant. While risk management and safety features can be "added on" to a plant design, or an operating plant, at any time in its life cycle, safety is most effectively and economically addressed early in the life cycle. At this time, the designer may have considerable flexibility in choosing alternative starting materials and reaction sequences to produce a specific product. As process and product development proceed, these options become less readily available. By the time a plant is actually built, it may be extremely difficult to change the basic manufacturing technology because of the large commitment of resources to the existing technology, and the designer may have no choice but to add expensive safety devices, procedures, and mitigation systems to meet safety requirements.

Table 16–I. Evaluation of Six Alternate Manufacturing Processes for Methyl Methacrylate Using a Proposed Inherent Safety Index (Edwards and Lawrence, 1993).

Process Route	Inherent Safety Index
Acetone cyanohydrin	~120
Ethylene based/propionaldehyde	~75
Propylene based	~70
Ethylene based/methyl propionate	~50
Isobutylene based	~50
Tertiary butyl alcohol based	~50

Safety strategies can be categorized as inherent, passive, active, and procedural. Inherent and passive strategies generally relate to the basic process technology and plant design, and are nearly always implemented early in the design life cycle. They focus on elimination of hazards, or minimizing the degree of hazard, rather than on management of hazards. Active and procedural strategies are usually also a part of a chemical process risk management program—it is not often possible to eliminate all hazards. Active and procedural strategies should also be considered during the design of a plant—safety devices and procedures are most reliably and economically implemented if they have been considered in the initial design rather than when retrofitted to an existing design.

Process hazard analysis tools are used to understand the hazards of a chemical process, and to aid the designer in selecting risk management strategies. A wide variety of tools is available for use at all stages of a chemical process life cycle. Tools used at the earliest stage of development and design (What if, interaction matrices, process chemistry hazard analysis) tend to look at the process broadly, with a focus on general categories of hazard rather than detailed incident scenarios. Other design tools (HAZOP, FMEA, logic model based tools) look at a well developed design in great detail, with the objective of understanding specific potential incident scenarios and identifying appropriate risk management strategies for the incident scenarios identified.

It is important to remember that the safety of a chemical process cannot be viewed in isolation from other process and plant design criteria. The chemical plant must meet many requirements from workers (safety, long term health, employment and wages), owners (operating costs, capital investment, profitability), customers (product quality, reliability of supply, cost), neighbors (safety, health, environmental impact, economic impact), and government (compliance with laws and regulations). All of these are important, and they may often be in conflict. The chemical process designer is best able to understand these design objectives and select the optimum design that maximizes the benefits to all concerned stakeholders if they are considered throughout the life cycle of the process. Ultimately, the plant must satisfy all of the stakeholders or it cannot be successful. Indeed, if the design does not satisfy all of the stakeholders, it probably will not be built at all, or, if it is, it will not operate for very long. Early and continuing attention to safety, along with all of the other design requirements as part of an integrated design process, is the key to designing safe, environmentally friendly, and economically competitive chemical plants.

REFERENCES

1. Center for Chemical Process Safety (CCPS). *Guidelines for Hazard Evaluation Procedures, Second Edition With Worked Examples.* New York: American Institute of Chemical Engineers, 1992.

2. Bollinger RE, Clark DG, Dowell AM, et al: *Inherently Safer Chemical Processes: A Life Cycle Approach.* New York: American Institute of Chemical Engineers, 1996.

3. Crowl DA, Louvar JF: *Chemical Process Safety Fundamentals With Applications.* Englewood Cliffs, NJ: Prentice Hall, 1990, pp 14–15.

4. Center for Chemical Process Safety (CCPS). *Guidelines for Engineering Design for Process Safety.* New York: American Institute of Chemical Engineers, 1993.

5. Center for Chemical Process Safety (CCPS). *Guidelines for Design Solutions for Process Equipment Failures.* New York: American Institute of Chemical Engineers, 1998.

6. Marshall VC: The social acceptability of the chemical and process industries. *Trans. IChemE* 68, Part B (May), 1990, pp 83–93.

7. Wade DE: Reduction of Risks by Reduction of Toxic Material Inventory. *Proceedings of the International Symposium on Preventing Major Chemical Accidents,* Feb 3–5, 1987, Washington DC. 2.1-2.8. New York: American Institute of Chemical Engineers, 1987.

8. Carrithers GW, Dowell AM, Hendershot DC: It's Never Too Late for Inherent Safety. *International Conference and Workshop on Process Safety Management and Inherently Safer Processes,* Oct, 8–11, 1996, Orlando, FL. New York: American Institute of Chemical Engineers, 1996, pp 227-241.

9. Gowland RT: Applying inherently safer concepts to a phosgene plant acquisition. *Process Safety Progress* 15, 1 (Spring), 1996, pp 52–57.

10. Center for Chemical Process Safety (CCPS). *Guidelines for Safe Automation of Chemical Processes.* New York: American Institute of Chemical Engineers, 1993.

11. Kletz TA: Inherently Safer Design - The Growth of an Idea. *Conference on Inherent SHE: The Cost Effective Route to Improved Safety, Health and Environmental Performance,* Jun 1997, London, London: IBC UK Conferences Limited, 1997, pp 16–17.

12. Kletz TA: *Plant Design for Safety.* Bristol PA: Taylor & Francis, 1992.

13. Kletz TA: Process Plants: *A Handbook for Inherently Safer Design.* Bristol PA: Taylor & Francis, 1998.

14. Osterwalder U: Continuous process to fit batch operation: Safe phosgene production on demand. *Symp. Pap. - Inst. Chem. Eng., North West. Branch,* 6.1-6.6. Rugby, Warwickshire, England: Institution of Chemical Engineers, 1996.

15. Wilkinson M, Geddes K: An award winning process. *Chemistry in Britain,* Dec 1993, pp 1050–1052.

16. Hochheiser S: *Rohm and Haas: History of a Chemical Company.* Philadelphia: University of Pennsylvania Press, 1986.

17. Davis G, Kincaid AL, Menke D, et al: *The Product Side of Pollution Prevention: Evaluating the Potential for Safe Substitutes.* Cincinnati, OH: Risk Reduction Engineering Laboratory, Office of Research and Development, U.S. Environmental Protection Agency, 1994.

18. Kharbanda OP, Stallworthy EA: *Safety in the Chemical Industry.* London: Heinemann Professional Publishing, 1988.

19. Center for Chemical Process Safety (CCPS). *Tools for Making Acute Risk Decisions With Chemical Process Safety Applications.* New York: American Institute of Chemical Engineers, 1995.

20. Dow Chemical Company. *Dow's Fire and Explosion Index Hazard Classification Guide.* 7th Edition. New York: American Institute of Chemical Engineers, 1994.

21. Dow Chemical Company. *Dow's Chemical Exposure Index Guide.* 1st Edition. New York: American Institute of Chemical Engineers, 1994.

22. Mansfield DP, Malmen Y, Suokas E: The Development of an Integrated Toolkit for Inherent SHE. *International Conference and Workshop on Process Safety Management and Inherently Safer Processes,* Oct 8–11, 1996, Orlando, FL. New York: American Institute of Chemical Engineers, 1996, pp 103–117.

23. Turney RD, Mansfield DP, Malmen Y, et al: The INSIDE Project on inherent she in process development and design:The toolkit and its application. *IChemE Symposium Series,* No. 141, 1997, pp 203–215.

24. Edwards DW, Lawrence D: Assessing the inherent safety of chemical process routes: Is there a relation between plant costs and inherent safety? *Trans. IChemE* 71, Part B, (Nov), 1993, pp 252–258.

25. Edwards DW, Lawrence D, Rushton AG: Quantifying the Inherent Safety of Chemical Process Routes. *5th World Congress of Chemical Engineering,* Jul 14–18, 1996, San Diego, CA, Vol. II. New York: American Institute of Chemical Engineers, 1996, pp 1113–1118.

26. Hendershot DC: Measuring inherent safety, health and environmental characteristics early in process development. *Process Safety Progress* 16, 2 (Summer), 1997, pp 78–79.

27. Greenberg HR, Cramer JJ (eds): *Risk Assessment and Risk Management for the Chemical Process Industry.* New York: Van Nostrand Reinhold, 1991.

28. Wells G: *Hazard Identification and Risk Assessment.* Rugby, Warwickshire, UK: Institution of Chemical Engineers, 1996.

29. Lees FP: *Loss Prevention in the Process Industries,* 2nd ed. London: Butterworth-Heinemann, 1996.

30. Skelton B: *Process Safety Analysis: An Introduction.* Houston, TX: Gulf Publishing Company, 1997.

31. Center for Chemical Process Safety (CCPS). *Guidelines for Chemical Process Quantitative Risk Analysis.* New York: American Institute of Chemical Engineers, 1989.

32. Urbenv PG (ed): *Bretherick's Handbook of Reactive Chemical Hazards,* 5th ed. London: Butterworth-Heinemann Ltd, 1995.

33. *Chemical Hazards Response Information System.* Volume 2, Hazardous Chemical Data Manual. Washington DC: U.S. Government Printing Office (GPO Stock No. 050-012-00329-7), 1992.

34. Farr JK, Freeman W, Odojewski SS: New program for chemical compatibility." *Chemical Health and Safety* 5, 6 (Nov/Dec), 1998, pp 33–36.

35. INSIDE Project. *Conference on Inherent SHE: The Cost Effective Route to Improved Safety, Health and Environmental Performance,* 16–17 Jun, 1997, London, London: IBC UK Conferences Limited, 1997.

36. Chastain JW, Jensen JHS: Conduct better maintenance and operability studies. *Chemical Engineering Progress* 93, 2 (Feb), 1997, pp 49–53.

37. King CS, Walker DA, Long MP: Lessons Learned From an RCM at Ashland Petroleum. *5th Annual Conference of the Society for Maintenance and Reliability Professionals,* Oct 5–8, 1997, Pittsburgh, PA, 1997.

38. Alley M, Long M, Walker D, et al: Integrating Reliability-Centered Maintenance Studies With Process Hazard Analyses. *International Conference and Workshop on Reliability and Risk Management,* Sep 15–19, 1998, San Antonio, TX. New York: American Institute of Chemical Engineers, 1998, pp 419–441.

39. Hendershot DC, Post RL, Valerio PF, et al: Let's Put the 'OP' Back in 'HAZOP'. *International Conference and Workshop on Reliability and Risk Management,* Sep 15–18, 1998, San Antonio, TX. New York: American Institute of Chemical Engineers, 1998, pp 153–167.

Chapter 17

APPLICATION IN THE CONSTRUCTION INDUSTRY

by Craig B. Schilder

OBJECTIVES

This chapter will provide information about two important aspects of construction design safety. The obvious one is safe design of the facility, bridge, highway, equipment, or other tangible end item to ensure the user or maintenance person or disposal person is not injured. The other aspect is the adequate design to protect construction workers before the user takes possession.

DESIGN TO REDUCE CONSTRUCTION INJURIES

Taking the last first, the thoughtful planning and design to reduce the risk of construction injuries is challenging, but not hard to accomplish. This design thoughtfulness is becoming more common. A person could view it in California when they were restoring the freeway ramps after a recent earthquake. The ramps were constructed on the ground and lifted into place, eliminating many fall hazards to construction workers.

Some buildings have atriums with glass skylights, which have been built on the roof and slid into place to avoid fall hazards for the welders and glass installers. Sometimes the common construction hazards can be eliminated during constructablity reviews, and other times by a system safety review board.

DESIGN FOR SAFETY TOOLBOX

The Construction Industries Institute (CII) developed a software program, "Design for Safety Toolbox," in cooperation with the University of Washington and the University of Texas.[1,2] The Toolbox operates in the Windows environment, maintains multiple project safety data, utilizes a matrix management tool to ensure comprehensive design team involvement, and includes a database, which contains 14 general hazard knowledge areas (for example: fire protection and prevention, electrical, fall prevention, lift operations, excavation, general access and egress) .

The system's flexible user interface allows the designer to conduct the safety analysis in three organizational modes: by project systems, by construction site hazards, or by project components. Each mode is keyed to the knowledge database, which can be updated and accessed from any part of the system. User files also store general project information such as project title and job number, project description, job location, last assessment date, project designer, and so on.

DESIGN TO REDUCE USER INJURIES

Now back to the obvious, safe design for the user. The typical system safety design effort is easily adapted to the "design-to-protect-user" concept. Just as is done with weapons systems or aircraft or automobiles, user safety can be easily accomplished with a simple team approach. User safety needs must include the operator or tenant or maintenance person or the disposal person at the end of the useful life. Very frequently the daily user is the only "operator" considered. But the maintenance person usually needs to climb up or down to fix or lubricate a part, turn a valve or repair equipment. Fall and burn hazards and other physical hazards need to be eliminated with early identification and proper design. (See "Building Design Safety Checklist" at the end of this chapter.)

Figure 17-1. Cooling tower without work platform for maintenance workers.

Before describing a simple process to resolve hazards, here are a few examples.

EXAMPLE 1.

Maintenance person needs to maintain the spray nozzles in a water cooling tower. A set of stairs and work platform is needed to keep the workers from falling into or off the equipment while opening access panels and performing maintenance functions. However, if the tower is part of a larger construction project, these hazards can get overlooked and a later fix must be accomplished to meet OSHA standards.

EXAMPLE 2.

Maintenance worker must walk the top of rounded equipment, whether an aircraft wing or fuselage or a fuel tank car. The worker will need fall protection equipment, appropriate training and close supervision, or adequate work platforms can be planned, designed and constructed to reduce the risk of fall.

EXAMPLE 3.

In offices, proper designs are needed to eliminate the ergonomic injury potential and keep valuable productive workers on the job. The obvious hazards are the lighting, aisle widths, sharp edges and corners, proper heights of monitors and working surfaces, and so on. Buying systems furniture does not remove the hazards. The interior design needs to be accomplished by a professional trained in ergonomic design. During the recent construction of a beautiful office building, "ergonomic" side chairs, that weighed 41 lbs and had rubber feet that did not allow movement except by the strongest employees, were purchased.

Many offices had four of these chairs in their cubicle that the visitors could barely lift. Complaints came from the office workers and their visitors. Although the purchasing group thought if the chairs were sold as "ergonomic" they must be appropriate to order. Actually due to the weight, the back injury risk is quite high and back injury prevention training would be needed. Several calls to the vendor, who wanted to please the customer, resulted in agreement to replace the 500 heavy chairs with lighter chairs.

EXAMPLE 4.

Maintenance workers need to access equipment on this low sloped roof. Fall protection

Figure 17-2. Aviation fuel recycler without work platform and access ladder for operators.

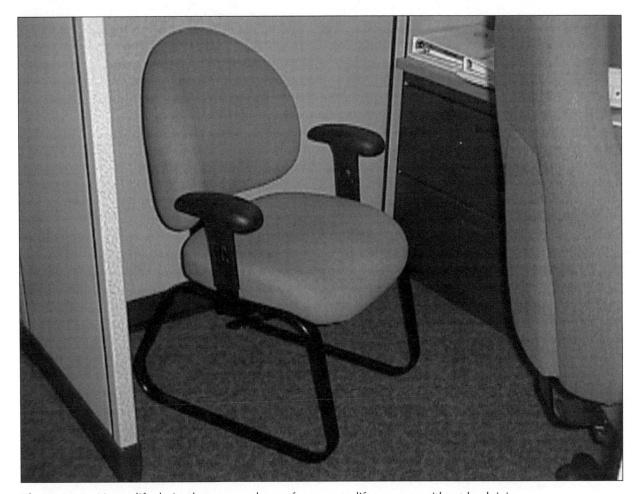

Figure 17-3. Heavy lift chairs that are too heavy for users to lift or move without back injury.

Figure 17-4. Slippery rooftop requiring fall protection for maintenance workers.

becomes a major problem since this rooftop has an epoxy coating which is very slippery when wet and the building is located in the Pacific Northwest where it rains frequently. The after construction solution was to install roof anchorages; however, the design solution is to understand the effect of the outdoor environment on roof coatings.

WHO OWNS THE PROBLEM?

Somehow the designer or design manager will be blamed for all the user accidents and the construction worker will be blamed for his "operator errors" that many professionals claim occur in 80% of the incidents. Interestingly enough, the designer can solve the problems in both cases, with the safety through design process.

SAFETY THROUGH DESIGN PROCESS

This simple process starts with the *planning team* asking the customer what specific hazards need to be controlled. Usually the planners and other functional area experts can team up to

offer wide design coverage. The team obtains customer input, offers solutions and tracks construction compliance. The planning team should include the customer, appropriate design engineers, architects, a safety engineer, an industrial hygienist, an environmental engineer, a fire chief or fire inspector, and other specialties depending on type of construction. Each member should have a knowledge base and will have important contributions when risk management recommendations are required. This team can be called a *facility system safety working group* (FSSWG pronounced "FIZ WIG")

FACILITY SYSTEM SAFETY WORKING GROUP RESPONSIBILITIES

Like other system safety working groups, the main responsibilities are to identify the potential hazards, track resolution and observe that the design was properly constructed; very simple tasks. Computer spread sheets can be used to track the hazards or sophisticated safety software tools can be used. The standard Preliminary

Hazard List (PHL) or Preliminary Hazard Analysis (PHA) can easily be adapted to obtain customer input and list solutions. After construction of the project, the FSSWG can use the PHL or PHA as a pre-occupancy checklist. After the customer has occupied the facility for a period of time (six to eight months) a post-occupancy survey is needed to check on latent safety issues or warranty items that still need to be fixed from the original pre-occupancy issues.

CUSTOMER INPUT

Everybody says the customer is always right, so getting the customer involved right up front is most important. The FSSWG must determine the customer needs, wants, and desires. The customer must be involved in the planning process to avoid cost over runs. It is mandatory the customer stay involved with the planning, design and construction of the facility. The customer cannot simply ask for a 200,000 square foot building and become separated from the process.

TEAMWORK AND COMMUNICATIONS

Customer communication is also most important. During one FSSWG, the user, a middle grade employee, asked for a safe entrance for parents to drop off their children at this proposed child care facility. This would enable the children to avoid crossing any busy streets or parking lots as the facility was sited in the same area as the base exchange, commissary, and gas station. This was a major issue for the user, and hopefully the planners and designers would have figured it out by themselves.

Children's safety would have been jeopardized or the project would have cost more money depending on what design or construction stage this deficiency would have been caught. There is a need to maximize input from the customer operator and maintainer. The customer can include a few individuals, but most importantly the person that will actually manage or operate the facility. Teamwork with the customer, designers and safety and health practitioners is most important.

CORPORATE LEVEL INTEGRATION POLICIES
ENVIRONMENT SAFETY AND HEALTH

A new acronym you may be seeing more frequently, is PESH (*programmatic environmental safety and health*). If "evaluations" is added to PESH, it becomes PESHE. And, if "analyses" or "assessment" is added, the term becomes PESHA. The Defense Department requires this integration for major weapon systems and the concept equally applies to facility construction.

The importance is self evident with hazardous material and hazardous waste requirements (discussed later); it is a combination of the safety and health and environmental expertise to design out hazardous conditions that will affect the system developer, user, maintainer, disposer, public and the environment. This greatly expands the envelope and requires out-of-the-box thinking.

For the PESHE, the requirements are for the program manager to *identify* and *evaluate* system safety, health and environmental hazards, *define* risk levels and *establish* a program to manage the probability and the severity of recognized hazards.

RISK MANAGEMENT

MIL STD 882C, System Safety Program Requirements[3], describes several levels of severity of an unplanned event and several levels of probability of that event. A combination of the severity and the probability, arranged in a matrix displays several risk levels. In real world analyses, each risk level needs to be empirically defined. For example, a confined space that maintenance personnel need to enter daily or weekly that could contain toxic or explosive vapors would be listed as a *risk 1*. Obviously, the high level risks need to be lowered to the lowest risk level possible.

CORPORATE RISK ACCEPTANCE

Hazards that cannot be designed out of a system or building or cannot be designed significantly low level require special approvals. A senior executive must be the final approval authority for acceptance of *high* risk hazards. For *serious* risk hazards, the corporate design director or chief engineer can accept the risk. In all cases, the management decisions must be formally documented and formally accepted.

It is significant that the vice president or design director risk-decision-making is assigned above project design level. The level of risk acceptance must be directly related to the seriousness of the hazard. This allows top management to be involved with serious and high level hazards the company will live with after construction is complete.

SYSTEM SAFETY PRECEDENCE

The late Joe Stephensen, in his book *System Safety 2000*[4], lists the sequence to reduce the risk levels in the following manner:

➤ Design for minimum hazard;
➤ Provide safety devices;
➤ Provide warning devices;
➤ Control with procedures and training; and
➤ Accept the remaining residual hazards.

For the maintenance confined space scenario, we would design the space to avoid the source of the toxic vapors, or design the space with several entrances, or design so no entry was required or enter with a reduced frequency, and so on. The higher up the precedence levels, the better the solution should be. In some applications, logarithmic weighting factors are applied to each level.

HAZARD TRACKING

Hazards identified by the FSSWG planners and designers need to be resolved and corrective actions tracked. Unresolved hazards will stand out and attention will be focused to reducing their risk, hopefully through design. Who should track the hazards? Either the technical experts or the design safety team should be responsible, depending on how the design teams are organized. But there needs to be *one* master list that records the resolutions. The formats for preliminary hazard analyses (PHA), as described in *System Safety 2000*[4] (e.g., Figure 8-3), can readily be used to track corrective actions.

EXPERIENCE REPORTS

The FSSWG needs to review experience reports (e.g., worker complaints and suggestions, incident reports, security reports, legal reports, inspection reports, rework and change order reports, external and internal audit reports, fines, and penalties) from similar facilities. Special safety conditions may come from the group such as "why have a confined space for the maintenance person", the group advised to "hinge the top open rather than have a small access hole."

The FSSWG needs to meet before critical milestone reviews, determine if acceptance testing is needed for other than the fire protection systems, and approve risk acceptance recommendations for hazards that cannot be designed out. They must participate on pre-occupancy walk-through inspections and post-occupancy evaluations.

The workers' compensation database can be used to target high-risk injuries such as back and neck, and allow redesign of the workstations or the work procedures. Environmental Notices of Violation reports and can determine how better design could minimize hazardous material spills.

SAFETY ANALYSIS TOOLS

MIL STD 882C lists numerous analytical tools available to the planners, designers and FSSWG. All are discussed in the MIL STD and in *System Safety 2000*. The PHA is an expanded Preliminary Hazard List, which is to be secured from customers. Even a simple PHL can provide great information from the user/customer. The Fault Tree Analysis, Failure Mode & Effects Analysis, and Software hazard analysis (3) are more complex techniques that are rarely used in facility design unless it is a complex process facility.

CONSTRUCTION CRITERIA BASE (CCB)

The National Institute for Building Sciences (NIBS) is a government-funded organization that collects technical design information from all government agencies and sells quarterly updates on CDs or for viewing on web pages. The CCB is most useful to planners, designers, and FSSWGs. All of the Army, Navy, Air Force, GSA, EPA, DOE, etc. design and construction specifications and standards are included, as well as many industry standards. The NIBS phone number is 202-289-7800 and Internet address (http://www.ccb.org).

OCCUPANCY ISSUES
PRE-OCCUPANCY INSPECTIONS

Jumping to the end of the construction milestone, assuming all hazards have been identified and resolved to the lowest risk; the FSSWG needs to conduct a pre-occupancy walk thru of the facility. This can be part of a formal test and evaluation (like in weapon system safety) or simply using the expanded PHA as a checklist to validate what action was taken. This will eliminate turnover surprises, and if needed, ensure safety and health items are posted on the "punch list" of identified deficiencies. The FSSWG has a key to making a successful occupancy.

POST-OCCUPANCY EVALUATIONS

Even if the punch list didn't have any safety and health items listed, some occupancy issues may have occurred during the first 6 months that can be corrected before the construction warranty runs out. This time the FSSWG may be represented by the safety manager, who has the list of employee complaints already tabulated and each must be resolved. The original design safety analyses (PHL or PHA) would be good to review at this time to determine the efficiency of the corrective actions taken.

CONTEMPORARY FACILITY DESIGN SAFETY AND HEALTH ISSUES

ERGONOMIC INPUT ERROR REDUCTION

Many engineers and safety practitioners are starting to trust the Internet security systems and are ordering products via web pages. On the order receiving side, ergonomic designs for Internet ordering process is important to ensure quality. The employee in photo 5 is recording customer orders to start the work process. This organization has an extremely low production error rate; however, it determined the main source of errors was due to incorrect input of the order (another false example of the 80% human error). Better workstation design will reduce employee fatigue, potential injury and eliminate input errors. At the same time direct web page ordering to avoid operator input error is being accomplished; however, for the next few years not all customers will have access to web page ordering and the operators will continue to be needed.

POLLUTION PREVENTION (P2)

Pollution Prevention (P2) and other support equipment needs to be evaluated for safety and health risks. When constructing or operating a facility where P2 equipment is needed, ensure at least the common physical hazards of high/low temperature, high voltage, high amperage, fall hazards, vibration, emergency controls, and

chemical hazards are controlled (see a checklist at www.navfac-safety.navy.mil.navy/p2). After using a checklist to evaluate the equipment, provide a TSDS (Technical Safety Data Sheet, like the Material Safety Data Sheet) to let the user know the safety and health characteristics of the equipment. (For further information on TSDS see Internet address: http://www.navfac-safety.navy.mil/p2.htm.)

HAZARDOUS CHEMICALS

HAZMAT/HAZWASTE process or maintenance chemicals need to be considered during planning and design. If left out, a separate facility may need to be constructed on exterior, or interior space modified rather than integrated into facility. The planning analysis (FSSWG) may reveal a considerable amount of space is needed for chemical storage and waste storage. This would be the perfect time to convince the process engineers to reduce the need for hazardous materials. One IBM plant[5] did this very well. All of the various chemicals were reduced to three or four innocuous chemicals.

FALL PROTECTION

As a leading killer of workers, fall hazards need to be eliminated through complete design. Eliminate hazards to the construction worker and to the user/maintenance person. The edge of building roofs are hosting numerous video cameras for security and high intensity lighting fixtures that need to be maintained. Roof-mounted HVAC systems are typically located near the edge of a facility (usually due to placement of interior process exhaust systems). See Figures 17-6a and 17-6b. However, protection is needed to prevent the HVAC mechanic from stepping back off the building.

FALL PROTECTION FOR SKYLIGHT MAINTENANCE

The 1998 National Safety Congress was held at the Los Angeles Convention Center. The designer of this facility was quite aware of the need for maintenance, repair, and cleaning of the skylights surrounding the foyers. Notice in Figure 17-7 the electric scaffold with permanent steps and handrails that rotates around the entire span of the skylights.

Figure 17-5. Customer order input workstation increasing ergonomic injury potential.

Figure 17-6a. Maintenance fall hazard, too close to edge of roof.

Figure 17-6b. No parapet to protect maintenance workers.

Figure 17-7. Maintenance scaffold provided for glass skylight access

SOFTWARE SAFETY

More and more, building systems are being controlled by computers. It is important to understand how the software system reacts when various abnormal conditions occur. The failure modes that effect safety and health hazards must be understood. It must be known exactly what occurs, when the power fails or when the system changes over to emergency power, or other scenarios. The security system in a recently completed office building has a keyless entry system with motion detector magnetic locks. The powerful magnets lock the doors at a preset time and do not allow entry or exit. Multiple exit routes no longer exist. Designers must be cautious about the software systems and analyze the failure modes to ensure no high-risk situations will occur.

DESIGN BUILD

The current trend is to specify less and use the Design-Build acquisition strategy. This strategy does not alleviate the need for adequate design safety planning and tracking. It might require less use of specific standards and more use of performance standards. However the FSSWG is still needed to ensure customer safety controls are communicated to the designer and constructor and that these are accomplished. For information about this strategy check the Design-Build Institute of America's web site: www.dbia.org.

INTERIOR DESIGNERS

As ergonomic awareness increases within the workforce, there will be more demands for "creative" ergonomic designs to satisfy our employees. Interior designers need to be trained in ergonomic design considerations which should increase customer satisfaction with workstation and other interior hazard elimination through design (see Example 3).

FUTURE OF DESIGN SAFETY

Customers and owners will continue to want smaller, quicker constructed, best value facilities, and their awareness of the need for design safety will be increasing. Since most customers and owners have occupational safety and health professionals, their user expertise will need to be tapped by the FSSWG. Planner and designer awareness of unique safety and health design issues need to increase. Liability will continue to grow for those who design in death traps of confined spaces, allow fall hazards for maintenance personnel, or allow ergonomically bad designs for workstations and industrial processes.

Life cycle costing is important in facility design. Costs of designs to eliminate high risk level hazards need to be compared against the long term cost of incidents, like those workers' compensation payments, that continue for 15 to 20 years after the initial injury medical payments. Design safety cost benefits need to be developed by designers for customers to understand and agree to purchase rather than upgraded landscaping, carpeting, or lighting fixtures.

The effects of change need to be considered more intensely. Field changes need not only to increase the value and decrease the cost, but the injury risk levels need to be minimized. There are millions of maintenance tasks done every day by thousands of workers where a better designed tool, process or facility can reduce the potential for human error to below 10%.

REFERENCES

1. Gambatese J, Hinze J, Haas C: A tool to design for construction worker safety. *ASCE Journal of Architectural Engineering,* vol. 3 no.1, Mar 1997 pp 32–41.

2. Brown D, Matuszak P, Hinze J, et al: Design for Safety. Construction Industry Institute publication no.101-1, 1997. NOTE: "Toolbox" is available from the CII, phone number 512-471-4319, or www.construction-institute.org.

3. MILSTD 882C, Department of Defense, System Safety Program Requirements, Jan 1993.

4. Stephenson J: *System Safety 2000.* New York: Van Nostrand Reinhold Publishers, 1991. National Safety Council. ISO-Safe at IBM Charlotte, *Proceedings from 1997 Symposium.* Institute for Safety Through Design, 1998.

Chapter 17 Appendix

BUILDING DESIGN SAFETY CHECKLIST

1. PLANNING AND ADMINISTRATION OF SAFETY AND HEALTH (OSH)

1.1 **GENERAL:** Designing facilities and systems which are inherently safe for use or occupancy by customer personnel is an integral part of every Architect/Engineer contract issued. The A/E is responsible for ensuring safe facility designs.

1.2 **OBJECTIVES:** The principal objectives of Occupational Safety and Health Act are to preclude hazards, minimize hazardous exposure, and reduce systems rework and retrofit to assure the safety and health of all personnel using our facilities and systems.

1.3 **OCCUPATIONAL SAFETY AND HEALTH ACT (OSHA):** Our company has committed to a continuing program to ensure design criteria are consistent with OSHA requirements. The A/E shall ensure facilities are designed in compliance with Title 29, CFR Part 1910 OSHA Requirements, as well as company criteria. However, if conflicts between OSHA and company or other Federal criteria are noted, the conflicts should be referred to the Contracting Officer Technical Representative (COTR) for resolution. The A/E should follow-up to ensure resolution is achieved though the system safety process.

1.4 **SAFETY ENGINEERING:**

Customer: A list of customer special safety and health concerns (for example, confined spaces, back injury, repetitive motion, fall hazards, energy sources, hazardous materials, etc.) shall be obtained, provided to the A/E and status reports provided to the customer. Planning and design shall ensure customer safety and health needs are identified and special controls are designed into facility projects. The Facility System Safety Working Group (FSSWG) is a safety process tool to link customer safety and health needs to the designer. FSSWGs should include the safety manager, industrial hygienist, environmental engineer, planner, user, and the safety engineer, as well as any other discipline needed based on the project. The FSSWG should develop a list of hazardous operations that are of concern and review the control methods that will be used. The safety engineer will assist in developing the list of customer safety and health concerns and coordinate with the FSSWG to determine adequacy of controls. The safety engineer will ensure that appropriate design safety reviews are conducted and recommendations/comments are provided to the project engineer or A/E.

Designer: The A/E may need to conduct their own analyses to ensure all hazards are identified, risk evaluated and engineering controls provided. Designs should minimize hazards to construction personnel, maintenance personnel and users. For complex or high hazard facilities, the A/E shall prepare a Safety Assessment Report (SAR) (refer to Mil-Std 882, DI-SAFT-80102A). The SAR report shall identify all customer requested controls, residual unsafe design characteristics, quantify risk of hazards not eliminated, and identify any controls, inhibits, or safety procedures. Whenever possible the designer should try to include safety features to minimize construction safety hazards.

REFERENCES: Title 29, CFR Part 1910 Occupational Safety Health Standards for General Industry, MIL STD 882 (current series) Department of Defense, System Safety Program Requirements.

II SPECIFIC DESIGN CONSIDERATIONS

2. AMERICANS WITH DISABILITIES

2.1 **DESIGN ELEMENTS:** Accommodate employees with disabilities to prevent injuries and illnesses. Provide "clean offices "for sensitized individuals. Provide computer assisted equipment and software.

2.2 **REFERENCES:** Planning and Design Policy Statement, Barrier-Free Design Accessibility Requirements; Americans with Disabilities Accessibility Guidelines (ADAG).

3. CONFINED SPACE

3.1 **GENERAL REQUIREMENTS:** Eliminate all possible confined spaces from the design. Remaining confined spaces shall be evaluated for accessibility, methods of isolation, maintenance and inspection.

3.2 **REMAINING CONFINED SPACES:** For each remaining confined space, wherever possible, design the space for continuous human occupancy, prompt egress, ease of ingress and elimination of hazardous atmosphere wherever possible.

3.3 **ACCESSIBILITY:** Design all confined spaces with multiple, large accesses. Access shall be equipped with platforms, which are large enough to support all required equipment and personnel. Access must not be restricted by objects such as pipes or ducts. Locations of ladders and scaffold mounts inside the space shall be identified. Consider fall protection issues such as anchorage points.

3.4 **ISOLATION METHODS:** Design isolation methods to isolate confined spaces from hazards. Isolation design considerations include planning for equipment removal through accesses, full isolation of confined space(s) from electrical, mechanical, hydraulic, pneumatic, chemical, thermal, radioactive and other hazardous energy such as falling object(s); to provide for complete isolation of all flows into and out of the confined space(s) such as valve blocking, spools, double blocks and bleeds, flanges, and flushing connections.

3.5 **MAINTENANCE AND INSPECTION:** Design the confined space(s) so that maintenance and inspection can be performed from the outside or by self-cleaning systems. Position maintenance points for ease of access.

3.6 **REFERENCES:** ANSI Z117.1 (latest version) Safety Requirements for Confined Space; Title 29 CFR Part 1910.146, Permit-Required Confined Spaces.

4. ELECTRICAL SAFETY

4.1 **GENERAL REQUIREMENTS:** Consider voltage and amperage levels, high voltage effects, ground connections and isolation. Design for safe operation, maintenance and inspection.

4.2 **PROTECTIVE DEVICES AND GROUNDING:** Design ground fault circuit interrupter (GFCI) systems for all high humidity areas and areas where liquids are, or may be used in applications such as spraying, splashing, pooling, or any other use by personnel. Reduce voltage and amperage levels by substituting equipment or systems; fuses, circuit breakers, and line capacities to meet anticipated future requirements. Eliminate grounding connections to gas or steam pipes, electrical conduits and sprinkler system piping to prevent accumulation of static electricity. Engineer ground devices to ensure maximum protection for unique sites such as rooms with flammable atmospheres; to provide lightning protection on buildings and electrical structures.

4.3 **INTRINSICALLY SAFE EQUIPMENT:** Design equipment or systems with consideration of combustible gases or vapors that may be encountered and account for differences in flash points, explosive limits and ignition temperatures.

4.4 **EQUIPMENT HEAT GENERATION:** Design to accommodate for the effects caused by heat generation from equipment and to control the temperature for flammables stored near this equipment.

4.5 **ISOLATION OF HIGH VOLTAGE EQUIPMENT:** Design to isolate indoor and outdoor high voltage equipment by using enclosure vaults, security fences, lockable doors and gates. Non-insulated conductors such as bus bars on panel boards, switchboards or high voltage equipment connections in accessible areas must be enclosed or protected to eliminate or reduce electrical hazards associated with maintenance and inspection.

4.6 **ENERGY ISOLATION:** Ensure all equipment and systems can be locked out. (See lockout/tagout section.)

4.7 **REFERENCES:** NFPA 70 National Electric Code; ANSI Z244.1 (latest version) Requirements for Lockout/Tagout; Title 29 CFR Part 1910, Subpart S, Electrical; and 29 CFR Part 1910.147 Control of Hazardous Energy (lockout/tagout); ANSI C2 (National Electric Safety Code).

5. ERGONOMICS

5.1 **ANTHROPOMETRY:** Design for the 5th and 95th percentiles (smallest and largest) such as clearances for the 95th percentile and visual fields for the 5th and 95th percentile. Determine the range of movement expected in the job or task and provide adjustable equipment wherever possible. Eliminate gender specific tasks and consider future workforce (older population with more females), force requirements such as grip strength and reach envelope. Eliminate spatially restricted spaces that require kneeling and crawling.

5.2 **PROCESS DESIGN:** Design layouts that do not require personnel to: Twist and turn when moving an object from one conveyor belt, table or machine to another; lift an object from floor level to a conveyor, table or machine; work with elbows above waist level; use hands and elbows in a twisting motion while performing job tasks; hyper-extend or hyper-flex wrists while performing job tasks.

5.3 **WORK-STATION DESIGN:** Design for range-of-motion of the worker; for field of vision of worker; to reduce repetitive motions required per task, duration and pace of a task; to provide adequate support for back and legs (such as back supports or floor mats); adjustable work surfaces that are easily manipulated from position of the work; delivery bins to accommodate height and reach limitations; work platforms that move up and down for various operations; for powered assists to eliminate the use of extreme force; for the use of suspension devices for heavy tools; the use of diverging conveyors off main lines so that certain activities can be performed at slower rates.

5.4 **PERSONAL RISK FACTOR:** Gender—Determine and understand which tasks negatively affect which genders. Age—Determine tasks that affect workers based on age. Anthropometry—Know the range of the work force. Work method—Design proper procedures for task accomplishment. Senses—Poor vision, hearing, and smell should be considered in ergonomic design. Physical strength—The strength required to accomplish a task must be considered. Weight—The weight of the worker can affect the design of a workstation.

5.5 **UPPER EXTREMITY RISK:** Design: to eliminate the need for repetitive and/or prolonged activities; to eliminate forceful exertions with the hands such as reducing the number of hand pinch grips required in task accomplishment. Design out the need for prolonged static postures (add chairs, arm rests etc. where needed) and maintain symmetry between the worker and the task (avoid awkward postures). Eliminate the need to reach above the shoulders, reach behind the back, perform unusual twisting of wrists and other joints, maintain continued physical contact with work surfaces or use tools with excessive vibration in task accomplishment.

5.6 **ENVIRONMENTAL RISKS:** Design to maintain constant workstation temperatures and avoid excessively hot conditions or excessively cold conditions; for appropriate lighting; to eliminate excessive vibration. Consider the type of floor surface and platforms required for safety and stability at the workstation.

5.7 **REFERENCES:** ANSI A-365 (latest version) Draft Ergonomic Standard; NIOSH lifting equation.

6. FALL PROTECTION

6.1 **ELIMINATION OF HAZARDS:** Design stairways with standard guardrails instead of straight ladders where feasible; parapets or guardrails at roof edges; warning lines and cables to keep personnel away from fall hazards; for cranes or personnel lifts to provide safe access. Install supply and exhaust fan equipment at ground level or on roofs with sufficient space and protection to adequately perform testing and routine maintenance.

6.2 **MAINTENANCE AND INSPECTION:** Design equipment so that fall hazards are minimized during maintenance repairs, inspection or cleaning. Consider future degradation of installed equipment in maintenance and inspection activities.

6.3 **ENGINEERING CONTROLS:** Design the job or operation to eliminate work at heights. When not feasible provide prevention systems such as guardrails, catwalks, and platforms. Consider fall arrest issues such as anchorage points; compatibility of the control measures with the job tasks and work environment.

6.4 **FALL PROTECTION SYSTEMS:** Install anchorage points. Design horizontal cable or I-beam trolley systems in areas where employees require continuous mobility and where platforms or guardrails are not feasible. Ensure proper test methods are used to ensure systems are capable of proper support.

REFERENCES: ANSI A92.5 (latest version) Aerial devices elevated work platforms; NFPA 101 Life Safety Code; Title 29 CFR Part 1910, Subpart F, Powered Platforms, Manlifts and Vehicle-Mounted Work Platforms.

7. FIRE PROTECTION

7.1   **GENERAL:** Mil-Hdbk 1008 provides detailed guidance for the incorporation of fire protection engineering measures in the design and construction of DOD facilities. The handbook can be used in the purchase and preparation of facilities planning and engineering studies and design documents used for the procurement of facilities construction.

7.2   **STANDARD FIRE SUPPRESSION EQUIPMENT:** Design so standpipe fire suppression equipment is protected against mechanical damage and located to facilitate prompt use of hose valves, hoses, and other equipment at the time of a fire or other emergency. Locate hose outlets and connections high enough above the floor to avoid being obstructed and to be accessible to employees. Ensure that reels and cabinets are conspicuously identified.

7.3   **TOTAL FLOODING SYSTEMS:** Total flooding systems should provide a pre-discharge employee alarm which is capable of being perceived above ambient light or noise levels before the system discharges, giving employees time to safely exit from the discharge area.

7.4   **FACILITY EVACUATION:** Design doors and pathways of sufficient size to allow complete dispersal of employees from a specific department or location. Consider safe areas inside of primary facilities for personnel who cannot escape. Design internal evacuation routes so that during an emergency occupants will readily know the direction of escape from any point. Provide means of egress remote from each other to prevent the blocking of any single exit due to fire or smoke. Discharge exits directly into the street, or yard, court, or other open space that gives access away from the facility and allows for adequate space to accommodate the discharge of occupants. Mark and arrange every exit so it is clearly visible and immediately recognized as an exit in order to minimize the possibility of confusion during an evacuation. Provide adequate and reliable illumination at all exit locations with exit signs at the point of exit from the building. Mark doors, passageways, or stairways which are not (or do not lead to) an exit by a sign reading "Not an Exit" or by a sign indicating its actual character, such as "To Basement," "Storeroom," "Linen Closet," etc.

7.5   **REFERENCES:** Mil-Hdbk-1008, Fire Protection for Facilities Engineering, Design and Construction; Title 29 CFR Part 1910 Subpart L (Fire Protection); Title 29 CFR Part 1910, Subpart E, Means of Egress; NFPA 101, *Life Safety Code*.

8. FIRST AID AND MEDICAL SERVICES

8.1   **FACILITY DESIGN:** Design medical facilities IAW Mil-Hdbk-1191: Provide for emergency communications and ramps where needed to deliver or pick up patients by ambulance. Provide adequate ventilation in first aid facilities. Design surfaces of doors, walls, floors, and ceilings in the medical work area to be water-resistant for ease of cleaning. Ensure access doors to the medical work area are self-closing. Consider emergency access points for ambulance crews and emergency responders.

8.2   **WASHING FACILITIES:** Provide medical facilities with an automatic or elbow/foot operated sink for washing hands to be located in the work area. Provide adequate washing facilities using potable water, soap, and single use towels or hot air drying machines; hand-washing facilities that are readily accessible to personnel working in first-aid stations.

8.3   **MEDICAL WASTE:** Provide areas for the isolation of medical waste; adequate ventilation in waste storage areas. Provide adequate marking of "biohazard" storage areas.

8.4   **COMPRESSED GAS:** Provide safe storage of compressed gases used for medical purposes. Minimize use of equipment or fixtures having potential for an ignition source. Provide storage of compressed gases outside of the immediate medical facility whenever feasible.

8.5   **PATHOGEN EXPOSURE CONTROL:** Provide medical work areas that minimize splashing, spraying, spattering, and generation of droplets involving blood or other potentially infectious materials. Plan for tables, countertops, flooring, and other routinely used work surfaces to be constructed of nonporous materials to aid in exposure control.

8.6   **LAUNDRY REQUIREMENTS:** Design for storage and recycling of launderable materials, contaminated laundry to be bagged or contained at the location where it was used and not sorted or rinsed in the location of use. Design to accommodate wet contaminated laundry that may soak-through or leak from the bag or container.

8.7   **CONTAINMENT EQUIPMENT:** Plan for and/or install certified biological safety cabinets (Class I, II, or III) or other appropriate combinations of personal protection or physical containment devices for all activities involving with infectious materials that pose a threat of exposure to droplets, splashes, spills, or aerosols for pathogen control.

8.8   **MAINTENANCE INSPECTION:** Properly position bulky or hard-to-maintain equipment to provide ease of access. Specify that maintenance access points be positioned for safe access.

8.9   **REFERENCES:** NFPA 99, Health Care Facilities; NFPA 99B, Hypobaric Facilities; NFPA 101, Life Safety Code; Mil-Hdbk-1191; Title 29 CFR Part 1910.151; Title 29 CFR Part 1910.1030; CGA Pamphlet P-2 Characteristics and Safe Handling of Medical Gas; EPA PB-86199130 Guide for Infectious Waste Management.

9   HAZARDOUS MATERIALS

9.1   **GENERAL STORAGE REQUIREMENTS:** Design storage facilities to maintain and separate both hazardous and non-hazardous storage; emergency ingress and egress points from hazardous materials storage areas. Determine whether underground or above ground storage is best for the site. Locate compatible waste streams in the same region of the site to reduce potential widespread contamination. Define well installation requirements (if necessary). Consider waste compatibility, hazard classes, fire suppression guidelines, containment requirements and recovery actions needed to properly store and dispose of hazardous materials.

9.2   **CHEMICAL COMPATIBILITY AND STORAGE:** Design diking between incompatible materials; collection sumps under the acid and alkaline storage areas for leakage that can be drained after any incident and/or neutralized before disposal; explosion-proof rooms for Flammables/ Combustibles. Design: floor drain passages; leakproofing method to prevent ground or ground water contamination; to eliminate chemical compatibility issues; to isolate materials; separate sumps for containment; eye wash and showers into appropriate locations; use a containment material to retain all emergency water.

9.3   **FLAMMABLE STORAGE:** Design explosion-proof rooms for flammable and combustible materials storage. Utilize spark resistant equipment, fire doors, blow-out walls, etc. Review all fire extinguishing requirements. Store fuels away and separate from oxidizers.

9.4   **LOADING/UNLOADING LOCATION AND DESIGN:** Place loading docks on opposite side of prevailing winds. Ensure all dock areas are designed with a sprinkler system. Provide dikes and/or containment systems for loading/off loading areas for tankers or railcars.

9.5   **STORAGE ABOVE/BELOW GROUND:** Provide secondary containment; spill prevention controls; overfill prevention controls; diking for tank farms. Design to protect from corrosion; leak detectors; all tanks to be grounded.

9.6   **ALARM AND WARNING SYSTEMS:** Design: systems to provide sufficient time for escape from the facility; alarms that are capable of being perceived above ambient noise or light levels by all personnel in the affected portions of the workplace; alarms that are distinctive and recognizable as a signal to evacuate the work area or to perform emergency actions; standardized systems to eliminate confusion in an emergency; to allow maintenance of alarm systems. Install redundant systems in areas with corrosive atmospheres or where devices are subject to unusual wear or possible destruction. Incorporate tactile devices in areas where personnel would not otherwise be able to recognize an audible or visual alarm.

9.7   **REFERENCES:** NFPA 30, Flammable and Combustible Liquids Code; NFPA 43D Pesticide Storage; NFPA 49 Hazardous Chemicals Data.

10. LIGHTING

10.1   **GENERAL REQUIREMENTS:** Incorporate supplemental lighting around moving machinery, conveyors, steps and stairways. Consider color perception changes under yellow sodium vapor lights. Design lighting that is comfortable to the eye; provides adequate security; and adequate for the work to be performed.

10.2   **EMERGENCY LIGHTING:** Provide emergency lighting: where necessary for personnel to remain at machines or stations to shut down equipment in case of power failure, at stairways, passageways, or aisleways used for emergency egress.

10.3   **LIGHTING IN HAZARDOUS CONDITIONS:** Determine NFPA Class and Division ratings for the location where lighting is considered. Ensure all associated switches and electrical equipment are approved for the location. Portable battery powered lighting equipment, used in connection with the storage, handling, or use of flammable gases or liquids must be of the type approved for the hazardous location.

10.4   **OUTSIDE LIGHTING:** Locate outdoor lamps below all live power line conductors, transformers, or other electric equipment unless adequate clearances or other safeguards are provided. Eliminate high contrast light and dark areas that may contribute to accidents from people or vehicles entering or leaving lighted or non-lighted areas.

10.5   **REFERENCES:** NFPA 101, Life Safety Code; IESNA Lighting Handbook (latest version); IES RP07 Practice for Industrial Lighting; IES RP-1 Practice for Office Lighting; NFPA 70, National Electric Code.

11. ENERGY CONTROL

11.1 **GENERAL REQUIREMENTS:** Specify or design energy isolation devices capable of being locked-out. Layout machinery and equipment to ensure safe access to lockout devices and provide each machine/equipment with independent disconnects. Specify lockout devices that will hold the energy isolating devices in a "safe" or "off" position.

11.2 **MACHINE AND EQUIPMENT SPECIFICATIONS:** Ensure equipment and utilities have lockout capability and that any replacement, major repair, renovation, or modification of equipment will still accept lockout devices. Design emergency and non-emergency shutoff controls for easy access and usability. Integrate actuation controls with warning lights and alarms to prevent personnel exposure to hazards.

11.3 **LOCKOUT DEVICES:** Ensure selected devices are capable of withstanding the environment to which they are exposed and are standardized within the facility.

11.4 **REFERENCES:** Title 29 CFR Part 1910.147, Control of Hazardous Energy (lockout/tagout); ANSI Z244.1 Requirement for Lockout/Tagout; NFPA 70, National Electric Code.

12. MACHINE GUARDING

12.1 **GENERAL REQUIREMENTS:** Design guards to be affixed to the machine whenever possible and ensure the guard does not itself create a hazard. Utilize structural barriers such as exterior or interior walls to isolate moving parts of machines. Specify guards that are interlocked with the source of power to the machine to prevent them from being removed by unauthorized personnel. Use vibration isolators to dampen or eliminate noise transmission and mechanical failure.

12.2 **BARRELS, CONTAINERS, AND DRUMS:** Ensure revolving barrels, containers, and drums are elevated and/or guarded by an enclosure which is interlocked with the drive mechanism.

12.3 **ANCHORING MACHINES:** Anchor all machines to prevent movement or vibration. Ensure the floor surface is appropriate for the weight and stress.

12.4 **MAINTENANCE CONSIDERATIONS:** Design maintenance access points to be located outside guards and are accessible. Provide adequate space between pieces of equipment.

12.5 **LOAD LIMITS:** Mark maximum rated limits on all machines, hoists, etc. Design out the ability for "quick-starts" to reduce mechanical stress. Install bumpers, shock absorbers, springs or other devices to lessen the effects of repeated impacts.

12.6 **REFERENCES:** OSHA 29 CRF 1910, Subpart O, Machinery and Machine Guarding; ANSI/ASME B15.1 (latest version) Safety Guarding and Devices.

13. MATERIAL HANDLING

13.1 **PLANNING FACTORS:** Consider load-handling factors for optimum storage and movement. Determine container specifications. Ensure equipment maximum load specifications are displayed prominently and that the size, weight, and center of gravity of the load are considered. Analyze types and quantities of materials to be staged indoors. Design receiving points and material handling processes to accept just-in-time deliveries.

13.2 **FACILITY WIDE CONSIDERATIONS:** Combine compatible operations to reduce multiple handling. Minimize transport distances in the facility by analyzing material routing techniques and necessary movement. Automate process if possible.

13.3 **WORK-STATION DESIGN:** Bring workers into the design process. Plan for objects to be between shoulder and knee height. Plan for adjustable work heights. Minimize travel distances. Place items within reach distance (plan for a range). Eliminate unnecessary handling. Choose proper containers for the task. Optimize equipment/material layout. Consider relationship of worker to work station (reduce twisting, bending, reaching). Minimize negative environmental factors. Insure load stability in movement.

13.4 **MANUAL TASK:** Automate load movement by using mechanical lift tables, lifting platforms, lift trucks, cranes, hoists, etc. Have material delivered at proper height. Increase unit quantity and load per movement. Reduce weight & size for easier handling. Change load movement to pushing and pulling operation.

13.5 **INDUSTRIAL TRUCKS:** Use industrial trucks when load movement is intermittent, over long distances, or over a variable path.

13.6 **MONORAILS, HOISTS, CRANES:** Consider use of monorails and cranes when the load transfer is required from one point to another in the same general area. Consider use of hoists to facilitate the positioning, lifting, and transferring of material within a small area.

13.7 **AUTOMATED SYSTEMS:** Consider driverless, automatically guided vehicles (AGV) for small load applications. Consider automated retrieval systems (ARS) for parts and storage retrieval.

13.8 **STORED MATERIALS:** Plan for storage areas that can be kept free of tripping, fire, and other hazards. Determine and observe height limitations when stacking materials; stacking limitations for lumber, blocks, bags and bundles. Design to allow drums, barrels, and kegs to be symmetrically stacked.

13.9 **MATERIAL SHIPPING & RECEIVING POINTS:** Minimize heating and cooling losses through the use of suspended dividing flaps or other doorway enclosure techniques. Install self-leveling docks, truck levelers, forklifts, cranes, and other devices to maximize efficiency and reduce manual material movement and handling. Provide separate receiving points for hazardous and non-hazardous materials.

13.10 **RAMPS:** Provide adequate width for material transport without the removal of guard-rails and toe-boards. Ensure that the slope of any gangway, ramp, or runway does not exceed specifications and rise to run ratio. Construct floor with maximum loading as a prime consideration and so that floor cannot tip, sag, or collapse under maximum anticipated loads.

13.11 **REFERENCES:** Title 29 CFR Part 1910, Subpart N, Materials Handling and Storage.

14. NOISE LEVEL CONTROL

14.1 **FACILITY EVALUATION:** Evaluate size and shape of rooms and departments, proposed layout of equipment, work stations, break areas, surface materials (e.g., ceiling/steel; walls/cinder block; floor/concrete), and noise from other sources (spill-over noise).

14.2 **NOISE INTENSITY CONTROL:** Separate personnel from noise sources by the greatest reasonable distance. Install noise barriers between the source and the operators. Locate equipment and workstations so that the greatest sources of noise are not facing the operators. Take advantage of reflective walls and floor surfaces to properly channel sound. Use building construction materials that absorb sound energy. Design an enclosed room for the equipment operator. Mount equipment that may vibrate on solid foundations. Locate noisy equipment in sound enclosures to reduce ambient noise levels. Install insulating material over surfaces creating or transmitting excessive noise. Provide noise absorbent linings on air ducts and mufflers on openings.

14.3 **EQUIPMENT SELECTION:** Select equipment with low vibration and noise characteristics. Stipulate permissible maximum noise levels in specifications for new equipment. Use equipment with low velocity fluids or gas flows. Where possible, lower machine or conveyor speeds or high pressure air exhausts.

14.4 **MAINTENANCE:** Design for maintenance minimization of vibration and noise. Use slow-acting valves or accumulators in water systems to eliminate water hammer. Substitute high noise processes with lower noise producing processes, such as squeezing processes instead of drop hammer processes; welding processes instead of riveting processes; chemical cleaning processes instead of high speed grinding/polishing processes.

14.5 **REFERENCES:** Title 29 CFR Part 1910.95, Occupational Noise Exposure.

15. TOXIC MATERIALS

15.1 **GENERAL REQUIREMENTS:** Review Material Safety Data Sheets (MSDS) for toxic materials selected for use. Consider current Threshold Limit Value's (TLV's) in the selection of materials. Design: for "just-in-time" storage and use of toxic materials on site to limit the type of substances, amount (dose) of exposure, and the number of entry routes to the body. Reduce the possibility of reactivity of chemicals in the same work area. Incorporate toxic material source reduction techniques in the design phase through closed process systems when extremely hazardous materials are used, eliminate or minimize flanges, connections, pump seals, valves, valve stems, etc., and closed process control rooms for operators. Incorporate shower and change rooms to prevent contamination outside of the facility. Ensure standardized labeling and marking of equipment, tanks, lines etc. Ensure access ports are of adequate size to permit entry while using personal protective equipment (PPE). Provide deluge showers and eyewash fountains.

15.2 **GASES:** Design: ventilation systems capable of handling routine and emergency releases; safe and adequate storage and staging facilities or workstations where gases are used. Consider line systems fed to work stations to eliminate indoor gas storage and staging. Install: emergency shut-off controls for maximum accessibility during emergencies: systems to detect and warn building occupants of threatening air concentrations.

15.3 **VAPORS:** Install spring-loaded covers where possible on open surface tanks to reduce evaporation; fusible links on covers of all open surface tanks not having spring-loaded covers. Install systems to detect and warn building occupants of threatening air concentrations. Design ventilation systems capable of meeting indoor air quality requirements.

15.4 **FUMES:** Install proper ventilation in areas where hot work (welding, brazing, etc.) is performed. Design ventilation systems capable of meeting indoor air quality requirements.

15.5 **AIR PARTICULATES:** Install HVAC and other control systems capable of meeting indoor air quality requirements; systems to warn against concentrations reaching lower level explosive limits (LEL) or other specified action level.

15.6 **ACIDS AND BASES:** Design: facilities to incorporate separate staging and storage of opposing pH material; ventilation systems so that different hazard classes do not mix in the air streams.

15.7 **METALS:** Design to reduce, eliminate, control, or substitute non-carcinogens for carcinogens such as lead acetate and cadmium. Limit employee contact through the use of rollers, grappling devices, etc. Incorporate the use of dust filters at the point-of-operation in process to limit the spread of metal dusts through proper ventilation.

15.8 **SOLVENTS:** Select process solvents carefully, many different hazard types exist (flammable, acidic, alkaline etc.). Select solvents that satisfy process requirements, and reduce engineering controls and PPE. Incorporate solvent filtration units to reduce handling and extend life if possible.

15.9 **ASBESTOS:** Perform an asbestos survey, including sampling and testing of suspected asbestos containing materials (ACM), for all areas of the project to be demolished, renovated or disturbed. The work shall be conducted under a safety and health plan and in full compliance with all applicable safety, health and worker protection regulations. The survey will consist of the four following components.

A review of existing building records and drawings for references to ACM used in construction, renovation, or repairs.

An inspection of the building(s) and all associated tunnels, chases, and crawl spaces to identify those materials that may contain asbestos. The A/E will be responsible for repairing any damage to the building caused by the inspection of inaccessible spaces. The survey will include the identification of friable and non-friable ACM. The locations of all ACM will be determined, reported, and photographed.

Sampling and testing of the suspected materials identified in step 2. The number of samples to be taken will vary according to the condition, but sufficient samples must be taken to assure that all ACM is identified and documented. Samples will be taken of the various troweled or sprayed on surfaces, pipes, and boiler insulation, tile, siding, shingles, and other suspected materials. A lab certified by the National Voluntary Laboratory Accreditation Program (NVLAP) using polarized light microscopy will analyze samples. The results of each sample analysis shall become part of the final report.

The A/E shall prepare comprehensive drawings and specifications as required for the removal of the ACM in a final report.

A drawing showing all locations of ACM, the estimated quantity, and sample points. Also note locations where removal of ACM will require temporary relocation of other systems such as HVAC ducts and piping.

The test results.

Photographs.

Recommended actions with a cost estimate.

Any other information, field notes or forms which provide pertinent data.

15.10 LEAD: 1) Perform a lead-containing paint (lead>0.5 percent by weight dry film) survey, including sampling and testing of painted surfaces, on all areas of the project to be renovated or disturbed. The number of samples to be taken will vary according to the conditions, but sufficient samples shall be taken to assure that all lead-containing paint that may be disturbed as part of this project is identified and documented. Each sample shall be removed cleanly to the substrate. The sample shall include only paint scrapings and must not be contaminated with material such as rust or mill scale, wood, concrete, or any part of the substrate. Each sample shall be sealed in a separate plastic bag or container that will not contaminate the sample, and shall be identified with the following information: project site, date, and location of sample, name and signature of person taking the sample. The sample bags or containers shall be sealed and sent to a laboratory certified by the Environmental Lead Laboratory Accreditation Program (ELLAP).

2) For projects including total or partial demolition, the A/E will also analyze a representative core sampling for Toxicity Characteristic Leachate Procedure (TCLP) using EPA Sw-846. Sub-samples should be taken from walls, windows, floors, ceiling, doorframes, and other building components. (The sub-samples are normally taken by using a 1-inch drill bit or similar device.) The size of each sample taken will be based on the volume of that particular building component relative to the total volume of the anticipated debris. The composite sample must be thoroughly mixed before being analyzed for TCLP. If the test results are below the EPA limit of 5 ppm, the construction debris shall be identified as non-hazardous and can be disposed of at a regular construction landfill (subtitle D). For test results exceeding 5 ppm, the construction debris be managed under Resource Conservation and Recovery Act hazardous waste regulations.

3) Shall prepare comprehensive drawings and specifications as required for the removal and disposal of lead-containing paint. Complete documentation of the survey and all test results are required along with mapping all areas and the locations of all sample points to confirm lead-containing paint. Complete forms, field notes, photographs, and all other information including assessments, condition of paint, and anticipated physical difficulties involved with any abatement action shall be part of the survey report. A photographic record may be used to determine the validity of the proposed corrective actions if deemed necessary. The work shall be conducted under a safety and health plan and in full compliance with all applicable safety and health, and worker protection laws. The survey report shall include as a minimum the following information:

Qualifications of the laboratory.

Type of test analysis conducted.

Drawings showing location of samples and homogenous areas of lead containing paint including the estimated quantity.

Photographs (if used).

Results of both TCLP and total lead analysis in % concentration of lead in paint and ppm TCLP.

Recommended actions and a detailed cost estimate.

REFERENCES: Title 29 CFR Part 1910, Subpart Z, Toxic and Hazardous Substances; NFPA 30 Storage of Hazardous Materials; NFPA 491 Hazardous Chemical Reactions; CGA Pamphlet: Handbook of Compressed Gases

16. INDUSTRIAL VENTILATION

16.1 **GENERAL REQUIREMENTS:** Locate all emission sources. Characterize each constituent to determine specific requirements. Review: ways to reduce personnel interaction with the source reviewed, personnel location, and work practices; to determine incompatible air streams (cyanides and acids etc.). Consider effects of outside wind speed and direction: weather and seasons.

16.2 **ASSESS HAZARDS:** Review: Material Safety Data Sheets (MSDS) to determine specific of chemicals used in the process; exposure limits; use most conservative exposure limit determined. Mass-balances considered to determine actual loss rates. Comply with manufacturer recommendations for venting.

16.3 **COMBUSTIBLE HAZARDS:** Ensure: concentrations are below the levels specified; flammable or explosive limits are controlled by using intrinsically safe equipment. Incorporate explosion venting techniques into ventilation and collection systems.

16.4 **MAINTENANCE:** Install gauges to measure pressure drop at exhaust ducts. Design controls that are easily accessible to operators and maintenance crews.

16.5 **ALARMS AND WARNING SYSTEMS:** Ensure automatic controls are installed to provide audible or visual alarms if ventilation systems fail and provide sufficient time for safe escape from the facility. Automatically shut down operation if ventilation fails. Ensure alarms are designed that are capable of being perceived above ambient interference and that tactile devices are used where personnel would not be able to recognize an audible/visual alarm.

16.6 **HOODS:** Design and orient to ensure ventilated materials will fall or be projected into the hoods in the direction of the air flow and that minimum air flow specifications are achieved at any point in the capture zone. Ensure air flow specifications are strong enough to overcome other forces acting on the contaminants (doors, HVAC, etc.).

16.7 **DUCTWORK:** Design inlet and exhaust ductwork: to be adequately supported throughout its length and is sized in accordance with good design practice(s). Provide inspection or clean-out doors in ducting as required. Provide drains as required.

16.8 **MAKE-UP AIR:** Provide clean "dedicated" fresh Make-up air.

REFERENCES: ANSI/AIHA Z9.5 (latest version) Laboratory Ventilation; ANSI Z9.2 (latest version) Fundamentals Governing the Design and Operation of Local Exhaust systems; Title 29 OSHA 29 CFR 1910.94, Ventilation; NFPA 496, Purged and Pressurized Enclosures for Electrical Equipment.

Chapter 18

APPLICATION IN THE ELECTRONICS INDUSTRY

by Richard L. Parker
Mollie A. Foster

INTRODUCTION

As the world's largest producer of semiconductor devices, the Intel Corporation is also a very large consumer of manufacturing, assembly, test and office equipment. Novellus Systems, Inc. is a semiconductor equipment supplier, and a leader in chemical and physical vapor thin film deposition. Intel and Novellus culture is defined by a set of distinct values, one of which is safety.

The goal of supplier, and device maker, equipment environmental, health and safety (EHS) programs is to provide the best possible EHS performance for equipment purchased, operating and maintained by supplier and device maker.

There are many aspects to a total EHS program, which are required to operate an incident and injury free environment. Establishing a formal disciplined approach to integrate the myriad of program aspects ensures that (1) supplier and device makers expectations are met, and (2) EHS aspects are optimized and integrated into tool design and through the equipment life cycle phases. Adequate consideration is given to safety as early as possible in the equipment design and selection phases. Examples of expectations needing to be met include but are not limited to the following:

➤ Design, construct, and install safe, environmentally responsible products.
➤ Maintain a single configuration product meeting all requirements for worldwide use.

Both supplier and device maker must establish the equipment/product safety program as a quality driven and consistent approach with suppliers focusing on a documented, ISO 9001 process for both new design and also fielded equipment. Results of this Design for EHS process are as follows:

➤ Significantly decreased "time to money;"
➤ Improved product liability through effective and safe tool development through end user-supplier-original equipment manufacturer partnerships for safety;
➤ Optimized system design for conformance with all applicable requirements;
➤ Operational effectiveness and success;
➤ Customer satisfaction; and
➤ Budget commitments met.

BACKGROUND

The key issue that separates the semiconductor industry from most others is the extraordinary rate of change in manufacturing and product technologies. This rate of change far exceeds the rate of change by the various EHS codes, standards or guidelines. The objective of both supplier and device maker objective is to ensure safe processes and products despite often-antiquated codes and standards.

A unique aspect within the semiconductor industry is the collaborative effort between suppliers and device makers when working with environmental, safety and health issues. The industry has an excellent EHS record as a result, despite the young age of the semiconductor industry. Most of the large device manufacturers and their suppliers use voluntary EHS guidelines known as SEMI® EHS Guidelines.

OBJECTIVE

An explanation is provided of a successful semiconductor equipment design for EHS from both a device maker and equipment supplier viewpoint. This process is complicated since device makers can often state conflicting expectations, which can cause significant strain on an equipment supplier's ability to perform at a level acceptable to all customers. This text will examine how the world's largest semiconductor manufacturer drives a consistent program based on industry-wide expectations, and how a supplier consistently performs at a high level of EHS performance while meeting many demands.

The Intel and Novellus equipment EHS design program from tool design through installation and operations will be reviewed. Some basic processes and activities will be shared with the reader for potential use within their own organizations.

TERMS

The terms used are defined as follows:

➤ *CE Mark*=Label affixed to products indicating conformance to European Union product requirements.

➤ *Device Maker*=A producer of semiconductor devices or related products such as microprocessors, memory and digital processors.

➤ *EHS*=Environmental, Health, and Safety, or Environmental, Safety, and Health (ESH), or Design for Environmental Health and Safety (DFEHS).

➤ *Hazard Analysis*=A systematic examination of process and support equipment, design intents, or procedures through the application of specific methods to identify potential hazards and their consequences, which results in a qualitative and/or quantitative assessment of risk.

➤ *Semiconductor Equipment and Materials International (SEMI®)*=Global trade association representing semiconductor, flat panel display equipment, and materials industries. Founded in 1970, SEMI® is a worldwide organization (2,000 member companies). EHS professionals of member companies developed thirteen EHS voluntary guidelines. Two core guidelines:

• *S2-93A Safety Guidelines For Semiconductor Manufacturing Equipment* includes references and requirements from: NFPA 318 Protection of Cleanrooms, NFPA 79 Electrical Standard for Industrial Machinery, ANSI S1-13 Methods for the Measure of Sound Pressure Levels, ANSI/UL 1262 Safety Standard for Laboratory Equipment, ANSI/UL1301-1 Safety Standard for Electrical Equipment for Laboratory Use, ANSI Z136.1 Safe Use of Lasers, ANSI Z535.4 Product Safety Signs and Labels, 21 CFR 1040 Laser Safety; Performance Standards for Light-Emitting Products, 89/392/EEC Machinery Directive, 72/23/EEC Electrical Equipment Designed for the Use within Certain Voltage Limits (Low Voltage Directive), EN 60204-1 Safety of Machinery – Electrical Equipment of Machines, EN 418 Safety of Machinery – Emergency Stop Equipment, Functional Aspects Principles for Design, and 92/31/EEC Electromagnetic Compatibility (EMC) Directive.

S8-95 Safety Guidelines For Ergonomics/Human Factors Engineering of Semiconductor Manufacturing Equipment.

➤ *SEMATECH (SEmiconductor MAnufacturing TECHnology)*=A non-profit technology development consortium of U.S. semiconductor manufacturers formed in 1987. The SEMATECH Application Guide for SEMI® S2-93A and SEMI® S8-95 provides interpretations for certain areas within the two Industry guidelines.

➤ *Supplier*=A producer of equipment, chemicals or contract services used in the support or manufacturing of semiconductor or related devices.

➤ *Tool*=A term used for process equipment used in the manufacturing of semiconductors.

INTEL EHS NEW EQUIPMENT PROCUREMENT PROCESS

The equipment safety design process is summarized in the flowchart (Figure 18-1). Intel and other device makers rely on the SEMI® EHS guidelines for the common set of equipment EHS design expectations. Details of the specific SEMI® EHS guidelines are not required for this discussion. It is the process and concepts that are important. These EHS guidelines establish the minimum requirements that a supplier shall apply when designing and selling a tool. Intel and several device makers embark on tool variations and details, which often results in designs that exceed any known requirements. However, by using these voluntary industry guidelines device makers are able to move tools throughout the world to new or expanding manufacturing operations with little impedance. Performance to these EHS guidelines are measured through a third-party auditing system, analogous to a nationally recognized testing laboratory verification. A key difference is that tools are not labeled since third-party evaluations go well beyond electrical compliance and SEMI® guidelines are not "standards."

SEMI® guidelines allow new technologies to emerge while maintaining and often improving already excellent EHS performance. Device makers, in most cases, refer to the SEMI® EHS guidelines in purchase specifications and require submission of a qualified third-party report. Third-party qualifications are also established through a SEMI® EHS guideline. Most device makers also require that tools be either CE marked or CE mark-able in order to meet the European requirements. Commonly asked questions are as follows:

➤ Question: *Is a UL (Underwriters Laboratories)-type label acceptable in place of these third-party reviews to SEMI® guidelines?*
Answer: *Only if the application of the tool is consistent with the labeling criterion, the tool is <600V, 2400w and there are no hazardous process materials.* and ...
➤ Question: *Does a CE-marked tool preclude the need to meet any of the aforementioned guidelines?*
Answer: *No, until there is complete alignment with North American requirements, such as NFPA (National Fire Protection Association) and NEC (National Electrical Code) standards, a multiple set of requirements must be met.*

With so many requirements and technology that is often years ahead of existing codes and standards, how Intel must work closely with suppliers and other device makers to develop and use safe and clean equipment becomes abundantly clear.

INTEL EQUIPMENT SUPPLIER DEVELOPMENT

New technologies in chips, demand new equipment process capabilities (Figure 18-1), compo-

nent 1). Intel has always been proactive in educating the supplier and device maker communities. Most aspects of EHS are not considered proprietary so device makers attempt to share copious information with suppliers currently doing business with Intel and those that are not doing business with Intel. This process is facilitated by organizations such as SEMI®, the Semiconductor Industry Association (SIA), and the Semiconductor Safety Association (SSA).

EDUCATION PLATFORMS

The Intel Supplier Day is a two-day annual event sponsored for all equipment and facilities suppliers and key contractors held in the United States and Japan. Each year a management team is brought together to develop an event theme so that all areas of focus are integrated. Attendees are by invitation only, CEO or executive staff management level. This event is used to communicate critical expectations and to *listen* to suppliers concerns and suggestions. A floor area with booths and demonstrations is used to communicate messages from and to Intel. EHS is a key area on the floor with one to two Intel EHS corporate managers and one to two technical experts on hand to answer questions, discuss Intel and supplier expectations. This event is often followed with an EHS road show to individual suppliers, which allows more detailed technical exchanges. In order to maintain a high level of synergy, Intel, suppliers and other device makers will often form teams to develop EHS performance goals.

INDUSTRY ALIGNMENT

Intel works to ensure that other device makers, such as Texas Instruments and IBM, and equipment suppliers are commonly aligned in EHS performance expectations. While much energy is expended in maintaining this alignment, the ultimate payoff comes in realizing extremely safe and clean tools for work and surrounding environments. Suppliers benefit by having shorter design lead times and being presented with fewer EHS design variations, all of which lead to reduced tool development cost and a more valued design by device makers.

Example
Wafers are thin slices of silicon, the primary manufacturing media for making semiconductors.

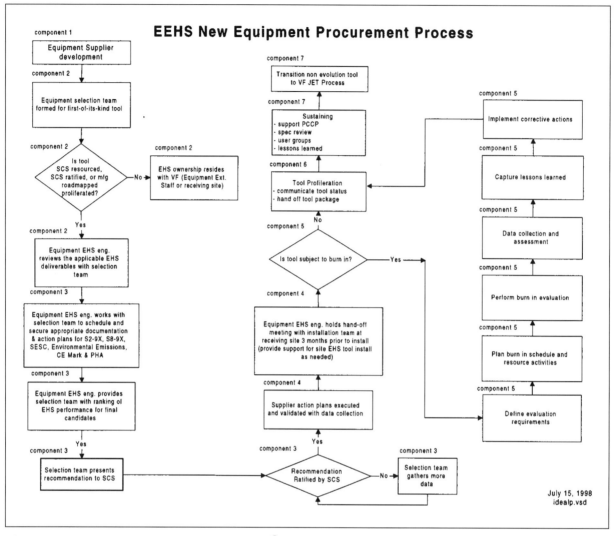

Figure 18-1. Equipment Design Review Process.©

They are also used as a common benchmark for determining manufacturing and quality improvements. The industry is attempting to move from an 8-inch diameter silicon wafer to a 12-inch wafer and an accepted measurement benchmark to improve manufacturing efficiency and costs. There are EHS issues associated with such a transition: larger tools, more emissions, higher utilities consumption, increased weights in manual materials handling, and complex automation, to name a few.

Intel initial efforts began in 1993 even though such a transition may not occur until 2001 or later. It was determined as a minimum that emissions must be one-half that of an 8-inch wafer/per wafer in order to meet aggressive reduction goals. Utilities could not exceed the current 8-inch consumption model and should be reduced in water use areas. It was established that 12-inch wafers should not be manually handled due to weight and safety. Texas Instruments and Intel formed a working group to communicate these emerging issues to the industry at large. Areas where industry alignment has been established for 12-inch wafer technology key areas include the following:

1. S2-93A compliance;
2. S8-95 compliance (ergonomics);
3. CE compliance certification;
4. Supplier EHS management;
5. Environmental (Process Tool Emission Characterization Standards Package - Supplier is required to provide engineering analysis and measurements using supplier process to verify emissions goals are met);
6. Fire; and

7. Risk management (Preliminary Hazard Analysis)

Intel and Texas Instruments produced a joint video so that all suppliers and device makers could share in an understanding of the new challenges. Subsequently, training sessions were hosted by SEMI®, SEMATECH International, I300I (International 300mm Initiative), Intel and Texas Instruments to further communicate the issues, listen to suppliers' concerns and develop road maps to overcome obstacles in achieving excellent EHS performance. Areas where industry alignment is not possible are left to each device maker and supplier to manage and negotiate.

SELECTION

Activities of Manufacturing Tooling Suppliers Equipment selection teams or work groups are created whenever Intel embarks on a new wafer process (Figure 18-1, component 2). Teams are typically comprised of very specific engineering disciplines, including a corporate equipment EHS engineer. Intel uses a large percentage of existing technologies, as do other device makers, when moving to the newer technologies. This allows for faster manufacturing start-up to peak volume and fewer problems. The equipment EHS engineer's first role is to educate this team on the EHS requirements and the process that must be followed for success. The selection team then assesses various supplier capabilities using an established set of manufacturing specifications. EHS expectations are consistent, and do not vary from one supplier to the next.

At this point EHS begins a scoring process for each supplier, using the EHS Supplier Selection Score Card (Figure 18-2). It is used to assess two areas critical in the Intel supplier review process: 1) Do supplier and device maker have the data needed to assess the EHS design of the tool in 7 key areas, S2-93A, S8-95, CE technical file, Supplier EHS management (safety programs), Environmental characterization, Fire assessment, Process Hazard Analysis (PHA)?, And 2) What is the health of the tool based on this data, non-compliance to required codes, etc? Each supplier is scored based on the results in both these areas.

Suppliers are requested to produce third-party reports to SEMI® S2/S8, which also detail tool design parameters such as ergonomics, safe-ty, hazard analyses, emissions characterizations and utilities consumption. Additionally, the report must reveal where tool design features or processes do not meet criteria outlined in the SEMI® EHS guidelines. Each area determined to not meet the EHS performance criteria is risk ranked using a SEMI® S10 risk ranking guideline. In addition to a hardware design review, Intel assesses a supplier's EHS program, injury rates, required OSHA compliance, et cetera, which allows determination of other potential safety issues and provides focus for corrective actions prior to a supplier being selected. The Design For EHS is an iterative process (Figure 18-3), which requires that systems be established for collecting lessons learned for use in future equipment selection.

CORRECTIVE ACTION AND DATA COLLECTION WITH SELECTED SUPPLIER

This phase of equipment supplier review (Figure 18-1, components 3 and 4) includes approving supplier roadmaps to compliance and the equipment installation sign-off.

SUPPLIER ROADMAPS

A supplier roadmap is used to define the specific actions a supplier must take to produce a tool that is designed to EHS requirements. A goal of the equipment selection teams, and the corporate equipment EHS group, is to ensure all known issues are resolved prior to, or during the development phase, so that field retrofits are not required in a high volume production facility.

Prior to a selected tool entering Intel facilities, the equipment EHS engineer conducts a meeting with the first two sites scheduled to receive the new tool. These sites are typically the technology development site and the first site to go into high volume manufacturing. Within these meetings, this Intel team of site and corporate EHS engineers determines which issues have merit from those that are of no real risk to the employee, community or environment. Each action item has a required completion date, which is tracked by the responsible equipment engineer. Each equipment supplier is managed separately due to unique issues and capabilities. Intel will often work with a supplier to implement internal EHS program improvements, benefiting Intel and other supplier's customers. This

SCS Equipment EHS Supplier Selection Score Card

Supplier: _____

Equipment: _____

Selection Chair: _____

Date: _____   Total Score: _____

EHS Deliverables→	Scoring Criteria→	Score→	Total Score ←
S2-93A	1) non-compliance's? 2) If yes, how many(Low, Med. High)?	1) No= 1 2) Yes =-1 for each non-compliance item	
S8-95 (S2-93A Section 14.0)	1) non-compliance's? 2) If yes, how many(Low, Med. High)?	1) No = 1 2) Yes = -1 for non-compliance's non-compliance item	
PHA("What if or FMEA analysis).	Tools/subsystems with >/=600v, or class 3 or 4 HPM provide FMEA All other cases "what if?" analysis	+1 Data package complete or 100% compliance achieved -1 For each risk issue(Low, Med. High) Not applicable (NA) = 1	
CE Mark European directives (Appendix A of S2-93"A")	Intel agrees with the Declaration of Conformity submitted by the supplier	No = -1 Yes = 1 Not applicable (NA) = 1	
Combustible material (S2-93a section 19.0)	If combustible material is >20% of the surface area the material meets FMRC 4910 test standard	No = - 1 , Yes = 1 Not applicable (NA) = 1	
Safety Program Expectations	1) Operations manual contains OSHA approved LOTO procedures. 2) Identified means to receive LOTO and Electrical Safety training per OSHA requirements. 3) FSE presents completed training documentation prior to arriving at the site.	Yes = 1, No = -1	
Emissions Data (S2-93A section 24.1)	Report completion per Intel Emission data package or equivalent method	+1 Data package complete If the emissions are above trigger level -1 if the emissions are >1 - 3X goal(low) -2 if the emissions are >3X goal(high) Trigger level HAPs = 0.0005lb/ws VOCs = 0.001 lb/ws PFCs = 2lb CE/ws	

TOTAL SCORE (maximum possible 7) _____

Figure 18-2. EHS Supplier Selection Score Card. ©

then clears the path for streamlined performance in the future.

EQUIPMENT INSTALLATION SIGN-OFF

Tools that are installed within an Intel facility must undergo an " Equipment Sign-Off" process. This sign-off occurs in each level 1, level 2 and level 3.

LEVEL 1 ELECTRICAL SYSTEMS/SUBSYSTEMS

Level 1 consists of a review of electrical systems and subsystems associated with the equipment or process that must be completed prior to electrical power being supplied. This includes a review of disconnects, guarding of energized circuits, and emergency shutdown capabilities.

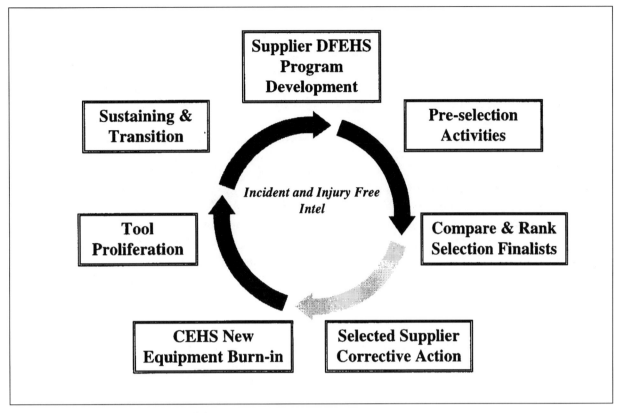

Figure 18-3. Design for EHS model.

A lockable disconnect is required for all hazardous energies. All hazardous energies are to remain locked and tagged out until Level 1 sign-off is complete.

Tools may be powered up to test Emergency machine off (EMO) functionality ONLY after all Level 1 checklist items have been verified. Tools must be returned to a locked-out state until Level 1 sign-off has been completed.

LEVEL 2 ENGINEERING QUALIFICATION

All EHS requirements are reviewed, including labeling, gas delivery systems, gas detection systems, interlocks, exhaust, chemical disposal, leak detection (if applicable), and so on. Hazardous production materials (HPMs) may be introduced into the equipment or process only after completion of Level 2 sign off.

LEVEL 3 RELEASE TO PRODUCTION

All punch-list items & equipment specifications have been completed and are ready for safe operation. Validation that all tool specifications are met, all problems are closed, tool is ready for full operation.

Should a tool fail at any level, corrective action is taken to resolve the issue before proceeding to the next level. This process ensures that the tool is installed, energized and operated to the highest EHS standards available, regardless of operating country.

DESIGN VALIDATION AND DEVELOPMENT (BURN-IN)

The Design Validation and Development process assesses the tool design, performance and layout at an Intel new product/process development facility (Figure 18-1, component 5). Focus is placed on maintenance and operational issues, which are based on supplier manuals and tool reliability. Intel knows that manufacturing environments will impact procedures and/or task design, which cannot be detected by the third-party evaluation processes. This process has been most beneficial in identifying ergonomic issues and verifying operating response plans to various tool conditions (alarms, error messages). Additionally, the process allows Intel EHS professionals to collect chemical monitoring baseline data eliminating the need to perform this process at each new facility. This process reduces EHS resource requirements and manufacturing delays in facilities receiving this new equipment.

The process objective, then, is delivery of tools to high volume manufacturing (HVM) without EHS roadmap issues or retrofit requirements. The following steps identify the basic process elements during the Design Validation and Development phase:

Planning with the Design Validation and Development Burn-In Tool Team

The first step is to meet with the process tool owner, identify key contacts, discuss roles and responsibilities, and obtain supplier documentation on the tool that will be used to determine which activities require analysis.

Negotiate EHS resources for Design Validation and Development Activities

Step 2, equipment EHS engineer meets with the EHS content experts (Industrial Hygiene, ergonomics, safety, fire and environmental) to define the scope, content, and time requirements for the specific EHS Burn-in activities. Activities in maintenance, servicing or operation of the equipment will be critically assessed for potential EHS issues.

Schedule Activities

Step 3, schedule the review activities identified in step 2. Meetings are held with the process equipment owner to integrate the EHS activities into the process equipment development schedule.

Conduct Analysis

Step 4, EHS content experts will conduct the scheduled analyses and evaluations identified during the Pre Burn-in meeting. Documentation, if required, will be developed indicating the scope of analysis activities and issues identified. These issues will be risk-ranked using SEMI® S10, and tracked by the equipment EHS engineer to closure in the Burn-In Corrective Action Plan. Risk ranking ensures that issues can be consistently communicated to other suppliers and other device makers, facilitating the sharing of knowledge within the industry. All Burn-In documentation is captured in the Tool Specific Package (TSP), and then delivered to the Capital Equipment Development (CED) tool owner to be included in the Technology Transfer document to the HVM sites.

PROLIFERATION OF TOOLS TO MANUFACTURING LOCATIONS

The TSP (Figure 18-1, component 6) is a comprehensive data package unique to the Intel EHS program. The package contains all data needed for a manufacturing site to learn about the EHS characterization of a specific tool. It contains data normally collected at other sites installing the tool, thus reducing duplicated efforts, and assists in reducing tool start up time.

EXAMPLE

An example of the TSP content is shown below; most recently completed for a purchased assembly and test tool.

Section 1 – Initial Installation Data, Selection Acquired
    S2/S8 Letter of Compliance
    Declaration of Conformity to CE Mark
    Hazardous Energies Control Point Listing
    Interlock Matrix
    Radiation Identification Table
    Chemical/Gas Listing
    PPE/Emergency Safety Equipment Assessment
    Ventilation/Exhaust Summary Matrix
    Tool/Subsystem Electrical Data Table
    Tool/Subsystem EMO Table
    Laser Inventory Sheet
    Tool Footprint Block
    Supplier Ergonomics Success Criteria
Section 2 – New Equipment EHS Burn-in Wrap-up Report
Appendix 1 – Safety Assessment/Reports Safety Burn-in Worksheet
Appendix 2 – Environmental Assessments/Reports
    Air Emissions Measurements Report
    Chemical/Water Mass Balance Report
Appendix 3 – IH Assessment/Reports
    IH Assessment
    Evaluation & Exhaust Optimization Report
Appendix 4 – Ergonomic Assessments/Ergonomic Assessment Report

SUSTAINMENT OF EVOLVING DESIGNS; TRANSITION OF OUTDATED DESIGNS

To ensure continuous improvement, several quantitative and qualitative performance indicators or communications programs have been implemented (Figure 18-1, component 7). A brief summary of some of the more unique situations follows.

EQUIPMENT EHS PERFORMANCE REPORT CARDS

Twice a year each equipment EHS engineer is required to submit a standard report card to internal customers and peers. The report is designed to assess the engineer's performance relative to tool selection activities using predetermined performance criteria. This would be analogous to a college student's semester report card. Report card results are used to improve EHS system performance. Since implementing these report cards, team performance has improved by over 35% annually.

THIRD-PARTY PERFORMANCE

Third parties are those entities that contract directly with suppliers to assess tool design and compliance to SEMI® industry guidelines and local code requirements. Intel does not manage third parties since contracting is between the third-party and the equipment supplier, but does however, have a quarterly meeting, with all third parties attending, to review issues seen in the previous quarter and provide suggested actions. This is a single meeting involving all third parties, approximately 12, where issues are defined without directly implicating any one of the third parties. These representatives then go off to work the issues and respond to the Intel request for corrections or feedback.

SUPPLIER PERFORMANCE

Long term supplier performance is tracked in two key areas:
1. Safety bulletin incident (SBI), and
2. Safety, For Your Information (SFYI). These are near misses or incidents with potential for serious injury, property damage, agency inspections, or environmental violations that occur with a supplier's tool. Severity of events determines SBI or SFYI classification.

PRODUCT SAFETY NOTIFICATION

The *product safety notification* (PSN) is a written communication from an equipment supplier, which states there is an equipment or component defect, and there is the potential to create an unsafe condition. Upon identification of a component and/or piece of equipment defect that may compromise the EHS of Intel's employees or property, it is the supplier's responsibility to perform the following:
1. Provide notification as defined within the PSN guideline.
2. Develop an action plan and response timeline.
3. Implement the action plan.
4. Issue a letter to Intel stating all PSN issues are closed. PSNs are viewed as a proactive approach to resolving issues found within designs due to latent defects or some undiscovered problem.

THE NOVELLUS SYSTEMS INC SYSTEM SAFETY PROGRAM

Novellus is a semiconductor equipment supplier to the Intel Corporation and a leader in chemical and physical vapor thin film deposition. The following sections describe their new product development and system safety program.

DESIGN TEAM DEVELOPMENT

The successful introduction of any new product depends upon the cooperative efforts of many departments, cross-functional teams, and individual contributors. Comprehensive plans, clear communications, and accurate documentation are required. A New Product Introduction Guide applies to all programs for developing and introducing new products and processes, including joint development programs and major continuous improvement program (CIP) activities. It is applicable across all corporate and business unit departments. A program manager is appointed and chartered with the ultimate responsibility for ensuring the program's success, including safety and system effectiveness for the respective products. The program manager develops and manages the program of prescribed checkpoints, or design reviews. The guideline specifies the content and output required at each phase which assist to assure that goals, market needs, schedules, quality and EH&S issues are addressed throughout the project.

Product managers for new and released products have assigned the responsibility for defining and implementing the product safety program to the Novellus System Safety Department. The safety staff has the responsibility for implementation of each product safety task and has approval authority over each phase of the new tool system design through customer delivery. This approval authority together with the engineering product team review, ensures the identification, resolution, and verification of each identified hazard in accordance with the engineering order of precedence and system compliance with stated requirements and regulations.

Within the Novellus organization, the System Safety Manager reports through the Systems EHS Sr. Director, directly to the Executive VP of Systems Development, Engineering & Operations. Since the system safety staff does not organizationally report to the product managers, this relationship ensures staff objectivity by allowing the performance of safety analyses and design, and safety problem resolution independent of direct control from the product team. Each product team and each released product group, function with the system safety staff to form a cross-functional team, which includes professionals from related disciplines, such as field and maintenance engineering, reliability, manufacturability, technical publications, purchasing, supplier quality, and other product groups. The product safety staff is physically located in a central location to ensure day-to-day communications of design issues as they occur. The Novellus Intranet and Design Guidelines allow individual access to design requirements and rationales, and assure tool design will meet SEMI® EHS guidelines.

Thus, the Novellus product safety program emphasizes a direct working interface with the cognizant design engineers and other related disciplines to effectively identify, evaluate, and eliminate or control hazards at the highest feasible order of precedence. The techniques of hazard analysis and control are employed throughout the system life cycle by timely application and verification of safety criteria. These criteria and the systematic, iterative analysis process are input to the customer data collection activities, and are explained in the following paragraphs.

INPUT TO CUSTOMER DATA COLLECTION

The Novellus Systems' approach to product safety is an engineering approach, whereby the methodical application of various scientific and engineering principles is provided to achieve an acceptable level of protection from hazards to personnel, equipment, and the environment. In this process, hazards are identified and risks are minimized throughout all phases of the system life cycle. The independent system safety engineering hazard evaluation conducted for each product is an interactive process consisting of an examination of the system/subsystems in each activity phase, and as it is to be installed in the end user's fabrication facility. The system safety analyses, together with the third-party evaluation, identifies all components and equipment whose performance, performance degradation, functional failure, or inadvertent functioning could result in a hazardous incident. The culmination of this process is input to the customer data collection process for analysis and review of new equipment.

The Novellus Systems' system safety approach is an interactive and integrated process (Figure 18-4). Results of each action are compared against previous actions or retained for future reference. By continual review of the information compiled and updated as the program progresses, a closed-loop system of identification, analysis, correction and validation, and documentation is established. This system safety approach is instigated at the beginning of programs where steps can be easily monitored internally and for released or installed systems as part of a continuous improvement program or customer engineered specials programs. Although this approach is integrated, for discussion purposes it is broken down into five steps. The new product development phases are included for clarity where typical with a new development project, however the system safety approach remains continual and interwoven. The following paragraphs briefly discuss this overview of the Novellus Systems' system safety approach.

PRODUCT SCOPE AND REQUIREMENTS DEFINITION

During this phase of the process, the technical and business strengths and weaknesses of the new product idea are evaluated. Feasibility studies are undertaken to determine if the product is technically viable, and marketable. During these Concept and Feasibility Phases, the system safety staff identifies, investigates, and reports on

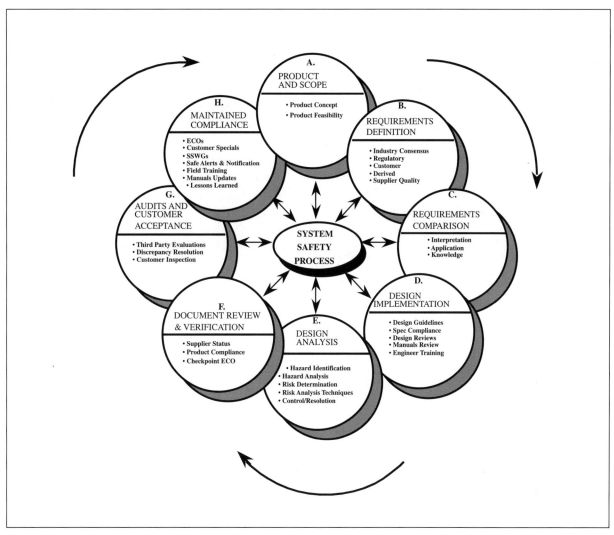

Figure 18-4. Novellus System Safety.

specific areas where studies and investigations are appropriate to identify high-risk or establish special safety requirements or procedures. Hazardous gases, high temperatures, or reactive processes are examples of potential high-risk criteria to weigh into the feasibility of the developing system. This process ensures that incident risk assessments are significantly highlighted and given appropriate weight as decision drivers.

During this segment of the system safety process, a basic review of requirements for the new or released design or supplier component is accomplished. These requirements include the following:

1. Adopted industry consensus guidelines, such as SEMI® or ANSI documents;
2. Regulatory directives and requirements, such as OSHA, Uniform Fire Code , or Uniform Building Code;

3. Customer internal requirements, as outlined on the procurement specification;
4. Derived requirements (derivation of new requirements), such as from hazards analyses or pertinent to state-of-the-art technology; and
5. Supplier quality control.

For the latter, supplier requirements are established consistent with the requirements of the overall Novellus product safety program, tailored to the supplier's product and safety criticality within tools. System safety requirements for SEMI® S2/S8 and CE Mark compliance are defined in the purchase orders and/or in design specification documents to ensure consistency with the overall requirements for each product. The system safety staff may attend the supplier's equipment design reviews where safety factors are relevant, or where such involvement will clarify design approaches and enhance system safety aspects of the Novellus tool development. As needed, there is participation in the evaluation of the supplier equipment designs and monitoring of the status and schedule to ensure timely compliance with contractual and other product safety requirements. For example, the product safety staff may facilitate a supplier through a third-party evaluation and track appropriate closure of each identified discrepancy compatible with the particular tool development.

REQUIREMENTS COMPARISON

System safety requirements are extracted from the various regulatory and industry standards/guidelines. These include international standards such as CE Mark. In this comparison, system requirements and design implementation are compared against pertinent safety requirements. These are combined with specific customer and derived requirements and form the basis of compliance requirements against which the equipment is judged.

At Novellus, the review, application, and conformance with consensus standards, such as the SEMI® guidelines, is not a guarantee of a safe product for three main reasons. First, consensus safety standards are written to address all possible situations, based on experience, but professional standards/guidelines organizations can never anticipate all environments and uses for a product. Second, all requirements must be interpreted and applied in an effective manner to meet the requirement intent. Requirement documents seldom fully explain the intent of any particular requirement. Better understanding of standards development can be gained, and is encouraged through active participation in consensus standards committees, such as SEMI®. Finally, while probably not unique to the semiconductor industry but certainly in the forefront, is that consensus standards cannot be current with the state-of-the-art technology increasingly pushed for new product designs.

It is therefore essential that regulatory and consensus requirements be interpreted and applied with the aid of a system safety professional. These are often identified during the early design phases by brainstorming sessions with the product design engineers and involvement in early cross-functional team meetings. This early involvement during technology discovery and applications facilitates better understanding of the evolving tool design. The application and interpretation of safety requirements, standards or principles to the product design, then, are not merely the research and imposition of written, consensus and regulatory requirements. It necessitates the identification and interpretation of those requirements and development of design/process solutions to apply these requirements. The ability to do this is based upon knowledge of the following:

➤ System or product;
➤ Principles of the system safety discipline; and
➤ Intent of the consensus or regulatory requirements.

This knowledge helps assure a process is established which will lead to a "safe" equipment design.

DESIGN IMPLEMENTATION AND ANALYSIS

In this step, the product design team's implementation of system safety requirements, such as obtained from engineering training sessions and/or design guidelines on the Novellus intranet, are reviewed by the system safety staff and analyzed for compliance with specifications and safety standards. In the corresponding Prototype Phase, a fully functional unit is fabricated and tested. This unit is designed to meet all specifications and criteria for release to production and must operate under total software control.

Review of documentation (drawings, memos, supplier analyses, and manuals) is augmented with attendance by the system safety staff at cross-functional team meeting, design or checkpoint reviews, and interviews with supplier and Novellus design engineers. Hazards and corresponding potential mishaps are also identified and, where not totally controllable by design action, are resolved at the highest feasible order of precedence. Derived system safety requirements are also developed based on additional data obtained as the design progresses. These derived requirements are the culmination of internal hazard analyses. For the preliminary and system technical hazard analyses, the hardware and software detailed system designs are ana-

NOVELLUS/THIRD PARTY
PRODUCT SAFETY EVALUATION PROCESS

PROCESS STEPS	NOVELLUS	THIRD PARTY
TOOL DESIGN	• Internal Hazards Analysis • Internal Safety Review • Corrective Actions	• Preliminary Assessment • Hazard Analysis Report
PLANNING PROCESS	• Define Scope • Define Schedule • Provide Key Information	• Prepare Comprehensive Proposal • Schedule Third Party Resources
ON-SITE EVALUATION PROCESS	• Tool Access • Engineering Availability • Manuals/Schematics • System Design Information	• Line-by-line Evaluation • Testing (e.g.: Electrical/IH) • Single Fault Failure Analysis
DRAFT REPORT PROCESS	• Provide Additional • Information Upon Request • Report Review/Alignment	• Prepare Draft Final Report • Quality Control Process • Electronic copy • Report Feedback/Alignment
SYSTEM DESIGN CHANGE TO MEET S2 REQUIREMENTS	• Review Issues From DFR • Implement Design / Labeling / Documentation Changes	• Review Responses • In office/On-site Consulting
RE-INSPECTION PROCESS	• Tool Access • Engineering Availability • Updated Manuals/Schematics • Modified Design Information	• Re-inspect Tool for Changes • Document Changes in Report
FINAL REPORT PROCESS	• Provide Outstanding Information Prior to "Drop Dead" Deadline to Meet Final Report Schedule	• Prepare Final Report Documenting Full Conformance with SEMI S2-93A

Figure 18-5. Product Safety Evaluation Process.

253

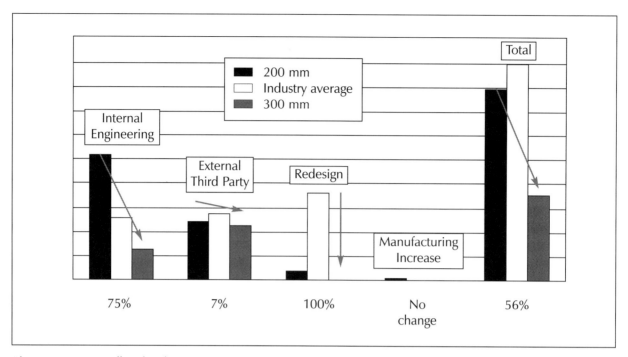

Figure 18-6. Novellus development cost reduction due to design for EHS. *Source:* Supplier's equipment safety cost data.

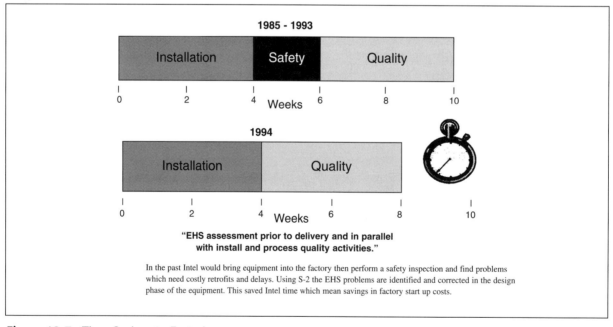

Figure 18-7. Time Savings to Factories.

lyzed and compared with previous safety analyses. This technical analysis can be quantitative as well as qualitative. Further, risks and the means to dispose of them can also be derived from the analytical results of other disciplines, such as FMEA (Failure Modes & Effects Analysis) or ergonomic assessments.

While various techniques for these analyses are discussed in other chapters, the basic hazard identification and control analysis is the principal element in the risk management process. The analysis method provides the collection of potential hazards identified from any source into a closed loop analysis and tracking system. Identified potential hazards remain open until an acceptable resolution is established and implemented by incorporation of design criteria or operational constraints in appropriate controlling documents, such as hardware drawings or operations/maintenance manuals.

The selected system safety analysis techniques and formats of documentation, such as the What-If, fault-tree, or other qualitative type hazard analysis are used to provide the following to the overall product safety review and evaluation of specific equipment:

(a) systematic and thorough analyses of potential hazards;

(b) assures a credible hazard is not overlooked;

(c) permanent record for hazard/risk data on compliance tracking database;

(d) quick reference of systems safety/ergonomic critical areas;

(e) identifies additional derived requirements; and

(f) point of reference for third-party evaluations.

These analyses are documented on internal Novellus hazard analysis worksheets and updated as the design matures. They are also shared with the engineering team for both currency and as input to design. During later design stages, these hazard analyses are provided to the third-party evaluator and later to the customer, as required, as input to their data collection process.

DOCUMENT REVIEW AND VERIFICATION

During the Development and Manufacturing Pilot Phases of the new product development process, several additional units may be built for process and reliability testing. Hardware and software designs are refined. All manufacturing documentation is released under engineering change order (ECO) to production. Some units are shipped to and installed at beta (prototype) test sites. The product safety compliance with the regulatory (such as S2 and CE mark), customer, and derived requirements must be completed at the end of this product development phase.

The system safety staff participates in formal product design or "checkpoint" reviews and informal reviews, such as weekly cross-functional team meetings, to ensure that safety engineering design factors are appropriately considered and the developing design is in consonance with product safety criteria. They may use system safety checklists, hazard judgment/practices to audit the particular tool design for system control requirement, and general safety engineering adequacy as a means of review. The primary objectives of the design reviews are to assess progress or perform an audit of the following:

- Compliance with program system safety design requirements, including regulatory, customer, and derived;
- Achievement of system safety design and procedural objectives;
- Adequate identification of potential safety hazards and their appropriate resolution;
- Effects of engineering decisions, changes, and tradeoffs upon system safety engineering requirements;
- Review of current design documentation for compliance with identified system safety engineering requirements;
- Identification of potential safety design or procedural problems affecting personnel safety or the environment;
- Status of supplier product safety engineering activities; and
- Status of previously approved design review actions.

AUDITS, CUSTOMER ACCEPTANCE, AND MAINTAINED COMPLIANCE

In the semiconductor industry, third-party evaluators are required to review the new product or significant change for concurrence with the safe design and related procedures. Later after discrepancies are resolved, the third-party evaluators are again contracted to audit the implemented corrections to satisfy compliance requirements, typically SEMI® S2-93A and SEMI® S8-95. Other standards or regulations, however, can also be evaluated. The third-party evaluation process for Novellus Systems (Figure 18-5) is a participatory partnership involving individual contributors from several engineering disciplines on both sides. Of course the final system approval is the customer acceptance from source inspection through review of the final compliance documentation as input to the data collection. This third-party evaluation plus customer acceptance process is essential for the new product releases as well as maintaining regulatory compliance for ECOs and customer specials.

ECOs and customer specials are evaluated on a case-by-case basis to determine the associated hazards, assess the associated risk, and predict the safety impact of the ECO on the existing system. Facilitated by internal training, the initiating engineer completes an initial checklist of the change and will notify the system safety staff depending on the nature of the safety criteria for that particular change. As a cross check, the system safety staff reviews the weekly lists of modifications, participates as a member of the change control and specials boards, and discusses planned modifications early with engineering and/or customers to better design safety features into the pending modification. The system safety staff will consider the ECO as a separate item for analysis and will be involved in the design review process, as needed, to aid the system safety hazard identification and control certification. Disposition of the ECO is documented in the department database and Intranet. Periodic system safety working group (SSWG) meetings are set for Novellus to present results from internal hazard analyses to the third-party evaluators for review. Further testing may or may not be needed as well as resolution.

Technical safety issues will be discovered after new product releases and the corresponding control measures effectively communicated to Novellus field service and customers. In the case of a serious incident, the system safety manager is notified within 24 hours. The system safety staff coordinates documentation of the particular safeguard with the Customer Satisfaction Department to assure *Safe-Alerts* are generated in a timely fashion and contain necessary information on the following:

➤ Nature of the potential hazardous incident;

➤ Corrective actions required; and

➤ Point of contact for further information.

The system safety staff remains current on training field engineering personnel and with revisions to procedures/manuals. The product training team contributes to the inclusion of cost and training effectiveness with the safe and hazard-controlled design of the equipment. The Novellus Technical Publications and Training Departments integrate all relevant information involving human performance with design for optimum system effectiveness and availability.

Product safety involvement ensures the freedom from those conditions that cause death, injury, occupational illness, or damage to, or loss of equipment, property, or the environment. These safety considerations do not affect or interface with human performance or cause an increased demand on staffing, personnel, and training resources. The training program with safety-related input links the aptitudes of operators, maintainers, and field support personnel with the type and amount of training necessary to maintain standards of expected human performance, safety, and control of hazards to achieve the equipment operational objectives.

The system safety staff reviews and provides input to the following documentation to determine the impact on product safety and to ensure the inclusion of appropriate cautions/warnings and procedures. It develops the appropriate product safety engineering requirements for input based on system requirements product safety criteria developed from the checklists and evaluations of the tool.

1. Technical manuals
2. Preventive maintenance instructions
3. OEM manuals
4. Operating procedures
5. Maintenance manuals

Finally, lessons learned from fielded systems or from the Novellus Applications lab provide a closed-loop back to the engineering design process. As discussed under Requirements Definition above, other requirements can be identified by researching past mishaps involving the same or similar products or processes and by analyzing other characteristics of the product or process; or by applying lessons learned during the development/testing of similar products or processes.

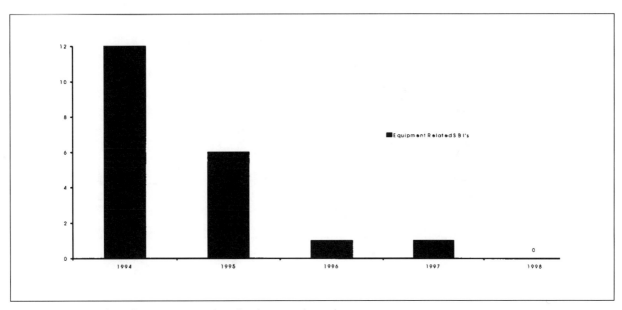

Figure 18-8. Reduced equipment-related safety incidents from 12 per year to zero per year.

TANGIBLE BENEFITS

In general, the semiconductor equipment suppliers and device makers have realized tangible benefits over the last seven years as a result of designing systems and processes to the SEMI® EHS consensus guidelines. For example, Novellus Systems has shown an approximate 50% reduction in the cost of compliance by implementing the *Design for Safety Process*. This reduction (Figure 18-6) compares the cost of safety compliance with the 200-mm systems to the newer 300-mm systems and again to the industry average as computed in a February 1998 VLSI Technology, Inc research study. In this metric, four areas are compared:

1. Internal: Labor, overhead, test equipment.
2. External: Outside consultants. Costs from third-party evaluators.
3. Redesign costs: ECOs.
4. Increase to manufacturing costs: Industry average showed 78% of companies reported 2.1 of system cost for additional safety compliance costs.

The Design for Safety Process implemented by Novellus Systems realized two primary goals for this significant cost reduction. First, frequent customer communications for the 300-mm design requirements at least six months prior to hardware design led to understanding and planning for the new products. Intel and Texas Instruments facilitated this understanding through advanced statements of compliance requirements. Next, the new product development cycle time was reduced by the following factors:

➤ *"Re-Use"*—push to design consistency across tool platforms. Internal up-front hazard analyses were standardized for better and more consistent design input.

➤ *"Learning"* from previous 200-mm effort.

➤ *Up-front* "design for safety" was incorporated into the design process per ISO 9001. Compliance was a requirement for completing the new product development process and ECO release.

➤ *Suppliers*—specifications were developed to mimic compliance requirements.

Intel has reduced the time it takes to produce product by two weeks (Figure 18-7). By implementing complimentary design for EHS systems, both parties realize gains in reduced injury (Figure 18-8), reduced operating costs as measured by scrubbed exhaust costs, and emissions reduction costs.

Reduction of scrubbed exhaust saving $21.6m/year capital cost avoidance and $1.2m Operating Cost Avoidance (Figure 18-9), and reduction in output of Volatile Organic Compounds (VOCs) (Figure 18-10).

KEY TO SUCCESS

The one key element to success regardless of a company's profile is senior management support. Intel EHS has the commitment of the highest

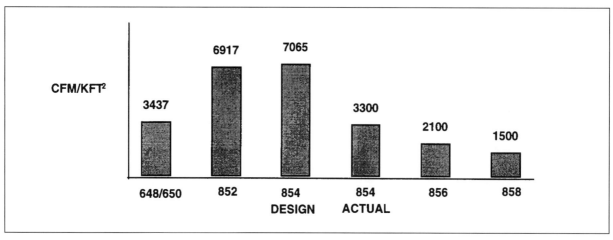

Figure 18-9. Reduced exhaust requirements from optimizing design efficiency, "more is not better", just more expensive.

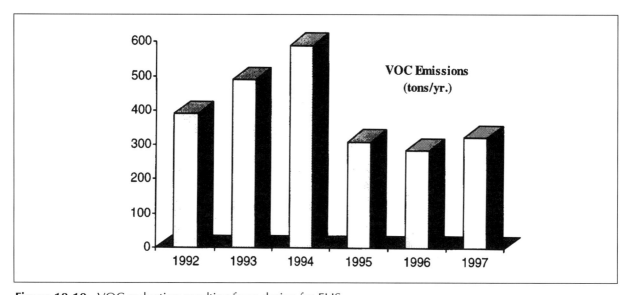

Figure 18-10. VOC reduction resulting from design for EHS.

possible management level as exemplified in the following quote from the CEO:

"We will comply with all applicable regulatory requirements as a minimum and implement programs and processes to achieve greater protection, where appropriate. We will work with stakeholders to develop responsible laws, regulations and innovative programs that provide safeguards for the community, the workplace and the environment while providing flexibility to meet the needs of our business. We (Intel) will be a responsible member of the communi-ties in which we live and work. We will continue to expand our knowledge and understanding of the effect of our operations on safety, health and the environment. We are committed both to continuous improvement in our operations and to sharing the knowledge that we gain with our employees, customers, suppliers, the communities in which we live and work, the scientific community, government and industry."

Craig R. Barrett, President and Chief Operating Officer.

Chapter 19

BEYOND THE MILLENNIUM— SAFETY THROUGH DESIGN IN 2005

by Wayne C. Christensen

INTRODUCTION

The observations offered herein are the result of viewing developments and trends in today's world to visualize where safety through design efforts will be in 2005, the tenth year of the Institute for Safety Through Design (ISTD). The author is not a futurist, forecaster, prognosticator, or visionary. This chapter is not meant to be a thorough in-depth analysis, but rather a brief look at trends, to whet your appetite, and excite you about the future. Comments are general since predicting just six years is extremely difficult, as readers recognize from personal observations of the speed of change today.

An advanced technological and information environment will exist in 2005 which will see safety through design efforts utilized by many companies. Keeping up with technology will be a major concern of corporations and individuals. Thus, a major emphasis of this chapter is on the use of computers in design engineering work. Two conclusions result and they are perhaps not surprising. First, there clearly is need for an extemely cooperative effort between engineers as designers, management and safety practitioners. Second, safety practitioners must upgrade their technological and computer design skills.

THE WORLD IN 2005

Efforts to incorporate safety through design concepts will be successful because corporations will recognize it is good business to design facilities, products, and processes with early consideration to safety, health, and environmental (SHE) concerns. Success will be reflected in decreased failure rates (incidents) and a variety of cost savings, including time decreases for changes in products, and productivity increases. At the same time the world in which this is accomplished will change substantially.

Engineers are already influenced, and safety practitioners and others will be strongly influenced, after the turn of the century by the acronyms CAD, CAE, CAM, CAPE, PDM, and ERP.[1]

- *CAD*=Computer Aided Design
- *CAE*=Computer Aided Engineering
- *CAM*=Computer Aided Manufacturing
- *CAPE*=Computer Aided Production Engineering
- *PDM*=Product Data Management (system to manage huge amounts of data created and shared for virtual manufacturing)
- *ERP*=Enterprise Resource Planning (Inventory control, scheduling, and so on)

These systems are already major contributors to safety through design efforts. The techniques to accumulate, manage and exchange information are in a state of great change; some have even suggested it is a revolution.

Readers only need to reflect on the spectacular growth in the number and capability of personal computers (PCs) and workstations, in the mid to late 1990s, to project an even greater magnitude of growth in the next six years. Add to that the decreasing cost of PCs, other hardware, and software and the capability to network workstations, and work via the Web. Another indication of future explosive growth is the lower hardware costs which will permit more and more companies to enter the "design on computer" era. Internet growth is expected to reach over 500 million users in the next couple years.[2]

As the century turns, and the Internet Age is upon us, we need to catch a glimpse of the marked changes in the world itself in 2005. Observations are based on major changes in business practice and technology occurring in a relatively constant environment, insofar as the absence of a major recession, deep depression, or significant Y2K hiccup. If any of the latter occur, projections retreat to a waste basket. Comments on government issues, social security, general education, or similar topics which can impact the world environment are beyond the scope of this chapter.

The space station scheduled for completion in 2004 will finally be completed in 2005 and technological innovation will continue to soar. The work on the space station, thus far, has gone incident free, as a result of excellent design engineering of the parts and the process. The ability to achieve this performance breeds hope that safety through design efforts will also yield safer workplaces.

Projections indicate there will be major population shifts throughout the world, with a slowing of population growth. People will be living longer as a result of improved medical care, food and shelter, and quantum leaps in prescription drugs and medical techniques. Urban redevelopment will occur as a result of the trend to an information society, due to the development of complete cities surrounding electronics/information centers. However, there will still be a need for manufacturing of large and complicated equipment such as airplanes, earth movers, farm machinery, and so forth.

Buildings and equipment will be needed in many countries of the world as they try to leap from the 19th century to the 21st century. Unfortunately, in the midst of great change some things never change, war will still be with us. Natural resource availability will be a limiting factor, causing increased concern and global commitment to consideration of environmental factors in design. The Environmental Protection Agency (EPA), ISO 14000, and similar environmental concerns will continue to have a substantive impact on the world around us.

Overall technology will accelerate. However, the public perception of safety and the level of acceptable risk, will continue to require education, especially since today large numbers of young people, and some older ones too, still engage in risky behavior like "car-surfing," using drugs, and excessive speed in vehicles. The worry is, they engage in this behavior today and will be in the workforce in 2005. Scientific research and data will continue at times to cause serious concerns, and extensive debate about safety in areas (food, chemicals, prescription drugs) where risk should be acceptable.

COMPANIES AND THE WORK FORCE IN THE NEW MILLENNIUM

COMPANIES

During the last two decades there have been major changes in management styles, and in the initiation of global efforts in product quality, safety, environmental affairs, and information exchange. In the years up to 2005, projections suggest,[3] manufacturing in the United States will continue to lose jobs, while the service, wholesale/retail, communications jobs will reflect growth. Major production facilities, where large products are produced, will change from "we do everything ourselves" to *modular facilities* where "we assemble all the pieces from our subcontractors."

Mergers and virtual companies worldwide will affect the safety through design efforts in the early years of the new millennium. However, the necessity of providing increased profit margins and quicker new product, process, and facility turn-around will force consideration of SHE in early design and production discussions. The reason may not be totally based on return on investment (ROI), but on the users needs, and the need of companies to stay competitive.

Computer designing will continue to reduce substantially the time to bring a process to fruition, together with accompanying efficiencies in the plant, and reductions in the number of parts and suppliers. The reductions expected in turnaround time are not measured in hours, days or weeks, but in months or years. In the auto industry indications are the five-year cycle for new vehicles has been reduced to 32 months and the talk is to further reduce it to 18 months. Constant and rapid technological improvement and redesign of products will fuel this compression.

An article, *Paperless Tigers*[4] indicated

> *Now Chrysler does have CATIA (Computer-aided three-dimensional interactive applications), all the way through the corporation, from design through manufacturing. The Concorde and Intrepid are Chrysler's first paperless cars. Almost everything was designed or engineered ... For instance, the intake manifold went through 1500 iterations on screen before a single tube was molded ... pre-CATIA times, engineers would have made four or five prototype versions ... and sent it into production ... more versions translate into more time ... On the LH it took three weeks to get the first chassis to fit into the first body. On the '98 it took 15 minutes. The entire program—from project approval to Job One—required only 31 months to complete, versus 39 for the first LH's.*

This CAD/CAM software is also used to design the Boeing 777 and by other companies.

Numerous reports have been noted of substantial time savings of one third or more from the use of three-dimensional graphics and similar programs in the design process. In the petrochemical industry an off-gas treating unit was designed in three-dimensional in nine months versus the 15 months normally required with two-dimensional design.[5] If that's the current status, it is highly probable the programs available in 2005 will be vastly superior, and the turnaround times even shorter.

Outsourcing will become a common practice for engineering design services in most companies. Without proper precautions this practice can complicate implementation of safety through design concepts. Minimal production engineering design will be done by in-house engineers; on the other hand those individuals who were "downsized" will probably be contractors for this service, so they should have some knowledge from their prior experience. Most detail work will be completed, on computers, by service companies who have long term contracts. Original equipment manufacturers (OEM) com-

panies will perform or be required to complete a *hazard analysis and risk assessment* as a result of growing requirements from standards, the European Community and companies. Since supplier qualifications are critical, outsourcing will require that purchasing personnel are brought into the safety through design loop.

There will be an increase in partnerships, between companies and their suppliers, to achieve common safety, health, and environmental expectations and to control costs. Those in full compliance with compatible safety, health, and environmental goals will, because of the reduced time to produce finished products, be in an excellent posture to receive contracts. Component manufacturers may adopt voluntary guidelines on safety through design, which may leave other suppliers out in the cold. Specific industries, such as the semiconductor industry, have already adopted guidelines (see Chapter 18), which move the process down to suppliers for consistent safety, health, and environmental programs.

MANAGEMENT

A major change by 2005 is management recognition in a much broader cross section of companies, not just the majors, that safe design of products, facilities, equipment, and processes will reap sizeable cost and competitive advantage benefits. Having undergone other substantive cultural changes, the transition to safety through design concepts will be accepted, but not without continued conflict. At the same time, many smaller companies will be running to "catch the train," as they have in quality and teaming. Many companies will be undergoing their umpteenth restructuring and management will continue facing the challenge of, and need for, continuous improvement.

Management will become more focused on participation and representation on standards and code committees to assure proliferation is minimized, that they maintain reason and practicality, emphasize simplicity, and hopefully limit proliferation of government regulations. They will also be concerned that regulations stay abreast of technology. Product liability lawsuits quite possibly will increase initially because attorneys discover the existence of hazard analysis and risk assessment documents, but the tide will turn and these documents will become excellent industry defense tools. Technology advancements will continue to be rapid and will contribute to safer products and as well as work environments.

In the area of research and engineering design activities company management will be increasingly focused on obtaining these services by contract through 2005. There are generally more projects than staff can be maintained to complete, and second, economics of the bottom line enter the picture. There will be concentrated research and major advances in chemistry and the materials produced. A whole range of new and improved products will be available as a result of breakthroughs in design as a result of new light-weight materials, adhesives, and so forth.

Throughout this era the conflict will ensue between those who feel zero risk is the only objective, and those who recognize that zero risk is not attainable, that there is some element of risk in everything that is done. Those who see that zero risk is unattainable, including a portion of the public at large, will grow. The tug of war over employees, between those who would have incident prevention efforts depend on personal cognizance of risk and those who foster increased effort to design for acceptable risk will continue. The emphasis on design will grow for business reasons indicated above.

WORKFORCE

Employment in the United States will increase with growth in workers over 55 years of age.[3] The workforce will become more diverse and possibly have less technical skills to apply in an increasingly technical work environment. User friendliness will become an increasing factor in product, equipment, process, and facility design.

Workers will benefit from a safer and healthier work environment, and will have significantly more input into the recognition and elimination of hazardous operations before they reach the production floor. However, workers will have to become computer proficient in order to operate equipment and participate in safety teams. The challenge to improve working conditions in the United States will continue, and the effort to materially upgrade working conditions in emerging countries will face increased pressure from many sources, including government, business and labor.

COMPUTERS UNLEASH CREATIVITY

In recent years computer hardware has made staggering leaps over where it was just a year or two before. Processor speed and hard drive capacity have doubled and doubled again making them operate at near lightening speed. Three-dimensional technology, providing the ability to capture things the way we see them and to be able to rotate parts, is available on workstations and on ordinary PCs. If the pattern continues and computers are revolutionized every 18 to 24 months, by 2005 there will have been at least three additional iterations.

In the software area, engineers already have design capabilities including digital prototyping and analysis functions, and the capability to simulate an entire facility, animate the process, and make the system search for specific safety problems. The design of a product may contain thousands of individual components which can be reflected in an assembled or in an exploded view. Structure, stress, vibration, finite element (FEA), motion and other analyses can be completed in the software programs, saving incredible amounts of time previously spent making models and in prototype testing.

Safety practitioners will have opportunities for participation in design, if they acquire the required technical skills. Both engineers and safety practitioners must make a commitment to life-long learning; all to satisfy the insatiable desire for increased technical capability to view entire facilities, processes, and products, driven by concurrent engineering, lean manufacturing, global design and manufacturing. Proposals and revisions using graphics will allow engineers and safety practitioners to market to management any recommendations in a manner that is time and cost-efficient, and will permit easy feedback and approval in a prompt and seamless manner.

In the educational (K–12) opportunities for the next generation, new dimensions in the use of PCs are being added continually, resulting from the development of simulation games and similar programs. Almost daily there are new software offerings that promise extended and speedier capability in design or design analysis that can be used on PCs. It will provide today's youth with skills which will be very necessary to function in their college education and in business.

There will be some fallout in the number of software systems used in business, as there was in word processing and accounting systems, through preferred systems and software company acquisitions. Many software systems already permit import and use of data from other programs. This will be advantageous to engineers and safety practitioners, since skill portability will not be impacted as greatly as if they were knowledgeable in one software package and had to acquire new software skills with each employer.

Information technology will lead the way to many changes in living and life styles. We have already seen growing numbers of workers functioning from offices in their homes, yet in intimate contact with their corporate office hundreds, even thousands of miles away. With the growing Internet capability for engineering, and marketing on the Internet, corporations will start rethinking their engineering, marketing and travel strategies.

Prototypes of major products, automobiles, aircraft, and buildings can be viewed in three dimensions, looked at from every angle, and tested without having to build models. The worker can be placed in a relationship to assembly of the product, and the production process simulated. At least one major auto manufacturer (Chrysler) has been considering, for several years, the ergonomics of the worker building the vehicle during the CAD/CAM design of a new auto.

The ability to prototype and test, including normally destructive testing such as vehicle crash tests, without having to construct models is already having a significant impact on the time to market and cost and will impact all product lines by 2005. Deneb/ERGO is another example of a tool for human motion and workplace assessment (Deneb Robotics, Inc) 3D graphics also have the capability of being translated into 2D drawings for construction. Activities now requiring super computers will become accessible on local networks or via the Internet.

Operating systems and software are available to allow collaboration by workgroups using local networks, or by the Internet which allows the operation or product being designed to have the design team interact on the same simulation no matter where in the world they are located. Virtual operating factories can already be simulated where a product goes through all production stages.

Several CAD/CAM/CAE/CAPE vendors claim to offer "design-through-manufacturing solutions" which user companies can use in virtual manufacturing if they use a common CAD system for product design and process factory design. Visualization, including stereoscopic viewing, and interactive simulation will play an important role in the solution to the projects given to teams.

A recent News Release[6] announced functions of great interest to safety through design efforts.

> *CATIA Version 5 ... provides a single system image and a platform-independent solution scalable across all levels of expertise ... delivers intuitive part and assembly modeling. Generative Drafting automatically creates associative drawings from 3D mechanical designs and assemblies. The Real Time Rendering application produces photo-realistic images ... The Advanced Shape Designers tools allow designers to quickly create free-form shape design deformations ... Advanced functions extend ... modeling functions to morphing complex, multi surface shapes. Other features include 3D fly-throughs and mock-up ... A Fitting Simulator application simulates mounting and dismounting operations for prevalidation during design of assembly and maintenance procedures.*

Simulation programs such as Mechanical Desktop (Mechanical Dynamics, Inc), CCPlant for manufacturing production plants (Dassault Systemes of America), MSC/Acumen (The MacNeal-Schwendler Corporation) and others are currently on the market and offer dramatic viewing of the production floor and a product proceeding through the entire production process. They have features which can be built in to alert, or check, for obstructions to product moving through a facility or the relationship of people to the product and operations.

CCPlant program for instance has Knowledge Engineering, which provides a capability of building in a whole library of safety rules and requirements for application in the actual design process and in post-design checking. In addition, questions can be raised and the design will be reviewed to ascertain compliance with other safety items. For instance, aisles may be examined by the program to assure they are of sufficient width to accommodate two-way fork lift truck traffic and a pedestrian. The downside is that many software systems do not contain design characteristics for safety, health, and environmental applications. Couple this with the absence of safety, health, and environmental expertise on the staff of many design engineering firms and the quality of safety, health and environmental service is substantially below industry needs.

Networking of workstations, use of the Internet, and the increasing capability to search for solutions to identified hazards will contribute to better quality in initial design considerations. Programs to link remote users exist, such as Deneb/VCE (Virtual Collaborative Engineering) Deneb Robotics, Inc and "CoCreate," CoCreate Software, Inc. PDM systems and the ability to import and export data have been improved, which assists in sharing models over the Internet.

The requirements for hazard analysis and risk assessment in the European Community and similar efforts in the U.S. machine tool industry will have created a demand for safety, health, and environmental guidance and it will be incorporated into CAD/CAE/CAM programs by 2005, rather than added by the user.

SAFETY THROUGH DESIGN CONCEPTS AND PRACTICE IN 2005

Retrofitting efforts, unfortunately, will still be required in a substantial number of buildings and equipment. Years of building of facilities and equipment without considering safety, health, and environment in the design will take a long time to be retrofitted or to move them into the decommission/recycle phase. Implementation of safety through design principles and practices will benefit those who adopted the concepts early. They will see the greatest return and consider it old news but sound business. It will surpass quality concepts in value added, as seen from evidence in earlier chapters. In 2005 there will be better designs in which engineers and safety practitioners have participated.

Culture change for safety through design which takes a number of years will still require continuing attention because of all the companies that have moved into designing safety into products, facilities, and so on. Safety through design efforts will bring the benefits of reduced injuries, illnesses, environmental damage, and cost savings, which will be realized and reflected in company annual reports.

Not only will the concepts of safety through design be widely accepted, but the intervening years will see a plethora of equipment and devices introduced to reduce risk to an acceptable level and thus make the workplace inherently safer. Zero energy systems will be built into equipment for protection if entry is necessary, devices will sense the presence of persons or inanimate objects in three dimensions not just one, and there will be major advances in the design of "permit required spaces" to eliminate the need for access, or to allow necessary work to be done by built-in equipment or by machines which make the entry (currently occurring—robots with TV entry into sewer lines to probe problems).

IMPACT ON ENGINEERS

The Accreditation Board for Engineering and Technology (ABET) Criteria for Accrediting Programs in Engineering in the United States, "Engineering Criteria: 2000,"[7] will have had a substantive impact on the amount of safety, health, and environmental knowledge acquired by engineers. The requirement is that in 2001 it be incorporated in degree programs. In 2005 over 50% of degree-granting institutions will have been reevaluated or have implemented materials in anticipation of an upcoming accreditation audit.

There is increasing talk about undergraduate engineering curricula focusing on "project-based engineering."[8] Many courses are already built on this concept, which permits engineering students to function as part of a multi-engineering disciplinary team, or even as part of a multi-university project team. The Internet will allow students to rapidly research trends and seek information from team members across the world. Engineering designs and practices may truly take an international flavor. Projects to develop and incorporate material into curricula will have yielded excellent materials to provide materials for the continuing education of engineers currently employed in industry. Much of this knowledge acquisition will come via the Internet.

ISTD has sponsored efforts to promote the use of hazard analysis and risk assessment software in engineering curricula and provided for entry into business, in the year 2000, of an initial cadre of graduates with this knowledge. By 2005 over 50% of engineering graduates will have been exposed to some form of hazard analysis and risk assessment software, either as a separate format or in procedures embedded in CAE/CAD/CAM programs. Professors and students will develop a greater appreciation of their responsibility in these areas.

A direct outgrowth of the ABET Criteria, and the growing practice of safety through design, will be an emphasis on incorporation of questions on these topics in the Professional Engineers (PE) examinations. The National Council of Examiners for Engineering and Surveying will have moved forward in efforts to incorporate questions on safety, health, and environment in the PE examinations. In 2005 as the cycle of incorporation of material into engineering curricula nears completion, questions will have been prepared and adopted for the exams, and may start appearing.

Engineers will face a shortened knowledge cycle and massive continuing technological change. It will require establishing a personal continuing education program that is followed rigorously. The move from two-dimensional CAD to three-dimensional will be forced on all establishments by the absence of software upgrades in two-dimensional, similar to the move from 5 1/4-inch disks to 3 1/2-inch disks.

As stated earlier process development times are growing shorter and will be even shorter in 2005, exerting increased pressure on engineers and safety practitioners to provide their input into the process early. Finally, in the midst of all the technological needs, engineers will also have to develop people skills, communication abilities, and an understanding of business economics. Engineers no longer stand or operate alone; they are a part of a design team.

IMPACT ON SAFETY PRACTITIONERS

A trend to decrease the number of corporate safety and health practitioners started in the mid-late 1990s and will have a profound effect on the knowledge safety practitioners must acquire. Corporate engineering and safety staffs and the capability of reviewing projects at the corporate level are disappearing. Not only because of the trend to decrease overall corporate staffing, but also because of the growth in outsourcing. Projects will be in the hands of teams from individual operations. Safety practitioners in the divisions and plants will no longer be able to rely on help from corporate and will have to be involved themselves at the beginning of the design of a project.

The growing practice of safety through design in business has necessitated that safety practitioners matriculating from safety degree programs will have received more technical courses than offered in 1999. It doesn't mean that they will have to have the total academic experience of an engineer, but they will have sufficient knowledge to have participated in cooperative capstone design courses with engineering and business students.

Safety practitioners will require, in addition to the basic skills in hazard recognition, evaluation and control, an ability to work with engineers directly in CAD/CAM/CAM programs, IF they are to influence the design effort in the early stages. Their efforts will be measured with respect to the number of modifications of process and equipment that are required once the product is ready for production or it reaches the factory floor. Skill in the ability to discern problems and assist in solutions during computer modeling will be essential. If, as an individual, you had problems visualizing and extracting information from two-dimensional drawings (blueprints) in the past, your difficulty may be eased with the three-dimensional imagery and simulation in the new systems.

Practitioners already in the field will have taken extensive course work to permit them to work cooperatively with engineers. In all cases computer knowledge will extend well past utilization of software to research or type term papers, play games, or maintain contact with friends and family over the Internet. In both cases, new practitioners and those already in the field, must be inspired, encouraged and given the vision to become qualified in the technologies being employed by business. Increasingly, safety practitioners and engineers will have to work as team members, rather than their current preferred practice as individual contributors.

In all focus thus far, on technological and computer skills, and a good understanding of business practices and economics, it must be remembered that culture changes will be necessary and people and communication skills will be necessary to lead and for team participation. There will be a need to be a change leader and to recognize when behaviors are reverting to old assumptions and attitudes.

IMPACT ON OTHERS

The wave of safety through design efforts will sweep through more than engineers and safety practitioners in the intervening years to 2005. It will include suppliers, service industries, and numerous others. Management schools will begin to incorporate information on safety, health, and the environment in their curricula, and students will experience the practical aspects in interdisciplinary project teams with engineering students.

The architectural field is currently undergoing change with the availability of computer three-dimensional graphics, visualization and simulation techniques, and the ability to take a virtual tour. Computer renderings for instance already include the ability to show the effects of indirect lighting; will the effects of noise be far behind? The tools now becoming available should permit the establishment of a library of safety rules and requirements for post-design checking as in industry. It will require stimulation, perhaps by the ISTD, to assure these considerations are in place by 2005.

While this chapter has focused primarily on the manufacturing industry, steps have been taken to introduce safety through design concepts into the construction industry. The "Design for Safety Toolbox" (Chapter 17) is an excellent start. Advances in methodology in manufacturing should spill over into construction and construction sites will be much safer in 2005.

Safety practitioners focusing on behavioral change will perhaps have to change their focus as incident prevention turns its face toward prevention through safe design rather than by exhortation. Cultural change practitioners will continue in vogue, since application of safety through design concepts requires a major cultural change in an organization.

SUMMARY

It is exciting to observe the changes in engineering design and the advances in 3D graphics and the visualization/simulation programs that are having a major impact on the design process. It is challenging and beneficial to safety, health, and environmental programs when compared to the efforts 15 to 20 years ago. The invigoration produces the desire to move to the front lines of design efforts just to be a part of the great age that will be experienced between now and 2005, in a substantive forward movement toward saving lives and reducing injuries.

One fact must be faced—the major compression of time in bringing a facility, process, or product from the concept stage to production, will no longer permit the luxury of reviewing after construction and placing a hold until "safety" measures are retrofitted. Management will not tolerate it. Safety, health, and environmental considerations must be incorporated in the design stage.

In the early days of developing its Mission and Vision, the Institute for Safety Through Design recognized that if the safety through design concepts were adopted they would minimize retrofitting in industry. The effort appears to be taking hold in 1999 and will probably reflect in 2005 that a substantial portion of facility, process, product, and equipment design considers safety in the very early stages of design effort.

Thus, on the tenth (10th) anniversary of ISTD (July, 2005) the Institute may have completed its initial Mission "To reduce the risk of injury, illness and environmental damage by integrating decisions affecting safety, health and the environment in all stages of the design process." What future actions of the Institute will be or will there be establishment of a son/daughter of ISTD remains to be seen.

There will be a high demand for those safety practitioners with the technical and computer skills to fit into the growing safety through design effort. And as stated at the beginning of the chapter, two conclusions result and they are perhaps not surprising. First, there clearly is need for an extemely cooperative effort between engineers as designers, management, and safety practitioners. Second, safety practitioners must upgrade their technological and computer design skills.

REFERENCES

1. Computer-Aided Engineering Glossary. *Computer-Aided Engineering,* Jul 1998, pp 50–54.

2. *Understanding e-business Solutions.* IBM Global Services, IBM Corporation, 1998.

3. Swartz G: *Employment Projections, 1996–2006 & Population Projections, 1997–2005.* Report to National Safety Council Board of Directors, Oct 27, 1998.

4. Vaughn M: Paperless tigers. *AutoWeek,* Oct 6–12, 1997, from a reprint.

5. Gorman M: Shaving time with 3D design, *Desktop Engineering,* Aug 1998, pp 12–16.

6. Briefings. *Desktop Engineering,* Helmers Publishing, Inc, vol. 4, no. 4, Dec 1998, p 8.

7. *Engineering Criteria 2000: Criteria for Accrediting Programs in Engineering in the U.S.* ABET (Accreditation Board for Engineering and Technology).

8. Huband FL: *Engineering Education—An Alternative Approach,* ASEE Prism, Jan 1999, p 4.

Appendix:

AUTHOR BIOGRAPHIES

Paul Adams functions as a Corporate Ergonomist and Safety Engineer on the Corporate Occupational Health and Safety staff, Owens Corning. In that position, he has successfully initiated and developed ergonomic processes within Owens Corning businesses and has led the effort to establish a corporate-wide process for incorporating safety into design. Prior to joining Owens Corning, he was an Assistant Professor in the Safety Degree Program at Illinois State University. He also has six years of experience as a loss prevention engineer at Olin Brass and Ammunition Operations. Paul holds both M.S. and Ph.D. degrees in Industrial and Operations Engineering from the University of Michigan, a M.S. in Industrial Safety from Central Missouri State University, and a B.S. in Industrial Engineering from Iowa State. He is a Certified Safety Professional, a Certified Professional Ergonomist, and a licensed Professional Engineer.

Donald Bloswick is an Associate Professor, Department of Mechanical Engineering, University of Utah, where he teaches and directs research in ergonomics, safety, occupational biomechanics, and rehabilitation engineering. He is Director of the Ergonomics and Safety Program, Rocky Mountain Center for Occupational and Environmental Health, and holds adjunct appointments in the Department of Family and Preventative Medicine, Department of Bioengineering, and Division of Physical Therapy. He has a B.S. Mechanical Engineering, a M.S.in. Industrial Engineering from Texas A&M, an M.A. in Human Relations, and a Ph.D. Industrial and Operations Engineering from the University of Michigan. He is a Registered Professional Engineer and Certified Professional Ergonomist, with ten years of industrial experience and 15 years as an ergonomic and safety consultant.

Tom Cecich is the VP Environmental Safety for Glaxo Wellcome. He is responsible for safety, industrial hygiene, environmental, fire protection, and emergency response activities. Previously he held safety and environmental management positions at IBM and Allied Chemical Corporations. He holds a B.S. in Industrial Engineering from University of Miami and a M.S. in Industrial Engineering from North Carolina State University, with a specialty in ergonomics. Tom is a Certified Safety Professional (CSP) and a Certified Industrial Hygienist (CIH). He served on the Board of Certified Safety Professionals (1993–98) and was President of BCSP in 1997. He is current Chair, Board of Directors of Manufacturers and Chemical Industry Council of North Carolina (state affiliate of CMA). He belongs to ASSE and is past president of the North Carolina Chapter.

Wayne C. Christensen is an Accident Prevention Consultant, and is Project Manager for the Institute for Safety Through Design and a Training Consultant for the National Safety Council. His career has focused on safety, fire prevention and protection, and disaster control and he has long advocated the safety through design concepts. He has also served as Managing Director, American Society of Safety Engineers (ASSE), Corporate Director of Safety, Owens Corning, and is a devoted husband to Betty. Mr. Christensen has a Fire Protection and Safety Engineering degree from IIT, is a Certified Safety Professional (CSP), a Fellow of ASSE, and a Registered Professional in Safety Engineering (CA). He is a Member, Society of Fire Protection Engineers, and a member of the American Society for Engineering Education and the American Society for Training and Development.

Michael J. Douglas is Manager Engineering for Health & Safety, General Motors North America, Industrial Engineering Department. He created the Task Based Risk Assessment (TaBRA) model used by GM, and has been a key leader in creating and implementing the UAW-GM safety specification (DHS 1.0). Michael also created Safety 21 standardized work process model for integrating design-in safety into the automotive engineering environment. Previously he was a Senior Electrical Engineer with GM Delco Electronics, and worked in a variety of engineering roles with Allison Engine Company including Turbine and Diesel. Michael has a BS in Electrical Engineering from Purdue and an MS in Business Administration from the University of Indianapolis.

Mollie A. Foster, Product Safety Manager, Novellus Systems, has 20 years' experience in systems safety engineering and systems hazard risk assessment in aerospace and Department of Defense projects. Currently she serves as the co-chair for the SEMI Environmental Safety, & Health Subcommittee, and is a member of the SEMI Compliance and Regulatory Committee. Ms. Foster has three children, Alicia, Nathan and Laurel, is a Certified Safety Professional (CSP), holds a B.S. in Safety Science, Oregon State University, and a M.S. in Systems Management, University of Southern California.

Robert T. George is Benchmarking Programs Manager, DuPont Company in Wilmington, Delaware. He helped establish the first benchmarking group within the DuPont Company, and has participated in benchmarking every type of business process. His first benchmarking study was on manufacturing teams and in 1990 he resourced a 12-person team to benchmark the product development process, which resulted in the institution of the Product and Cycle Time Excellence (PACE) methodology across the company. Today he leads the benchmarking process for the corporation as part of the group Consulting for Business Improvement (CBI). For the past three years he has led the Manufacturing Advisory Board for Engineering at Penn State and in 1997 spent part of his time under a National Science Foundation Grant as an Industry Fellow in Residence at the University.

Mark Hembarsky is with the Technical Operations Division, Glaxo Wellcome, and has led business process improvement efforts in Manufacturing, Logistics & Planning, Corporate Engineering, and Environmental Safety. He has led cross-functional teams, advised and coached senior managers and teams, and developed and delivered training. Previously, Mark was responsible for engineering and construction of several major research, development and manufacturing facilities in the United States and the United Kingdom. Mark held project management positions at Exxon Research & Engineering Co., and was responsible for engineering and construction of major petrochemical plant projects in the the United States, the United Kingdom, and Netherlands. He has a B.S. in Civil Engineering from Lehigh University, is a Professional Engineer (NJ), and a Certified Quality Manager (ASQ). He is a member of the American Society for Quality, National Society for Professional Engineers, and International Society for Pharmaceutical Engineering.

Dennis C. Hendershot is a Senior Technical Fellow in the Hazard Assessment and Environmental Engineering Department, Engineering Division, Rohm and Haas Company. He has over 25 years of experience in chemical process research and development, plant design and start-up, and process safety and loss prevention. Mr. Hendershot has served as a Director of the Safety and Health Division of the American Institute of Chemical Engineers, and was Chair of the Division in 1998. He has been a member of several subcommittees of the Center for Chemical Process Safety, including Risk Assessment (Chair), Hazard Evaluation (Chair), Inherently Safer Processes, and undergraduate Education.

Thomas A. Hunter, Ph.D. is Principal Consultant for Forensic Engineering Consultants, Inc, Westport, CT. Dr. Hunter is the author of Engineering Design for Safety and several papers on failure analysis and prevention for ASME. He has appeared as an expert witness in more than 100 trials, and performed more than 1,500 technical analyses of product failures. He has extensive hands-on design experience on military and commercial aircraft components, heavy industrial equipment, laminating and dry mounting presses, and was product safety director for a major manufacturer of portable powered equipment for the lawn, garden, and construction industries. He is currently a member of the Committee on Codes and Standards for the State of Connecticut.

Thomas J. Janicik, Safety and Health Manager, Mallinckrodt, has over 15 years of technical and managerial experience in safety, reliability and risk analysis spanning the Aerospace, Defense, Chemical Process, and Pharmaceutical industries. In 1993, the Texas Safety Association recognized him as Safety Manager of the Year. He serves as a member of the Center for Chemical Process Safety (CCPS) Technical Steering Committee and Risk Analysis Subcommittee and has provided numerous safety/risk analysis related presentations and tutorials. He received a B.S. in Environmental Engineering from Northwestern University, a MS in Industrial Hygiene from Texas A&M University, and a M.S. in Engineering Economic Systems from Stanford University. He is a Certified Safety Professional (CSP) and a Professional Engineer.

Bradley S. Joseph is Manager of Ergonomics in the Health Care Management organization, Ford Motor Company. His duties include coordinating development and administration of a comprehensive ergonomics program for Ford's Assembly, Manufacturing, Warehousing and Administrative workplaces. He is involved with the UAW-Ford National Joint Committee on Health and Safety monitoring implementation of the ergonomics process by developing a training materials and conducting research. Prior to joining Ford, he was an Assistant Professor, Medical College of Ohio (MCO) teaching ergonomics and industrial health related courses, and currently holds Adjunct Assistant Professor positions at Wayne State University and MCO. Dr. Bradley has a Master of Public Health degree, Master's Degrees in Industrial Engineering and Industrial Health, and a Ph.D. in Industrial Health and Industrial and Operations Engineering from the University of Michigan.

Wayne C. Loomis retired as Operations Safety Manager, Xerox Corporation. He serves as adjunct professor in safety and health for the Rochester Institute of Technology's Environmental Management degree program, and is chair of an advisory committee at RIT responsible for overseeing implementation of the proposed Safety Engineering Technology degree program. Mr. Loomis is a professional member of the American Society of Safety Engineers and the American Industrial Hygiene Association. He serves on the Board of Delegates for the National Safety Council and is past chairman of the Business and Industry Division of the National Safety Council. He is a Certified Safety Professional (CSP) and a Certified Industrial Hygienist (CIH).

Bruce W. Main is President of Design Safety Engineering, an Ann Arbor based engineering consulting firm specializing in safety through design. Has Mechanical Engineering degrees from MIT and the University of Michigan, and an MBA from the University of Michigan. He serves on the Advisory Committee for the Institute for Safety Through Design, and is a member of the ANSI B11 TR3 subcommittee on risk assessment. Mr. Main is a Professional Engineer, a Certified Safety Professional, and holds certification in product safety management. He is a member of several professional engineering and safety organizations, and has authored numerous articles and papers, as well as frequently lecturing on safety through design to industry and at universities.

Fred A. Manuele is President of Hazards, Limited. He retired from Marsh & McLennan where he was a Managing Director and Manager of M&M Protection Consultants. For several years, he served as a member of the Board of Directors of the American Society of Safety Engineers, and was a member and President of the Board of Certified Safety Professionals. At the National Safety Council, Mr. Manuele presently serves as a member of the Board of Delegates and the Advisory Committee for the Institute for Safety Through Design. A second edition of his book *On the Practice of Safety* was recently published. Mr.

Manuele was awarded the honor of Fellow by the American Society of Safety Engineers, and was inducted into The Safety and Health Hall of Fame International.

Richard L. Parker, Corporate Equipment, Environmental, Safety and Ergonomics Manager, Intel Corporation, has 16 years' experience in Aerospace, Telecommunications and Semiconductors in the areas of advanced manufacturing and EHS. He is co-developer and past chair of the SEMI S8-95 Ergonomics guideline development committee, and Past chair for National Foundation Industry University Ergonomics Research Board, Texas A&M. He is a Senior member of the Institute of Industrial Engineers, Past Director of IIE Ergonomics and Work Measurement Division, and is a Registered Professional Engineer in the State of Texas.

D. Thomas Peterson is Manager—Process & Systems in Engineering for the DuPont Company in Wilmington, DE. He has 29 years of experience in various DuPont engineering assignments in central engineering and at various plant sites. Experiences include specialty engineering (Power), regional engineering consulting, project management, Investment Manager and a variety of other supervisory assignments. Current work focus is the ongoing development, maintenance and application of competitive global project systems and processes. Included in this arena of responsibility is the task of providing support material and methods for project teams to assure that the right safety, health and environmental issues have been considered and properly handled early in their project execution. Mr. Peterson is a licensed Professional Engineer in Delaware.

Thomas W. Piantek is Director of Worldwide Safety Engineering Services, Johnson & Johnson. He has 36 years of manufacturing & engineering experience and a B.S. degree in Mechanical Engineering, from the University of Notre Dame. Mr. Piantek is an Instructor on Machine Safeguarding, New Jersey State Safety Council - 1996, 1997, 1998. He is a Member of Technical Advisory Group - Capital Good Standards Coalition, a Member of ANSI 244 Lockout Tagout Committee, and a Member of Johnson and Johnson Machine Safety Task Force.

Craig B. Schilder is Safety & Health Director, Naval Facilities Engineering Command, Washington, DC. His previous experience includes: Senior Safety Manager/Deputy to Commander, US Army Safety Center, Fort Rucker, AL; Safety & Health Branch Manager, US General Services Administration, Washington, DC; Safety Engineer, US Army staff, Pentagon, Washington, DC; Safety Engineer, US Army Electronics Command, Fort Monmouth, NJ; US Army Materiel Command Safety Engineering Intern, Texarkana, TX & Louisville, KY. Mr. Schilder has an Industrial Engineering degree from Newark College of Engineering, Newark NJ, and a Master of Engineering (safety) from Texas A&M University. He is a Certified Safety Professional (CSP), and a Professional Engineer (PE).

Steve I. Simon is co-founder of Culture Change Consultants, an organizational change consultant with 15 years guiding companies through successful culture change to improve safety performance. Dr. Simon pioneered culture change work in large organizations starting in 1983 and has co-authored numerous publications on the subject of establishing safety cultures, including the four book Grassroots Safety Leadership Series. He co-developed a Safety Culture Management Perception Survey, a validated instrument for assessing, in employees and management, twelve organizational and cultural factors that correlate to safety performance. Dr. Simon holds the Ph.D. degree in Clinical Psychology from Harvard University. He is a member of the American Society of Safety Engineers, and the Executive Committee of the Petroleum Section of the National Safety Council.

John M. Thaler, CSP, CHMM, Manager of Occupational Safety and Industrial Hygiene, Sikorsky Aircraft Corporation, Stratford, CT. He has over twenty years of experience in safety, industrial hygiene and environmental affairs. Mr. Thaler serves on the Aerospace Section Executive Committee of the National Safety Council and on the Connecticut Business and Industries Association Safety Advisory Board.

INDEX

A

Accreditation Board for Engineering and Technology (ABET), 49, 264
  criteria, 49
Aircraft manufacturing, application in, 185–193. See also Ergonomics
  building an infrastructure, 189
  cost analysis, 190–192
  data collection, 189
  and ergonomic principles, 186–188
  interdisciplinary approach examples, 190–192
  policy development, 188–189
    contract physicians, 189
    design and manufacturing engineering, 188
    employees, 189
    line management, 188
    line supervision, 189
    medical personnel, 189
    safety practitioners, 188–189
  training, 189
Americans with Disabilities Act (ADA), 99, 228
American National Standards Institute (ANSI), 75, 76, 91, 175
American Society of Engineering Educators (ASEE), 53
American Society of Mechanical Engineers (ASME), 91
American Society for Testing and Materials (ASTM), 75
Automotive industry, safety design in, 171–184. See also vehicle development process
  Chrysler Automotive, 171
  General Motors, 172–175
    application of principles, 179–184
    bubble-up phase, 176
    common standards development, 173–174
    data use, 173–174
    design-in safety principles, 179–180
    health and safety activity, 172–175
    task-based risk assessment, 174, 175
    vehicle development process, 175–179

B

Baccalaureate degree, 53–54
Benchmarking
  application of, 31–35
    build, 34
    design, 34–35
    dismantle phase, 32–33
    engineering process model, 31–32
    operate and maintain, 33–34
  and business improvement, 23–24
  change process, 30–31
  definition of, 23
  and engineers, 59
  and ISO 9000 standards, 70
  process, 25–30
    analysis and recommendation development, 30
    customer of services, 27–28
    data collection, 28–30
    design and implementation, 30
    front-end loading, 28
    line management, 27
    map of, 26
    and operations, 27
    participants in, 27
    planning, 25–28
    specialists, 28
    strategic management, 27
  and process measurement, 161–163
  and product reliability, 150
  requirements of, 24–25
    accountability, 25
    culture change, 25
    rigor, 24
    suspension of disbelief, 24–25
  vehicle development process, 176

Benchmarks for World Class Safety Through Design, 59
Bill of Materials (BOM), 177
Bill of Process (BOP), 176
Boiler plate specifications, 104–105
Building codes, 76–77
Building construction
   and building codes, 89
   certificate of occupancy, 89
   construction guidelines, 99
   purchasers, 90
   site assessment guidelines, 99, 100
Building Officials and Code Administrators (BOCA), 76

C
Capital approval process, 98–99
   phases of, 99
Carson, Rachel, 82
Case studies
   incident investigation and analysis, 135–136
   process implementation, 165–169
   product design, 77–78
   product liability prevention, 145–146
   research, 5–6
   risk management, 14–16
CE mark, 93, 95, 144, 242
Center for Chemical Process Safety (CCPS), 211
Center for Waste Reduction Technologies (CWRT), 211
   Certificate of Occupancy, 89
Chapanis, Alphonse, 6–7, 131–33
Chemical process industry, 195–215
   basic concepts, 198
      consequence, 198
      hazard, 198
      incident, 198
      likelihood, 198
   Center for Chemical Process Safety (CCPS), 211
   Center for Waste Reduction Technologies (CWRT), 211
   characteristics of, 195–196
      process safety, 196
   inherent safety measurement, 212
   INSIDE Project, 211
   life cycle, 196
   reliability in, 212
   and safety in design, 196, 198–206
      conflicts, 205–206

      design strategies, 198–200
      inherent safer design, 200
      moderate, 204–205
      protective layers, 200
      risk minimization, 204
      simplify, 205
      substitute, 204
   tools, 206–210
      and fault tree analysis, 206
      hazard/risk matrix, 206
      interaction matrix, 206–208
      Process Chemistry Guideword Hazard Review (PCGHA), 208–210
      process hazard analysis techniques, 206
Chemical processes
   and inherently safer concept, 75
   safety and, 10
Cleanup costs, 82
Code of ethics, engineers', 49
Computer
   and new millennium, 262–264
Computer Aided Design (CAD), 259
Computer Aided Engineering (CAE), 259
Computer Aided Manufacturing (CAM), 259
Computer Aided Production Engineering (CAPE), 259
Conference of American Building Officials (CABO), 77
Confined space, 228
Construction industry, application in, 217–226
   building design safety checklist, 227–239
   corporate level integration policies, 221–222
      corporate risk acceptance, 221–222
      experience reports, 222
      hazard tracking, 222
      National Institute for Building Sciences (NIBS), 222
      programmatic environmental safety and health (PESH), 221
      risk management, 221
      safety analysis tools, 222
   Design-Build acquisition, 226
   ergonomic input error reduction, 223
   facility system safety working group (FSSWG), 220–221
      customer input, 221
      responsibilities, 220–221
      teamwork and communication, 221
   and fall protection, 223
   and hazardous chemicals, 223

pollution prevention (P2), 223
post-occupancy evaluations, 223
pre-occupancy inspections, 222–223
reduction of construction injuries, 217
    software programs, 217
reduction of user injuries, 217–220
safety through design process, 220
software safety, 226
Consumer Product Safety Commission (CPSC), 80
Contracting services, 95–98
communication, 97
roles and responsibilities, 97–98
Cost analysis, 78–79. See also Product design
and aircraft manufacturing, 190
and product liability, 146–148
Culture change, 37–48
application of, 46–47
barriers of, 37–38
and benchmarking, 25
definition of, 39–40
elements for, 41–43
    driver for change, 41–42
    management support, 42
    structure for, 42–43
and hazard analysis, 18
and not applicable, 38–39
phases of, 43–45
    culture assessment, 43–44
    envision future, 43
    evaluation, 44–45
    implementation, 44
    recognition of need, 43
    strategic planning, 44
realignment of, 45–46
and risk assessment, 18
Simon Open System Model, 45

D

Data collection
and aircraft manufacturing, 189
and benchmarking, 28–30
Declaration of Conformity, 93
Delphi methodology, 53
Deming, W. Edwards, 4–5, 69
Department head, 54
Design. See also Product design
of machinery, 100–103
and maintenance, 111–114
process, 10
of product, 73–78

to reduce construction injuries, 217
to reduce user injuries, 217–220
requirements, 12–13
safety reviews, 159, 167–168
for safety toolbox, 217
Design process, 10
for assembly, 121–122
for error-free work, 121–122
incorporation of safety devices, 11
for minimum risk, 11
and operating procedures and training, 12
provision of warning devices, 11
purpose, 10
Device maker, 242

E

Education, safety, 57–58
EHS, 242
Electronics industry, application in, 241–258
data collection, 245–247
design validation and development, 247–248
education platforms, 243
equipment procurement process, 242
industry alignment, 243–245
report cards, 249
product safety notification (PSN), 249–256
selection, 245
system safety program, 249
    audits, 255–256
    data collection, 250
    design team development, 249–250
    document review and verification, 255
    implementation and analysis, 252–255
    product scope, 250–252
    requirements comparison, 252
third parties, 249
tools, 248
Electrical safety, 228–229
Energy control, 234
Energy Control Model of Accident Phenomena, 156–158
dissipation of energy, 156
and ergonomic risk factors, 158
and safe design, 157
strategies for harmful energy prevention, 157
Engineer, 49–63
Accreditation Board for Engineering and Technology (ABET), 49
    criteria, 49
baccalaureate degree, 53–54
and benchmarks, 59

code of ethics, 49
ISTD Symposium, 53–57
   challenges, 54–57
   format of, 53–54
   results of, 54
NETWORC, 61
and new millennium, 264–265
Professional Development Seminars, 62
safety education and training, 57–58
   implementation of, 58–59
   safety course topics, 60–61
and safety practitioners, 62–63
survey of, 50–51

Engineering design safety review, 159–160
Engineering design services
outsources, 164–165
teams, 120–121
Engineering for Health and Safety (EHS), 172
Enterprise Resource Planning (ERP), 259
Environmental costs, 81–82
Environmental Protection Agency (EPA), 82
Ergonomic risk factors, 158
Ergonomics, 119–130, 229–230
definition of, 122
design activities, 186–188
   backs, 188
   elbows/shoulders, 188
   hands and wrists, 187–188
engineering design life cycle, 119–121
Ford Motor Company design process, 119–120, 125–128
   design for ergonomics (DFE), 119, 121–124
   design improvement cycle, 127
   long term development, 127
manufacturing design, 122–128
principles of, 186–187
risk factors, 124–125
   awkward postures, 124
   direct contact trauma, 125
   environmental factors, 125
   high force, 124
   high frequency or repetition, 124
   inadequate rest, 124–125
   vibration, 125
Error
human, 7
provocative situations, 7, 131–133
European New Machinery Directives, 92
Exposure, 11

F
Facility system safety working group (FSSWG), 220
Failure Mode and Effects Analysis (FMEA), 58, 75, 117, 159, 222
Fall protection, 230
Fault Tree Analysis (FTA), 58, 75, 117, 222
Final safety walk-down, 160–161
Fire protection, 231
First aid and medical services, 231–232
Fitness-for-use criteria (FFU), 158–159
case study, 165

G
General industry, safety design in, 155–169
Generic safety circuits, 103–104
Global E-stops, 106
Globalization, 165

H
Haddon, William J., 10, 156
Hazard
analysis, 13, 16
definition of, 5, 11, 198
elimination of, 11
identification of, 11
probability, 11, 14
recognition and mitigation, 75–77
severity, 11, 14
tracking, 222
Hazard analysis, 75, 242
conducting of, 16
and confined spaces, 112–113
and contract specifications, 17–18
and culture changes, 18
and design process, 11
matrix, 13, 15
resources, 21
and retrofitting, 136
Hazard analysis matrix, 13, 15
Hazardous materials and waste, 232–233
Health costs, 81
Human error
and safety design, 7

I
Industrial ventilation, 239
Inherently safe, 75, 200
definition of, 10
example of maintainability, 114–116
measurement, 212

and retrofitting, 136
INSIDE Project, 211
Institute for Safety Through Design, 5
Interaction matrix, 206–208
International Conference of Building Officials (ICBO), 77
International influence
and safety design, 7–8
International Mechanical Code, 77
International Plumbing Code, 77
ISO 9000 standards, 70–71
ISTD Symposium, 53–57

K
Kletz, Trevor, 7, 9

L
Life-cycle costs, 83
Lighting, 233
Line management
and benchmarking, 27
Lockout/tagout, 112

M
Machine guarding, 234
Machinery
design, 100
global E-stops, 106
lockout requirement, 106
new construction, 100
recommended parts list, 100, 103
Machinery purchasing, 90–95
boiler plate specifications, 95, 96
CE mark, 93, 95
Declaration of Conformity, 93
European requirements, 92–95
generic safety circuit, 103–104
and OSHA requirements, 90–91
recommended parts list, 100, 103
Maintenance, 109–118
design considerations, 111–114
confined space, 112–113
fall protection, 113–114
lockout/tagout, 112
safety, 115–116
future trends, 117
maintainability/serviceability, 114–116
design criteria, 115
diagnosis/repair optimization, 114–115
principles, 114
serviceability considerations, 116

reliability considerations, 116–117
basic concepts, 117
types, 109
planned, 110–111
unplanned, 109–110
Malcolm Baldrige National Quality Award (MBNQA), 68, 69
Management
and new millennium, 261–262
Material handling, 234–235
Military Standard 882C, 9–10
Minimum risk, 10, 204

N
National Building Code, 76
National Electrical Code, 77, 91
National Fire Protection Association (NFPA), 75
National Institute for Building Sciences (NIBS), 222
National Safety Council, 5, 59, 62, 109
NETWORC, 61
Noise level control, 235–236

O
Operating procedure guide, example of, 19–21
OSHA, 227
and confined space, 112–113
hazard analysis requirements, 17
and health costs, 81
and machinery purchasing, 90–91
and retrofitting, 133–134
Outsourcing, 164–165
Overhead expenses, 79–80

P
Performance appraisals, 162
Performance-based codes, 76
Performance measures
benefits of, 1
Poka-yoke, 121
Policy and procedure statement, example of, 18–19
Preliminary Hazard Analysis (PHA), 58, 75, 221
Process Chemistry Guideword Hazard Review (PCGHA), 208
Process hazard analysis techniques, 206
Process measurement, 161–163
engineering performance assessment, 162

principles of, 161
project log, 161
process value validation, 162–163
Product Data Management (PDM), 259
Product design
  business practices, 85–87
    bottom line results, 86–87
    cost control/reduction, 86
    management objectives, 85
    operating margins, 86
    return on investment (ROI), 85–86
    survival, 85
  cost factors, 78–85
    allocation problems, 84–85
    cleanup costs, 82
    cost/benefit analysis, 80
    environmental costs, 81–82
    health costs, 81
    life-cycle costing, 83
    overhead costs, 79–80
    recycle costs, 83–84
    safety costs, 80–81
    social costs, 82–83
  process, 73–78
    building codes, 76–77
    case studies, 77–78
    hazard recognition and mitigation,
      75–77
    problem statement, 73–74
    solution development, 74
    user friendliness, 74–75
Product liability prevention, 139–151
  benchmarking, 150
  case studies, 145–146
  collateral standards, 150
  cost analysis, 146–148
    workers' compensation, 148
  databases, 150
  deep pockets, 143–144
  elements of proof, 140–141
  government standards, 149
  industry standards, 149
  international influences, 144
    CE mark, 144
  legal theories, 139–142
    negligence, 140
    warranty,140
  process, 141
  recalls, 145
  recommended practices, 149
  risk assessment, 142–143

  risk-utility test, 141–142
  technical literature, 150
  technical reports, 149–150
Professional Development Seminars, 62
Professor, 54
Project management, 98
Purchasing process, 89–108
  buildings, 89–90
  capital approval process, 98–99
  component lists, 100–103
  and corporate goals, 98
  generic safety circuits, 103–104
  machinery, 90–92
  prequalifying suppliers, 104–105

Q
Quality management, 67–72
  application of, 71–72
  and design, 4–5, 70
  and emergence of, 67–68
  ISO 9000 standards, 70–71
  Malcolm Baldrige National Quality Award
    (MBNQA), 68, 69
  and TQM, 68–70
Quantitative risk analysis (QRA), 206

R
Recycle costs, 83–84
Reliability, 116–117
Reliability Centered Maintenance (RCM),
  117
Retrofitting, 131–137
  definition of, 131
  error-provocative situations, 131–133
    axioms of, 131–133
  and evaluation, 134
  identification of needs, 133–134
  incident investigation and analysis, 134
    and case studies, 135–136
  and modification, 136
Return on Investment (ROI), 85–86
Risk
  acceptable levels of, 14
  assessment, 11, 13–14
  costs, 17
  definition of, 5, 10, 198
  and design, 5
  impact determination, 16
  minimum, 10
  ranking, 16
  residual, 17

Risk assessment
  conducting of a, 16
  and confined spaces, 112–113
  and culture changes, 18
  definition of, 11
  and design process, 10
  matrix, 13, 15
  and new millennium, 261
  and product liability, 141
  resources, 21
  task-based, 175
Risk assessment matrix, 13, 15
Risk management, 221
Risk-utitlity test, 141–142
Rucker, James C., 59

S
Safety
  costs, 80–81
  culture. See Culture change
  definition of, 5, 198
  education, 57–58
  and energy control, 156–158
  fitness-for-use criteria (FFU), 159
  and new millenium, 264
  practitioners, 62
  and TQM, 68–69
  training, 57–58
Safety through design
  and automotive industry, 171–184
  benchmarking, 23–36
  case studies, 5–6
  and chemical process industry, 195–215
  and construction industry, 217–239
  definition of, 3
  and electronics' industry, 241–258
  and error-provocative situations, 6–7
  and general industry, 155–169
  goal of, 3
  and human error, 6–7
  integration of, 158–161
    design safety reviews, 159–160
    final safety walk-downs, 160–161
    fitness-for-use criteria (FFU), 159
  and international influence, 7–8
  model, 3
    flowchart, 4
  operating procedure guide, 19–21
  policy and procedure statement, 18–19
  purpose, 10

  and quality management, 3–5
  and retrofitting, 131–137
  and theoretical ideal, 3–4
  and TQM, 68–69
Scannell, Jerry, 59
Simon Open System Model, 45
Social costs, 82–83
Space station, 260
Specification-based codes, 76
Standard Building Code, 77
Standard Building Code Congress (SBCC), 77
Strategic management
  and benchmarking, 27
Supplier, 243

T
Task-based risk assessment, 175
Tools, 245
Toxic materials, 236–238
TQM, 3–4, 42. See also Quality management
  definition of, 68
  and safety, 68–69
    through design, 69–70
Training
  and process measures, 161
  safety, 57–58

U
Uniform Building Code, 77

V
Vehicle Development Process, 175–179
  and benchmarking, 176
  Bill of Materials (BOM), 177
  Bill of Process (BOP), 176
  equipment build phase, 178
  preliminary design/layout, 177
  Product Engineering Department (PED)
    Process, 178

W
Walk-down, 160–161, 168
Walsh Healey Act, 82
Workers' compensation, 148
Workplace
  and new millennium, 260–261

Z
Zero Access™, 98